HEMISPHERIC DISCONNECTION
AND
CEREBRAL FUNCTION

Hemispheric Disconnection and Cerebral Function

Compiled and Edited by

MARCEL KINSBOURNE, D.M., M.R.C.P.

Senior Physician
The Hospital for Sick Children
Toronto, Ontario
Professor of Psychology
University of Waterloo
Waterloo, Ontario

and

W. LYNN SMITH, Ph.D.

Director
Cortical Function Laboratories
Colorado
Porter Memorial Hospital, Denver
California
White Memorial Medical Center, Los Angeles
Glendale Adventist Medical Center, Glendale
St. Joseph Medical Center, Burbank

CHARLES C THOMAS • PUBLISHER
Springfield • Illinois • U.S.A.

Published and Distributed Throughout the World by

CHARLES C THOMAS • PUBLISHER

Bannerstone House

301–327 East Lawrence Avenue, Springfield, Illinois, U.S.A.

© *1974, by* CHARLES C THOMAS • PUBLISHER

ISBN 0-398-02967-9

Library of Congress Catalog Card Number: 73 20276

*With THOMAS BOOKS careful attention is given to all details of
manufacturing and design. It is the Publisher's desire to present books that are
satisfactory as to their physical qualities and artistic possibilities and
appropriate for their particular use. THOMAS BOOKS will be true to those
laws of quality that assure a good name and good will.*

Library of Congress Cataloging in Publication Data

Cerebral Function Symposium, 3d, Coronado, Calif., 1971.
Hemispheric disconnection and cerebral function.

1. Brain damage—Congresses. I. Kinsbourne, Marcel,
ed. II. Smith, Wallace Lynn, 1922–   ed.
III. Title.   [DNLM: 1. Brain-Physiology—Congresses.
2. Brain—Surgery—Congresses. W3 C129K 1971h/ WL102
C414 1971h]
RC386.2.C37   1971   616.8   73-20276
ISBN 0-398-02967-9

Printed in the United States of America
CC-11

TO

PAULA AND SYLVA

CONTRIBUTORS

GEORGE M. AUSTIN, M.D.
Professor and Head of Section of Neurological Surgery
Loma Linda University, School of Medicine
Loma Linda, California

JOSEPH E. BOGEN, M.D.
Senior Neurosurgeon
Ross-Loos Medical Group
Los Angeles, California

MAUREEN DENNIS, Ph.D.
M.C.R. Fellow
Department of Psychology
The Hospital for Sick Children
Toronto, Ontario, Canada

HAROLD W. GORDON, Ph.D.
The Aba Khoushy Medical School
Israel Institute of Technology—Technion
P.O.B. 9649
Haifa, Israel

ROBERT J. JOYNT, M.D. Ph.D.
Professor and Chairman
Department of Neurology
University of Rochester Medical Center
Neurologist-in-Chief
Strong Memorial Hospital
Rochester, New York

MARCEL KINSBOURNE, D.M., M.R.C.P.
Senior Physician
The Hospital for Sick Children
Toronto, Ontario, Canada
Professor of Psychology
University of Waterloo
Waterloo, Ontario, Canada

BRUNO KOHN, Ph.D.
Assistant Professor of Psychology
Department of Psychology
York University
Downsview, Ontario, Canada

JERRE LEVY, Ph.D.
Assistant Professor
Department of Psychology
University of Pennsylvania
Philadelphia, Pennsylvania

ROBERT D. NEBES, Ph.D.
Assistant Professor, Division of Medical Psychology
Duke University Medical Center
Durham, North Carolina

AARON SMITH, Ph.D.
Director, Neuropsychological Laboratory
Department of Physical Medicine and Rehabilitation
University of Michigan Medical School
Ann Arbor, Michigan

W. LYNN SMITH, Ph.D.
Director, Cortical Function Laboratories
Porter Memorial Hospital
Denver, Colorado
White Memorial Medical Center
Los Angeles, California
Glendale Adventist Medical Center
Glendale, California
St. Joseph Medical Center
Burbank, California

COLWYN TREVARTHEN, Ph.D.
Lecturer, Department of Psychology
University of Edinburgh
Edinburgh, Scotland

PREFACE

Hemispheric Disconnection and Cerebral Function is the third publication of the Annual Cerebral Function Symposium. This annual series evolved five years ago from a growing awareness, among acquaintances representing a diverse spectrum of specialists, of an increasing need for recurrent and ongoing evaluation of the rapidly accumulating knowledge of neuro-behavioral correlates. The success of the first three meetings has been due to the remarkable ability of these scientists of markedly different persuasions to expedite and stimulate discussion, to facilitate exchange, to break down interdisciplinary barriers with unifying cross talk. This heterogeneous group included practicing neurologists, psychiatrists, pediatric neurologists, child psychiatrists, neurologic, otologic and ophthalmic surgeons, psychologists, clinical psychologists and clinical neuropsychologists as well as neurophysiologists, cardiological internists, anatomists, biologists, psychobiologists, biochemists, neurochemists, and psychopharmacologists.

A recurrent theme is evident in this ongoing series not only involving cerebral organization but also its underlying neuroanatomical/behavioral substrata, methods of investigation, behavioral changes resulting from psychopharmacological preparations and neurosurgical intervention, and the knotty problems faced constantly by clinical neuropsychologists in assessing these changes. *Hemispheric Disconnection and Cerebral Function* is a culmination of earlier chapters on commissurotomy and hemispherectomy of the first two meetings, respectively published in *Drugs and Cerebral Function* and *Drugs, Development and Cerebral Function*. Where the latter one focussed on developmental factors, the fourth meeting, *Aging, Dementia and Cerebral Function*, now in press, emphasized the decline end of the temporal continuum.

As this present volume appears, the next meeting *Dyssocial Behavior and Cerebral Function* will have been concluded; plans are largely completed for *Cognition and Cerebral Function* with *Neuropsychological Diagnosis of Cerebral Function* on the drawing board.

I want to take this opportunity to express my gratitude to Abbott Laboratories, Hoffmann-LaRoche, Inc., McNeill Laboratories, Inc., Smith, Kline and French, Inc., Wyeth Laboratories, and to a private foundation who wishes to remain anonymous, without whose generous support this last meeting would not have been possible.

My thanks go especially to Dr. Joseph E. Bogen who led off each of these three meetings with stimulating papers, moderated the final discussion of the first meeting, and wrote the Introduction to this present volume. My appreciation goes also to those who helped with this program and its publication: Dr. Robert T. Lewis, Professor of Psychology and Director of the Graduate Clinical Sequence, California State University, Los Angeles, and Associate Director of Cortical Function Laboratories; Mr. Murray Binder, Administrative Assistant of the Cortical Function Lab complex; to the contributors for their fine papers; and to Mr. Payne E. L. Thomas of Charles C Thomas Publisher for his continued encouragement and assistance in publishing this series.

W. LYNN SMITH

INTRODUCTION

The disconnection of one part of the cerebrum from another part, by the interruption of large fiber-tracts, was of intense interest to neurologists of the late 19th Century. It was, for example, a central concern of Freud's last major neurologic essay[1] before he committed himself almost exclusively to psychological investigation. Over the next half-century, disconnection attracted progressively less attention from brain theorizers. This decline stemmed in large part from Lashley's negative results from the interruption of intrahemispheric tracts,[2] and from the failure of Akelaitis[3] and Smith[4] to find effects following the interruption of the large interhemispheric commissures. Tomasch[5] wrote of the latter:

> They showed very clearly and in accordance with some earlier authors like Dandy, Foerster, Meagher and Barre, whose material however was not so extensive, that the corpus callosum is hardly connected with psychological functions at all.

In discussing the organization of states of consciousness, Fessard[6] expressed the generally accepted impression at midcentury:

> . . . , there is a great deal of data showing how unimportant is the part played by intracortical connections in such organization, as well as in those that control mental operations or sensori-motor performances . . . and section of important associative white tracts such as corpus callosum does not seem to affect mental performances. Other similar observations in man or animals are now accumulated in great number and variety. These results are so disturbing that one may be tempted to admit the irrational statement that a heterogenous system of activities in the nervous system could form a whole in the absence of any identified liaison.

A dramatic reversal of this opinion has occurred in the past fifteen years. The present intense, world-wide interest in the split-brain is the

---

[1] S. Freud, *On Aphasia* (original publication 1891) (New York, International Universities Press, Inc., 1953).

[2] K. S. Lashley, "In Search of the Engram," Symposia of the Society for Experiment Medicine, (London, Cambridge University Press, 1950) *4:* 454–482.

[3] A. J. Akelaitis, "A Study of Gnosis, Praxis and Language Following Section of the Corpus Callosum and Anterior Commissure," *Journal of Neurosurgery, 1:* 94–102, 1944.

[4] K. U. Smith, "Experimental Analysis of the Associative Mechanism of the Human Brain in Learning Functions, *Journal of Comparative and Physiological Psychology, 45:* 66–72, 1952.

[5] J. Tomasch, "Size, Distribution, and Number of Fibres in the Human Corpus Callosum," *Anatomical Record, 119:* 7–19, 1954.

[6] A. E. Fessard, "Mechanisms of Nervous Integration and Conscious Experience," in J. F. Delafresnaye ed., *Brain Mechanisms and Consciousness* (Springfield, Charles C Thomas, 1954).

result of Professor R. W. Sperry's paradoxically disciplined creativity and his persuasive exposition[7-16a] as well as his facility for guiding a host of energetic young investigators along fruitful lines of inquiry. These Proceedings of the 3rd Cerebral Function Symposium are a tribute to his central role in the resurgence of interest in disconnection, clinical[17,18a] as well as experimental.[19-21]

The experimental ingenuity of Sperry and his collaborators has been especially apparent in the utilization of a unique series of patients whose otherwise intractable seizures have been treated by the operation of cerebral commissurotomy. This operation was introduced by Professor

[7] R. W. Sperry, "Cerebral Organization and Behavior," *Science, 133:* 1749–1757, 1961.

[8] R. W. Sperry, "Some Developments in Brain Lesion Studies of Learning," *Federation Proceedings, 20:* 609–616, 1961.

[9] R. W. Sperry, "Problems Outstanding in the Evolution of Brain Function," *James Arthur Lecture* (New York, American Museum of Natural History, 1964).

[10] R. W. Sperry, "Brain Bisection and Mechanisms of Consciousness," in J. C. Eccles, ed., *Brain and Conscious Experience* (New York, Springer, 1966).

[11] R. W. Sperry, "Split-brain Approach to Learning Problems," in G. C. Quarton, T. Melnechuck, and F. O. Schmitt, eds., *The Neurosciences: A Study Program* (New York, Rockefeller University Press, 1967).

[12] R. W. Sperry, "Hemisphere Deconnection and Unity in Conscious Awareness," *American Psychologist, 23:* 723–733, 1968.

[13] R. W. Sperry, "Mental Unity Following Surgical Disconnection of the Cerebral Hemispheres," *Harvey Lect. Series 62* (New York, Academic Press, 1968).

[14] R. W. Sperry, "Plasticity of Neural Maturation," *Developmental Biology Supplement, 2:* 306–327, 1968.

[14a] R. W. Sperry, M. S. Gazzaniga, and J. E. Bogen, "Role of the Neocortical Commissures," in P. J. Vinken and G. W. Bruyn, eds., *Handbook of Clinical Neurology, Vol. IV* (Amsterdam, North Holland Pub., 1969).

[14b] R. W. Sperry, J. E. Bogen, and P. J. Vogel, "Syndrome of Hemisphere Deconnection," in P. Bailey and R. E. Fiol, eds., *Proc. 2nd Pan-Am Congress Neurol* (Puerto Rico, Dept. de Instruct, 1970).

[15] R. W. Sperry, "Perception in the Absence of the Neocortical Commissures," *Assoc Res Nerv Ment Dis, 48:* 123–138, 1970.

[16] R. W. Sperry, "Cerebral Dominance in Perception," in F. A. Young and D. B. Lindsley, eds., *Early Experience in Visual Information Processing in Perceptual and Reading Disorders* (Washington, National Academy of Science, 1970).

[16a] R. W. Sperry, "How a Developing Brain Gets Itself Properly Wired for Adaptive Function," in Tobach, Shaw and Aronson, eds., *The Biopsychology of Development* (New York, Academic Press, 1971).

[17] N. Geschwind, "The Clinical Syndromes of the Cortical Connections," in D. Williams, ed., *Modern Trends in Neurology* (London, Butterworth, 1970).

[18] M. I. Botez and E. Crighel, "Partial Disconnexion Syndrome in an Ambidextrous Patient," *Brain, 94:* 487–494, 1971.

[18a] B. Schott, F. Michel, D. Michel, and R. Dumas, "Apraxie idéomotrice unilatérale gauche avec main gauche anomique: syndrome de déconnexion calleuse?" *Revue Neurologique, 120:* 359–365, 1969.

[19] M. S. Gazzaniga, *The Bisected-Brain* (New York, Appleton-Century-Crofts, 1970).

[20] S. Dimond, *The Double Brain* (London, Churchill Livingstone, 1972).

[21] V. M. Mosidze, *et al., Rasheplen mosg (split-brain)* (Tbilisi, Metsniereba, 1972).

P. J. Vogel whose open-mindedness, surgical skill and unfailing patience have made possible a remarkably productive interdisciplinary research program. It was most appropriate that these Proceedings concluded with some of his informal remarks. The most extensive disconnection leaving a person capable of ordinary social obligations is hemispherectomy, which deprives the intact hemisphere of both commissural and brain stem communication with its fellow. Consideration of hemispherectomy was initiated in the 2nd Cerebral Function Symposium. The present volume continues where that one ended. It is also concerned more with the results of severing only the commissures, including some discussion of implications for certain psychic and social problems.

JOSEPH E. BOGEN

CONTENTS

HEMISPHERIC DISCONNECTION
AND
CEREBRAL FUNCTION

[PART I]

HEMISPHERECTOMY

[CHAPTER I]

DOMINANT AND NONDOMINANT HEMISPHERECTOMY

Aaron Smith

THE DEVELOPMENT OF CEREBRAL LOCALIZATION AND "DOMINANCE"

UNTIL A CENTURY AGO, the established beliefs of human brain functions were based on extrapolations of the results of animal experiments by Haller, Flourens, and others (McHenry, 1969). Thus, it had been believed that all parts of the brain were functionally equivalent. Flourens, the outstanding authority for most of the nineteenth century, had "established" that the cerebral hemispheres were incapable of producing any movement. Experimental hemispherectomies of twin-brained animals by Flourens (1824), Vulpian (1866), and Goltz (1888) supported the view that the two great cerebral hemispheres in man were functional as well as anatomical duplicates.

Generalizations of many of the findings in experimental animal studies to man were later shown to be in error. However, certain observations by Vulpian and later by Goltz (1888) anticipated not only the development of hemispherectomy in man but the significant differences between effects of hemispherectomy for IH (usually in children) and for tumor (usually in adults).

Vulpian reported, "When one attempts an experiment of this sort (hemispherectomy) on mammals, it is necessary whenever possible to make use of very young animals, for on the one hand, these support operation well, and on the other, the functional relations between the different parts of the encephalon are not yet as narrowly circumscribed *as they later become;* to such effect, that ablation from the brain has less influence on the action of other parts than in the adult animal" (Vulpian, 1866; translated by Kennard and Fulton, 1942, italics added).

Goltz observed the similarity in initial and residual effects of right and left hemisphere removals in dogs. Since "personality" was unchanged and loss of intelligence and other functions in the dog was "amazingly small," Goltz suggested that hemispherectomy might be feasible for removal of large lateralized tumors in man. (The first case of successful diagnosis, localization, and excision of a concealed intracranial tumor, however, had been reported only three years earlier [Bennett and Godlee, 1885]. Since surgical treatment of brain tumors was widely considered dangerous and ineffectual, Goltz's proposal was ignored.)

Accumulating studies of aphasics in the nineteenth century led to Broca's (1865) eventual claim that speech was localized in the third left frontal convolution. Although Jackson and others rejected the equation of localization of defects with the localization of functions, Jackson emphasized one of the most striking findings in studies of aphasics. "Damage to but one hemisphere will make a man speechless." Thus, the neat, rational dogma that man's twin brains were functional as well as anatomical duplicates was shattered forever.

Comparative studies had consistently failed to reveal any differences in the functions of the two cerebral hemispheres in infrahuman species. However, in addition to the special role of the left hemisphere in language, the asymmetry of human hemispheric functions was reflected in handedness. In contrast to random preference for either upper extremity in lower species, preference for the right hand in 90 percent of all normal adults also attested to the special status of the left hemisphere.

The suddenly elevated status of the left hemisphere thus invited detailed clinicoanatomical correlation studies of its component structure in efforts to "localize" other language and nonlanguage functions. Reports of defects in auditory comprehension, reading, writing, calculation, general intelligence, and other nonlanguage functions following variously situated lesions in the left hemisphere, and the absence of such defects in cases with corresponding right hemisphere lesions were cited as evidence of the existence of specific "centres" for the functions within the left hemisphere. Although based on correlations of impairment in visual ideation following right posterior lesions, Jackson's (1876) description of the right hemisphere as leading in "higher" nonlanguage reasoning capacities was largely ignored.

At the beginning of the twentieth century, Liepmann (1905) reported that the left hemisphere controlled the right in execution of purposeful left-hand movements. This added investiture of a directorial role in nonlanguage functions further enhanced the already elevated status of the hemisphere. Subsequent references to it as "dominant," "major," and "leading" reflected widespread views that man's left hemisphere was superior to the right in all functions. The "nondominant," "minor," and "subordinate" right hemisphere, or to use the apt title of the review by Bogen (1969a), "The Other Side of The Brain," was relegated to a vague, undefined, but unquestionably inferior role.

Thus, the concept of cerebral "dominance" developed as an offshoot of early claims of cerebral localization based on comparisons of patients with comparable lateralized brain lesions. Although even Broca had declared that the right hemisphere participated in comprehension, many writers subsequently localized all language functions exclusively in the left hemisphere (Smith, 1971). Commenting on Dandy's (1928) report of normal mental capacities following right hemispherectomy for tumor, Lhermitte (1928) pointed out that previous studies had long established that the left was "l'hémisphère intellectuèlle." Until recently, "it was possible to say that animals below man have two 'right' hemispheres, one on each side" (Teuber, 1967). Thus, man's proud perch atop the highest rung on the phyletic scale-ladder he constructed was solely due to his speaking, intelligent "dominant" hemisphere.

THE DEVELOPMENT OF HEMISPHERECTOMY FOR BRAIN TUMOR

The development of hemispherectomy by Dandy for otherwise incurable and inevitably fatal gliomas was based on his observations in surgical treatment of cerebral tumors. He reported that since each of the lobes in the right hemisphere could be removed without apparent mental impairment, it was logical to expect that the entire right cerebral hemisphere might be removed "with little if any change in the mentality of a right-handed patient" (Dandy, 1928).

In his initial report on five cases, Dandy (1928) noted that apart from relieving preoperative mental symptoms, removals of the entire right cerebral hemisphere for tumor had no discernible effects on language, general intelligence, or personality.

Since two subsequent similar cases also failed to reveal any mental abnormalities, Dandy might have cited his findings as confirmation of his expectation. However, if removals of the normally developed adult right hemisphere resulted in only the same left-sided sensory and motor deficits observed after limited right-sided lesions, what functions did the much larger areas of the right hemisphere not involved in sensory and motor functions serve? Was the right hemisphere a vestige organ that, apart from "lower" level sensory and motor functions, did not contribute to or participate in any "higher" intellectual or psychological functions?

Dandy probably pondered these questions between his 1928 and 1933 reports. For although he presented clinical studies demonstrating normal mental capacities in his 1933 report, Dandy was now also unwilling to say that right hemispherectomy had no effect on mentality, but rather that his cursory mental examinations and referrals "to the best available talent" had failed to disclose any abnormalities (Dandy, 1933).

The concept of plasticity of human cerebral functions was introduced by Dax (1836) and Broca (1865) in their reports indicating the localization of speech exclusively in the left hemisphere to explain exceptional cases in which speech was either preserved or recovered following total destruction of the so-called speech centers.

Dax called attention to the absence of aphasia in adults with slowly developing lesions in the same areas of the left hemisphere in which sudden lesions resulted in immediate aphasia. He thus suggested that the momentum of the lesion was a critical factor, and that in cases with gradual destruction of speech mechanisms in the left hemisphere, other unspecified intact cerebral structures were able to maintain normal language functions.

Although Broca concluded that motor speech functions were localized exclusively in the third left frontal convolution of the adult brain, he attributed the development of normal speech following destruction of Broca's area in childhood to the transfer of speech functions to the third right frontal convolution. He also suggested that the successful reeducation of adult aphasics might be due to the potentials of right hemisphere mechanisms to compensate for language deficits resulting from left hemisphere lesions.

The vast pertinent literature before and after the studies of Dax and Broca, and the development of current concepts of cerebral localization, dominance, and differences in hemispheric functions cannot be reviewed here. However, the accumulated findings in studies of hemispherectomy for lesions incurred at different stages in the development of the brain provide unique evidence of the principle underlying the development and organization of cerebral functions in the young brain, and of their disorganization and reorganization in the adult.

HEMISPHERECTOMY FOR INFANTILE HEMIPLEGIA

Following isolated cases by McKenzie (1938) and Williams and Scott (1939), Krynauw (1950) demonstrated the feasibility of hemispherectomy for IH in a report on twelve cases (10 left and 2 right hemispherectomy) with but a single operative death. Krynauw cited Osler's emphasis of the mental enfeeblement often following IH. He noted that many parents sought help for the mental state rather than hemiplegia or epilepsy. In these twelve patients with age at operation from eight months to twenty-one years, Krynauw reported that following removal of the entire left hemisphere in an infant, language functions developed normally without any apparent speech difficulties. Following left hemispherectomy in a nine-year-old girl, ability to use the right arm was only slightly impaired compared to the situation before operation, and she could speak, understand speech, read, and write without difficulty. In two cases, speech actually improved markedly after hemispherectomy.

Right or left hemispherectomy caused no more than a transient increase in hemiparesis. "Although return of function and power to the preoperative level was predicted and expected in these cases, improved tone and function beyond this level has been a happy by-product of this operation, and is perhaps a little difficult to explain" (Krynauw, 1950).

Krynauw noted that EEG abnormalities (a nonspecific dysrythmia) in IH were not confined to the pathological hemisphere. Following its removal, however, EEG tracings over the remaining hemisphere rapidly settled to normal limits, presumably for the first time since onset of IH. This indicated that radiation of effects from the pathological hemisphere had disrupted the natural physiological activities of the anatomically normal side, "particularly those more especially concerned with the highest intellectual integration" (Krynauw, 1950). In cases with limited surgical excisions, the remaining portions of the diseased hemisphere could continue to disrupt the anatomically normal side. Thus, Krynauw concluded, it was necessary to remove the entire pathological hemisphere.

Epilepsy, which had been present in ten of the eleven cases surviving hemispherectomy, ceased, and without requiring sedative medication. Personality and behavior disorders were markedly improved. Krynauw also observed that improvement in the mental sphere "*presupposes, and is dependent upon, the integrity of the remaining hemisphere and its ability to function normally once it has been released from abnormal influences from the pathological side*" (Krynauw, 1950, italics added).

Since no apparent defects in language were observed in any of the ten cases with left and one case with right hemispherectomy, Krynauw reasoned "hemispheric dominance had adjusted itself before removal of the affected hemisphere, and that it was the minor hemisphere which was removed in all cases" (Krynauw, 1950). Another observation is especially pertinent in considering preoperative disabilities and recovery of functions following hemispherectomy for tumor and for IH. "In the past many of our clinical deductions regarding localization and function in the central nervous system have been based on the concept of nonfunction and negative activity of areas of pathology, and due regard has not always been given to the fact that these areas may often be the site of increased, albeit distorted activity; in other words, zones of dysfunction rather than nonfunction" (Krynauw, 1950).

COMPARISONS OF HEMISPHERECTOMY FOR TUMOR AND FOR INFANTILE HEMIPLEGIA

In a report on an adult with right hemispherectomy for tumor, Mensh *et al.* (1952) reviewed the findings in forty-one previously reported cases of hemispherectomy for tumor and for IH. They cited the diverse and often contradictory descriptions of psychological effects of hemispherectomy and emphasized the need for systematic studies with standardized psychological techniques. Noting that previous reports emphasizing the absence of psychological impairment had been based on clinical studies, they summarized the results of repeated postoperative examinations with psychological tests. "The examination data reflect wide variations in functioning, with concreteness and perseveration of ideas, confused and psychotic-like thinking. . . . Also seen are premorbid levels of superior vocabulary and verbal facility and extremely compulsive behavior" (Mensh *et al.*, 1952).

In the first comparison of hemispherectomy for IH and for lesions occurring in the adult brain, Gros and Vlahovitch (1953) reported that the only difference was the capacity for transfer of cerebral dominance in IH cases to the remaining hemisphere. In a summary of the results in Gardner's ten tumor cases, Gardner *et al.* (1955) compared residual motor, sensory, language, and psychological functions with those reported by others in hemispherectomy for tumor and for IH. "When the functioning of the patients operated upon the brain tumour is compared with that reported in patients operated upon for infantile hemiplegia, it is apparent that, if one hemisphere is impaired, whether by developmental anomaly, birth trauma, or some disease process occurring shortly after birth, other parts of the brain do, *to some extent*, acquire the functions which otherwise would be performed by the parts that have failed to develop. In the adult nervous system, where physiological centres and pathways and engrams already have been laid down, other areas cannot "take over" the function of parts destroyed. In other words, the immature cortex of one hemisphere can acquire functions which nature planned for the cortex of the other side, but (with the possible exception of speech) once a function has become established in the cortex, it cannot be transferred. Since corticalization of function is an ontogenetic as well as phylogenetic phenomenon, the infant can part with his cortex with less resulting functional deficit than can an adult" (Gardner *et al.*, 1955, italics added).

The fact that less than fifty cases of hemispherectomy for brain tumor have been reported since 1928 reflects widespread doubts on the feasibility of hemispherectomy as a possible treatment for otherwise incurable malignant cerebral neoplasms (e.g. Pool, 1968), and extreme reluctance to attempt removals of a left "dominant" hemisphere in adults (Smith and Burklund, 1966). The reports reflect high operative mortality rates and, in most cases, death from recurrence of the tumor shortly after surgery. Although two adults survived after right hemispherectomy for tumor for fifteen and thirty years, respectively, the quality of postoperative survival was generally poor. Only one patient (Gardner *et al.*, 1955) was able to return to self-supporting work, albeit in a less responsible job.

Reviews of over five hundred cases of hemispherectomy for IH (White, 1961; Basser, 1962; Ignelzi and Bucy, 1968; Wilson, 1970), however, show a relatively low operative mortality rate (about 7%) with approximately equal proportions of left and right hemispherectomy. Although Wilson (1970) reported a high long-term mortality rate largely because of later occurring intracranial hemorrhages, Falconer and Wilson (1969) pointed out that, with prompt, correct diagnosis, these long term postoperative complications are remediable. Wilson also observed, "Although the better the original substrate the better the achievement after hemispherectomy, nevertheless roughly 42 percent of the patients assessed before operation as being of borderline or severely subnormal intellect proved to some degree educable or employable after hemispherectomy" (Wilson, 1970).

In general, the results of hemispherectomy for IH consistently show elimination or reduction of severe intractable seizures and/or severe behavior disorders in the overwhelming majority of cases followed removals of either hemisphere. Thus recent findings (White, 1961; Ignelzi and Bucy, 1968; Wilson, 1970) support earlier conclusions (e.g. Krynauw, 1950; Cairns and Davidson, 1951) that in properly selected cases of IH, hemispherectomy may be considered the treatment of choice.

Although many generalizations of the results of twin-brained animal experiments led to erroneous conclusions, certain findings reported by Vulpian (1866) were confirmed in comparisons of hemispherectomy for IH and for tumor. Despite the obvious differences in the underlying morbid anatomy, the markedly lower operative mortality rate in IH cases may reflect the younger age at operation as well as possibly less surgical difficulty in removing an atrophic hemisphere than one containing a neoplasm. The diverse and usually diffuse lesions resulting in IH (White, 1961) occur before, at, or shortly after birth. In a review of 420 cases, Ignelzi and Bucy (1968) reported brain damage occurred before birth in 75 percent; in the remaining 25 percent, onset occurred in infancy or very early childhood. Hemispherectomy for IH is therefore usually performed in early life (e.g. in 148 cases reviewed by White, mean age at operation was 12.9 years, range 7 months to 38 years).

Except for a fourteen-year-old boy (Hillier, 1954) and two girls aged nine and ten (Gardner *et al.*, 1955), all reported cases of right or left hemispherectomy for tumor were adults in whom the brain had matured normally until the development of a cerebral neoplasm. The reported age in thirty-one such cases listed in the literature ranged from twenty-three to sixty-seven, with a mean of forty years. (All three children survived 20 or more months postoperatively before death of recurrence of the tumor in 2 reported cases, the third not being reported.) The markedly lower operative mortality rate in approximately five hundred IH cases thus confirms Vulpian's observation for experimental hemispherectomy studies that younger subjects "support operation well."

Vulpian also pointed out that hemispheric ablations in older animals result in more marked disabilities because in younger animals the functions are not yet as narrowly circumscribed as they later become. He thus anticipated the concept of "chronogenic localization" enunciated by von Monakow (1911), and the striking differences between effects of lesions occurring at different stages in the development of the right or left hemisphere in man.

ASYMMETRY OF ADULT HEMISPHERIC FUNCTIONS

As Lhermitte (1928) had pointed out, studies of hemispherectomy in man provided opportunities for evaluating traditional concepts of cerebral localization and of similarities and differences in the functions of the right and left hemispheres. Early cases of right hemispherectomy for tumor revealed no apparent mental defects. However, the first reported case of left hemispherectomy for tumor (Zollinger, 1935) revealed that speech was present immediately after operation. Although the patient died seventeen days postoperatively, improvement of expressive and receptive language functions continued throughout the short period of survival. Thus, Lereboullet pointed out, "From a physiologic point of view, this case proves that the dogma of localization in the left hemisphere of word centers is not absolute and that the right hemisphere contributes to this function" (Lereboullet, 1936).

The marked differences between effects of right and left hemispherectomy for tumor with respect to the readily apparent severe aphasia immediately after left hemispherectomy, have been observed in all subsequent reported cases (Smith, 1966).

Failures in early studies of similar cases of right hemispherectomy or of adults with right-sided lesions to reveal any characteristic defects or to indicate any special role of the adult nondominant hemisphere in intellectual functions reflected the difficulties in dislodging the old popular concept of the left brain as "l'hémisphère intellectuèlle," as well as emphasis on verbal reasoning and language functions in clinical studies.

Standardized intelligence tests like the Stanford-Binet had been developed on the widely accepted rationale that "Language, essentially, is the shorthand of the higher thought processes, and the level at which this shorthand functions is one of the most important determinants of the level of the processes themselves" (Terman and Merrill, 1936). Thus, it is not surprising that Rowe (1937) reported that a preoperative Stanford-Binet IQ of 115 was unchanged six months after right hemispherectomy, and that similar IQ tests based on the rationale that intellectual processes are carried on and expressed in verbal symbols would frequently reveal no evidence of intellectual deficits following extensive lesions, or indeed total removals of the right hemisphere.

Early clinical studies by Jackson and others (Bogen, 1969b) had indicated that the right hemisphere played a leading role in nonverbal or visual ideational and constructional functions. Although subsequent psychometric studies (Weisenburg and McBride, 1935; Weisenburg, McBride, and Roe, 1936; Hebb, 1939) increasingly reported impairment in objective nonverbal reasoning tests, until recently (e.g. Strong and Elwyn, 1943), authoritative neurological textbooks continued to maintain that apart from sensory and/or motor disturbances, lesions of the right "nondominant" hemisphere produced no recognizable disturbances.

Use of a standardized neuropsychological battery of more recently developed psychological tests in studies of adults with hemispherectomy for tumor, however, revealed that, although language and verbal reasoning capacities were not appreciably impaired, removal of an adult right hemisphere that had developed normally until the growth of a tumor resulted in a consistent pattern of marked impairment in nonverbal reasoning and visual ideational capacities. In a comparison of effects of right and left hemispherectomy for tumor in adults, Smith (1969) reported:

1. Adult hemispheric functions differ quantitatively rather than qualitatively, with a markedly greater role of the left hemisphere in speech, reading and writing (but not verbal comprehension) than that of the right in nonlanguage or visual ideational functions.
2. Each adult hemisphere alone is capable of performing in more limited and varying degrees those functions in which the opposite hemisphere specialized.
3. The absence of the opposite hemisphere has little effect on the specific functions in which the remaining hemisphere specialized.

Despite marked differences in age, education, and postoperative intervals (from 10 days to 30 years), the Wechsler Verbal Subtest scores of all four patients with right hemispherectomy are within the normal range, with Verbal IQ's of 85 for R_2 (with the least education) fifteen years after right hemispherectomy, to 103 for R_4 only ten days postoperatively, and 99 for R_3 thirty years after nondominant hemispherectomy. This suggests that verbal reasoning, early acquired information,

TABLE I-I
RIGHT AND LEFT HEMISPHERECTOMY FOR BRAIN TUMOURS

	Right				Left		
	R₁(GE)	R₂(DB)	R₃(JP)	R₄(JH)	L₁(EC)		
Postop Interval	1 yr	15 yrs	30 yrs	10 days	10 mos	19 mos	20 mos
Age/Education (Years)	29/15	44/9	66/11	48/12	......	......	......
	Raw/Weighted Score (WAIS)			(WBI)	(WAIS)		
Information	17/11	13/9	17/11	14/10	......	......	......
Comprehension	21/13	13/7	13/7	12/11	......	......	......
Arithmetic	7/7	8/7	9/8	6/7	12/11	1/1	3/3
Similarities	13/10	12/9	9/8	8/7	......	......	......
Digit Span	10/9	8/6	10/9	10/7	(6/2)	0/0	0/0
Vocabulary	......	24/7	40/10	27½/13	......	......	......
Digit Symbol	29/6	3/0	0/0	0/0	3/0	0/0	0/0
Picture Completion	9/7	7/6	4/4	5/3	14/10	14/10	4/4
Block Design	18/6	8/3	8/3	3/3	36/11	28/9	8/3
Picture Arrangement	16/7	10/5	10/5	0/0	20/9	24/10	0/0
Object Assembly	21/6	11/4	6/2	0/0	29/9	29/9	0/0
Verbal IQ	99	85	99	103	......	......	......
Performance IQ	77	63	73	68	110	108	56
Full Scale IQ	89	74	87	84	......	......	......
Peabody Picture Vocab.	125	95	109	......	98	91	......
Visual Memory	2	2	0	......	6	2	1
Copying Designs	10	4	5	......	10	......	0
Colored Matrices	18	8	14	......	32	27	18
Visual Organization	29	10½	7	......	29	22	......
SDMT Written	25	0	0	......	4	7	0
SDMT Oral	35	0	0	......	......	......	0
Porteus Maze	......	5½	6	......	15	14	......
DSS (Face-Hand)	normal	bilateral	bilateral	......	right sensory	right sensory	bilateral

calculation, immediate auditory retention, and vocabulary are usually not diminished either ten days or thirty years after removal of a right hemisphere that has matured normally.

Comparisons of nonlanguage tests of visual ideational, spatial, constructional, and memory functions, however, reveal marked initial and enduring impairment in all four patients. Since normal visual acuity was indicated in ability to perceive small missing details in the Picture Completion Subtest, the subnormal scores in all other nonlanguage tests suggest the underlying disorder is not a "lower level" visual perceptual loss (e.g. a selective impairment of spatial attributes in the visual fields) but an impairment of "higher level" integrative functions unique to the mediation and processing of visual information. The marked discrepancies between Wechsler Verbal IQ's (ranging from 85 to 103) and Performance IQ's (ranging from 63 to 77) in the four cases of adult hemispherectomy were consistent with prorated IQ's reported by Bruell and Albee (1962) in a similar case (Verbal IQ, 121, Performance IQ, 76). Moreover, nonverbal analagous reasoning capacities or the ability to abstract in visual systems of thought as measured by the Raven Coloured Progressive Matrices, and visual memory as measured by the Visual

Retention Test, in R_1, R_2, and R_3 one to thirty years after right hemispherectomy were inferior to those of average eight-year-old children.

The markedly subnormal scores by all four right hemispherectomy cases (with left hemiplegia and homonymous hemianopsia) in nonlanguage tests standardized on adults with normal vision and bilateral manual dexterity might be interpreted as evidence of "lower level" sensory and motor defects, rather than impairment in the "higher level" visual ideational processes. However, despite right hemiplegia, right homonymous hemianopsia, and severe speech, reading, and writing defects, the same nonlanguage tests of visual ideational, constructional, and memory functions thirteen months after left hemispherectomy revealed no changes in the normal or above normal capacities demonstrated in preoperative tests by L_1.

The marked difference in effects of left hemispherectomy for tumour were apparent in the severe aphasia immediately after surgery. Although all language functions were profoundly impaired, speech was not abolished, and ability to follow simple verbal commands revealed some comprehension of speech. In L_1's attempts to answer questions immediately after surgery, he could produce isolated words, but after struggling to organize a meaningful reply, he uttered expletives and short emotional "nonpropositional" phrases. He also spontaneously articulated words and short phrases, but could not communicate an idea in speech. Speech slowly improved, and though still severely impaired a year after surgery, his ability to communicate in short spoken sentences had increased significantly. However, although L_1's speech had been dysarthric before hemispherectomy, despite the severe persisting aphasia, postoperative studies of language functions revealed no dysarthria.

The marked differences between effects of left and right hemispherectomy for tumour in all reported cases of children and adults thus reflect the increasing specialization of language functions in the adult left hemisphere. But this does not appear to be a totally exclusive or irrevocable assumption of all four language functions by the left hemisphere. Although severely impaired, L_1 demonstrated varying degrees of recovery in speech, reading, and writing. However, the ability to comprehend speech, which was least impaired initially, showed striking and continuing improvement until recurrence of the tumour. The marked recovery of auditory comprehension to nearly normal levels was reflected in clinical studies and in increasing scores in Peabody Picture Vocabulary Tests (98 at 13 months versus 85 at 7 months postoperatively, surpassing a score of 95 by R_2 15 years after right hemispherectomy). Other functions, variously dependent on comprehension of speech and auditory memory, showed marked improvement during the same period. His score in the Digit Span Subtest rose from 2 at 7 months to 6 at 13 months: in Arithmetic, from 4 to 12.

Thus, as Dr. Burklund and I have reported, and as the ingenious studies of patients with commissurotomy by Sperry, Bogen, and Gazzaniga (Sperry *et al.*, 1969) have also indicated, the right hemisphere alone is apparently able to sustain auditory comprehension and arithmetic reasoning.

In contrast to the marked initial and residual impairment in visuoideational functions and apparently intact language functions after right hemispherectomy for tumor, although speech, reading, and writing are profoundly impaired by similar left hemispherectomy, visuoideational functions are relatively intact. In fact, L_1's prorated WAIS performance IQ (110) thirteen months postoperatively places him in the 75th percentile of the general population in nonverbal reasoning capacities.

Thus, removals of a left or right hemisphere that has matured normally in man reveal systematic differences. Following left hemispherectomy, although nonlanguage mental functions remain intact, all language functions are initially profoundly impaired and subsequently show varying degrees of recovery, with only comprehension approximating normal levels one year postoperatively. (Although speech, reading, and writing had shown less recovery until tumor recurrence, the extent to which they may have improved with continuing survival remains unknown). It should also be pointed out that since the degree of hemispheric specialization in language function varies, all language functions may not be necessarily impaired after left "dominant" hemispherectomy.

Immediately following right hemispherectomy, although language functions were not noticeably impaired, nonverbal—visual ideational or reasoning, spatial, constructional, and memory capacities were severely impaired. Continuing severe nonlanguage defects in R_2 fifteen years postoperatively and in R_3 thirty years postoperatively do not indicate any capacity for other remaining structures (either in the left hemisphere or those remaining on the right side after hemispherectomy) to significantly amplify previously smaller contributions to these functions.

It is especially noteworthy that despite the severe residual language versus nonlanguage defects observed in one adult with left versus three with right hemispherectomy for tumour, *there was no evidence of psychosis, bizarre behavior, or impairment of volition or will. None of the patients revealed any suggestion of prosopagnosia, anogsognosia, color agnosia, word deafness, complete constructional apraxia, sympathetic dyspraxia, sensory or motor amusia, or other total defects variously described in cases with restricted lesions in either hemisphere.*

In some earlier reported cases of right hemispherectomy for tumour, findings based on psychological tests and on clinical observations were apparently confounded by effects of unsuspected recurring tumours which resulted in death not long after examination. For example in the first detailed psychological study of effects of right hemispherectomy for tumour (Mensh *et al.*, 1952), eight examinations from 18 to 134 days postoperatively showed generally declining scores in the later tests. However, the early recurrence and increasing invasion of the neoplasm were indicated in the appearance of seizures in the 6th postoperative month, and death 6.5 months after surgery. Marked mental changes (suicidal ideas) were reported with recurrence of the tumor 18 months after right hemispherectomy in a nine-year-old girl (Gardner *et al.*, 1955), followed by death 20 months postoperatively.

Another similar patient (Bruell and Albee, 1962) underwent hemispherectomy on November 24, 1954, was examined in March, 1955, and died in April, 1955, also apparently because of recurrence of the tumour. This is the only reported case I have discovered in the literature with bizarre behavior and a transient episode of anasognosia following right hemispherectomy for tumour. (Although psychological testing was necessarily limited, Bruell and Albee were the first to report the marked contrast between intact language and above normal verbal reasoning (prorated Wechsler-Bellevue Verbal IQ, 121) and gross impairment in nonverbal reasoning (prorated Performance IQ, 76) capacities following adult right hemispherectomy for tumour.)

Thus, although psychotic or bizarre behavior has been occasionally noted after right hemispherectomy for tumour, the emergence of behavioral abnormalities was associated with the recurrence of the tumour. The consistent pattern of marked initial and enduring impairment in visual ideational, constructional, and memory functions associated with normal capacities in verbal reasoning and language functions following removals of a right hemisphere that had matured normally in three right-handed and one left-handed adult supports Jackson's (1876) conclusion that just as the left hemisphere plays "a leading" role in language functions, the right hemisphere plays a similar role in visuoideational processes.

"STOCK-BRAINEDNESS" AND "PLASTICITY" OF HEMISPHERIC FUNCTIONS

Early reports of aphasia following right-sided lesions in left-handed adults had initially been interpreted as evidence that right or left hemisphere "dominance" for language systematically varied with handedness. Bramwell (1899) and Kennedy (1916), however, called attention to the "crossed aphasias," i.e. aphasias resulting from right-sided lesions in right-handed adults and from left-sided lesions in left handed adults.

Since the "crossed aphasias" clearly contradicted the assumption that language was systematically localized in the cerebral hemisphere opposite to the preferred hand, Kennedy proposed that right or left hemisphere dominance for language was hereditary and that "stock-brainedness" was independent of handedness.

The relationship between handedness and hemispheric specialization in language, however, has remained a source of historical controversy (e.g. Zangwill, 1967; Subirana, 1969; Smith, 1971). Roberts (1969) has concluded that "Dominance of the left cerebral hemisphere for speech is inherited." He also reported that, although the left hemisphere was dominant for speech in 95 percent of all dextrals and in two thirds of all sinistrals, the exact relationship between "stockbrainedness" and handedness (which also may be inherited) is unknown.

Early definitions of relationships between cerebral dominance and handedness were based on studies of patients with focal lateralized lesions. They reflected the view that in addition to intelligence, all language functions were localized exclusively in one "dominant" hemisphere. Citing reports of the absence of aphasia following left or right hemispherectomy for IH, Zangwill observed that "at birth the two hemispheres are virtually equipotential in regard to the acquisition of language and that dominance may be readily shifted in consequence of early brain injury" (Zangwill, 1960). However, in the normally developed brain, Zangwill described dominance as "a graded characteristic, varying in scope and completeness from individual to individual. Its precise relation to handedness and its vicissitudes still remains to be ascertained" (Zangwill, 1960). Thus, as Gardner *et al.*, (1955) and Zangwill (1960) have suggested, individual variations in hemispheric specialization in language and nonlanguage functions may be inherited and thus be a significant determinant of the results of hemispherectomy for tumour or for IH.

Early reports of improvements or development of language and mental functions following left or right hemispherectomy for IH were consistently cited as evidence that the hemisphere removed had been the "nondominant" one (Krynauw, 1950; Obrador, 1951; Gros and Vlahovitch, 1953; French *et al.*, 1955; Feld, 1953). However, these findings had been largely based on clinical observations and were limited to relatively short postoperative intervals. In a review of 150 reported cases, White (1961) noted general agreement that language was either acquired or improved following left or right hemisphere removals. He also observed that in contrast to disorders of spatial thought, body image, constructional apraxia, and other defects reported in adults with parietal lesions, mental capacities were not adversely affected. "Functional sites, in the same manner as mobility and sensibility, for speech, praxis and gnostic modalities have been 'reallocated' to other (healthy) areas of the brain in the course of development of IH. The transference of function can be spontaneously accomplished only before cerebral dominance is established. The age of establishment of cerebral dominance and the degree to which this dominance occurs are, without doubt, extremely variable among individuals" (White, 1961).

Although the extensive subsequent literature cannot be reviewed here, later studies using standardized psychological tests reported findings variously confirming and qualifying those of earlier clinical studies.

The reported differences between effects of hemispherectomy for IH and for tumour raise several critical questions. Gardner *et al.* (1955) suggested that following early lateralized brain insult, with the possible exception of speech, functions which would otherwise be performed by parts of the brain that failed to develop are to some extent "acquired" by the remaining presumably intact hemisphere. Like White (1961) and Lenneberg (1967), they also indicated that once a function has been "corticalized" or "established" in the right or left hemisphere, it cannot be transferred. To what extent may a specific function which later becomes "established" in either hemisphere be "transferred" to the opposite hemisphere following early lateralized brain damage?

The significance of age at time of brain insult and of the rate of "chronogenic localization" was also suggested by Teuber. ". . . we need to approach the problem in developmental terms; it is still not known how early the differentiation between hemispheres arises, whether before birth or soon after, whether predominantly as an effect of genetic factors, or as a result of use. We are all appreciative of the alleged plasticity of the infant brain, but we do not seem to have any strong evidence to suggest that the lateralization of different functions can really be reversed with complete impunity. One obvious task is to perform much more extensive studies than heretofore on childhood hemiplegia, since there is the strong possibility (we have some preliminary data) that right-hemisphere and left-hemisphere lesions, even in early infancy, produce reciprocally different syndromes, with right hemiplegia being associated with retarded language development and diminished ultimate language competence, while left hemiplegics show spatial and constructional difficulties" (Teuber, 1967).

In light of the specialization in language and verbal reasoning capacities by the left hemisphere, and in visual ideational, spatial, and constructional functions by the right hemisphere in the adult, it is logical to ask "Can a single hemisphere, either left or right, develop the normal levels of both language and nonlanguage capacities of the average adult

with two intact cerebral hemispheres? If not, there systematic differences in the subsequent development of these capacities as a function of
the side removed?"

Based on comparisons of preoperative and postoperative IQ tests of
twenty-eight cases of hemispherectomy and nine of partial lateralized
excisions for IH, McFie (1961) reported a greater increase in postoperative scores by the hemispherectomy group. However, he noted that the
increased IQ's occurred exclusively in hemispherectomized cases who
had sustained injuries in the first year of life, regardless of the side
removed or age at time of operation. McFie also reported that although
patients with normal EEG's in the remaining hemisphere showed the
greatest increase, the majority of unoperated patients with IH demonstrated ". . . a verbal deficit, amounting in some cases to dysphasia, irrespective of hemisphere damaged. . . . ," and ". . . these results indicate a limit to the capacity of the remaining hemisphere, imposed by the
mediation of the normal functions of both hemispheres by one hemisphere alone" (McFie, 1961). According to McFie, "by the end of the
first year, it appears likely that the conventional partition of functions
into right and left hemispheres has begun, and that subsequent injury
to a hemisphere does not entirely dislodge its functions to the other side,
with the result that removal of a hemisphere removes a certain amount
of functioning tissues." The limitation of a single right or left remaining
hemisphere "may bear particularly heavily upon language as opposed to
nonlanguage functions."

Subsequent studies of similar populations, however, reported different
findings. Griffith and Davidson (1966) presented comparisons of preoperative, initial postoperative, and four-year to fifteen-year postoperative IQ's in three cases with right and eight with left hemispherectomy
for IH. The remarkable outcome in Griffith's case No. 1 warrants individual consideration. Following onset of seizures at the age of ten,
hemiplegia at twelve, a right hemispherectomy was performed by Mr.
Huw Griffith of Oxford, England at the age of nineteen. He subsequently
obtained a university diploma. Tests fifteen years after the operation
revealed a WAIS Full Scale IQ of 109 (Verbal IQ of 121 and Performance
IQ of 91 versus a Verbal IQ of 101 and Performance IQ of 63 before surgery at the age of 19). Moreover, this thirty-four-year-old man was continuing successfully in a responsible administrative position with a local
authority. (This might be of special interest to one editorial writer in a
southern newspaper who, on learning of the normal nonverbal mental
capacities reported in Dr. Burklund's patient No. 9 (L_1) with left hemispherectomy for tumor, published the suggestion that L_1 might be better

suited for an administrative post in the Federal Government than many of the incumbents at the time.)

Since this young man and a second patient with right hemispherectomy had higher verbal than nonverbal reasoning capacities, and two similar patients with left hemispherectomy had higher nonverbal than verbal skills, Griffith and Davidson cited these findings as evidence that the transfer of intellectual faculty from one hemisphere to another after infantile hemiplegia or hemispherectomy for early lateralized lesions "may be incomplete, as it is for somatic functions." Although Griffith and Davidson recognized that this pattern was observed in only four of the eleven reported cases, they proposed that it was more easily detectable in the more intelligent patient. And, although these findings indicated subsequent development of language functions in all eight patients with left and three with right hemispherectomy, they also raised the question about earlier conclusions that the side removed was always "nondominant," regardless of whether it was the left or right hemisphere.

In contrast to earlier studies based primarily on clinical observations, standardized psychological tests in the above studies suggest systematic differences in effects of early lateralized lesions or hemispherectomy on the development of language and verbal reasoning versus nonverbal reasoning, visual ideational, spatial, and constructional capacities. However, other studies also using standardized tests reported different findings.

In comparisons of effects of IH on speech in 102 cases (54 left versus 48 right hemiplegics) and of effects of hemispherectomy in thirty-five of these patients, Basser (1962) reported no significant differences in preoperative verbal intelligence between right and left hemiplegics and no such differences after left and right hemispherectomy. Thus, Basser concluded ". . . speech was maintained and developed in the intact hemisphere and in this respect the left and right hemisphere were equal" (Basser, 1962). Although handedness is necessarily determined by the pathological involvement of either hemisphere, Basser noted the equipotentiality of the two hemispheres obtains irrespective of stockhandedness (and presumably, of stock-brainedness).

In the previously cited follow-up study of thirty cases with right and twenty with left hemispherectomy for IH (Wilson, 1970), earlier psychometric studies in the first thirty-four cases had been the bases for the findings by McFie (1961) described above. However, Wilson's later follow-up studies indicated different findings. Preoperatively, speech had been acquired or had developed in all but two youngest patients. Patients "who were hemiplegic before the acquisition of speech had no gross clinical disturbance of speech after hemispherectomy, irrespective of which hemisphere was removed. When the hemiplegia had followed the acquisition of speech, removal of the dominant left hemisphere led to failure of speech functions, but with later recovery in all but one instance" (Wilson, 1970).

With respect to general intelligence, Wilson observed, "The influence of hemispherectomy upon IQ levels has proved difficult or impossible to assess with accuracy." In the few patients with repeated postoperative tests ". . . changes were rarely more than a few points either way on the IQ scale" (Wilson, 1970). However, as noted above, he also attributed the level of residual functions to the quality of the substrate before hemispherectomy.

McFie's conclusions of impairment in verbal functions in the left and right infantile hemiplegics before and after right or left hemispherectomy were tested in a study of sixteen patients with hemispherectomy for IH and matched unoperated controls by Carlson *et al.* (1969). However, in addition to standardized IQ (Wechsler and Stanford Binet) tests, their testing battery included specific language tests for assessment of dysphasic disorders as well as tests of nonlanguage functions. In a summary of the overall findings, they reported no differences between effects of right and left hemispherectomies, and ". . . we have been unable to demonstrate any disturbance of language functions as measured by the tests we have used. Thus, not only have we been unable to confirm McFie's findings, but our patients have shown significantly higher verbal than performance IQ's when compared to the control group" (Carlson *et al.*, 1969). Although this pattern was also evident in comparisons of three patients with hemispherectomy before the age of six months and thirteen with hemispherectomy after two years of age, the mean IQ of the three early operated cases was significantly higher than that of the thirteen operated upon after the age of two years. Thus, their findings of greater residual language and nonlanguage functions in the early operated group are consistent with the report by McFie of larger increases in IQ in cases undergoing hemispherectomy for brain insults sustained in the first year of life.

Just as in psychological studies of "brain damaged" populations, the diverse findings in studies of hemispherectomy suggest inherent difficulties in precise definitions of the two fundamental variables, structure and function (Smith, 1962). Comparisons of effects of hemispherectomy for tumour are qualified by differences in the following: neurosurgical procedures and the extent of hemispheric removals; associated pathophysiological reactions, such as increased intracranial pressure, disturbances in the vascular supply, and radiation of effects to the opposite hemisphere which are often relieved by surgery; postoperative complications; age; postoperative intervals and secondary necrosis; individual variations in premorbid capacities and in the extent to which specialized functions have developed in each hemisphere; the absence of premorbid measures, as well as methods of testing; and, as noted above, the presence of unsuspected recurring gliomas which increasingly attenuate the functions of the remaining hemisphere.

Although preoperative studies contribute to definitions of effects of hemispherectomy for IH, the diverse reported findings suggest uncontrolled effects of the above and other factors. Assessments of effects based on comparisons of preoperative and postoperative studies may be confounded by the effects of prolonged large doses of anticonvulsant drugs which, while failing to eliminate seizures, may significantly reduce cerebral functions. Instead of the recurrence of tumours, the findings in earlier studies of operated and unoperated cases of IH are often similarly qualified by unsuspected damage to the presumably intact hemisphere, either concomitant with—or subsequent to—the initial early brain insult.

In most IH cases with severe seizures, hemispherectomy is performed only after prolonged efforts to control severe seizures have failed. Cairns, however, wrote, "it seems well established that fits can produce additional cerebral hemorrhages or infarctions" (Cairns, 1951). Carlson *et al.* (1968) urged early operation "to free the undamaged hemisphere from the disruptive influences of the damaged one and, more important, avoid the cerebral damage which occurs as a result of recurrent seizures" (Carlson *et al.*, 1968).

Progressive mental deterioration in this clinical material has been documented in long-term preoperative psychological studies reported by Ransohoff and Carter (1956). In their case Number 2, an IQ of 94 in a 9-year-old girl declined to 55 at the age of 14, and to 49 to one week before hemispherectomy at 16 years. One month postoperatively, her IQ was 56.

In a subsequent case (Ransohoff, 1970, personal communication), an IQ of 135 at 10 years of age declined to 85 just before surgery at the age of 17. One year postoperatively, the IQ had risen to 100. For many years before surgery, this patient had had up to 20 seizures daily.

Whether improvement in such cases is due to cessation of seizures, removal of the diseased hemisphere and elimination of disruptive influences on the remaining hemisphere, and/or discontinuance of sedative drugs, the findings indicate that in some cases hemispherectomy arrests and reverses underlying pathological processes that might otherwise result in irreversible mental retardation.

Ignelzi and Bucy (1968) reported that EEG evidence alone of abnormal activity on the side opposite the obviously damaged hemisphere does not contraindicate surgery unless other findings indicate bilateral lesions. This view is compatible with Krynauw's (1950) observation that, following hemispherectomy, abnormal EEG tracings over the remaining hemisphere rapidly returned to normal. McFie's (1961) report of the presence of abnormal EEG's over the remaining hemisphere in eighteen of thirty-one cases, however, suggested that preoperative damage had not been confined to a single hemisphere in approximately 60 percent of these early cases. It is therefore not surprising that the fifteen with lowest postoperative IQ's (ranging from 19 to 59) *included fourteen of the eighteen with abnormal postoperative EEG's.*

As indicated above, the methods of examination are also of critical importance. Early psychological studies of adults with right hemispherectomy for tumor failed to reveal any characteristic mental deficits because of the prevailing emphasis on projective tests such as the Rorschach as well as on tests of verbal reasoning capacities. The limited value of projective tests in such studies was also clearly indicated in the report by Bruell and Albee (1962). However, the marked differences in their patient's scores in the two nonlanguage tests also demonstrated that aggregate IQ scores in omnibus intelligence tests like the Wechsler scales may obscure specific defects resulting in markedly impaired performances in certain subtests.

Thus, in addition to possibly significant differences in individual natural endowment and other above cited factors, the wide variations in intellectual capacities in all reported studies of right or left hemispherectomy for IH may reflect differences in the tests used to assess mental functions as well as differences in the frequency and extent of unsuspected preoperative damage to the residual hemisphere.

It is therefore not surprising that in contrast to the pattern of systematic differential impairment of language versus nonlanguage capacities following "dominant" and "nondominant" hemispherectomy, neuropsychological tests of nineteen patients with left and thirteen with right hemispherectomy for IH showed wide individual variations in these capacities regardless of the hemisphere removed. However, to illustrate the marked differences between right and left hemispherectomy for tumour in adults and for lesions in early infancy resulting in IH, Table I-II presents the scores of two of eighteen *adults* with hemispherectomy for IH tested thus far.

As noted above, earlier studies had cited the subsequent development of normal language and improvement of mental functions as evidence that the hemisphere removed in IH, whether left or right, was the nondominant one. However, McFie (1961) reported that language and verbal reasoning deficits before and after right or left hemispherectomy for IH indicated greater attenuation in the development of language than nonlanguage functions. And Gardner *et al.* (1955) Griffith and Davidson (1966) and Teuber (1967), suggested that in such cases, transfer of (left hemisphere) verbal and (right hemisphere) spatial reasoning capacities may be incomplete. Griffith and Davidson (1966) also suggested that, although verbal-spatial disparities following hemispherectomy may diminish with time, such disparities remain more easily detectable in the more intelligent patients. Accordingly, Table I-II presents test scores of the most intelligent patient (PK) among our thirteen with right hemispherectomy, and of the most intelligent (BL) among the nineteen with left hemispherectomy.

In addition to providing evidence bearing on earlier diverse findings, presentation of the scores for these two young adults (Table I-II) permits comparisons with performances on the same tests by four older adults with right and one with left hemispherectomy. Since our neuropsychological battery includes several tests that were standardized in studies of normal adults with two intact hemispheres, Table I-II also

TABLE I-II
RIGHT AND LEFT HEMISPHERECTOMY FOR INFANTILE HEMIPLEGIA

	Right		*Left*
	IH₁(PK)		IH₂(BL)
Postop Interval	4 yrs		16 yrs
Age/Education (years)	24/13		21/12
		(WAIS)	
Information	17/11		22/13
Comprehension	14/8		27/19
Arithmetic	10/9		10/9
Similarities	15/11		17/12
Digit Span	9/7		9/7
Vocabulary	......		59/13
Digit Symbol	38/7		45/8
Picture Completion	9/7		17/12
Block Design	28/9		36/11
Picture Arrangement	22/9		24/10
Object Assembly	20/7		26/8
Verbal IQ	96		113
Performance IQ	85		98
Full Scale IQ	90		107
Peabody Picture Vocab.	109		125
Visual Memory	6		7
Copy Designs	10		10
Colored Matrices	31		32
Visual Organization	23		27½
SDMT Written	40		36
SDMT Oral	47		55
Porteus Maze	......		......
DSS (Face-Hand)	left sensory		normal

provides evidence of the extent to which language, verbal reasoning, and visual ideational and other nonlanguage functions may develop in a single remaining left or right hemisphere.

PK's reported medical history (No. 3 in Ignelzi and Bucy, 1968) lists encephalitis at the age of ten months, resulting in left hemiparesis, and mental and neurological retardation; and the development of seizures and frequent episodes of destructive behavior, neither of which were controlled by a variety of medications. At the age of twenty, she underwent a right hemidecortication, performed by Dr. Bucy. Comparisons of preoperative and postoperative findings, including the elimination of seizures and of mental aberrations in PK and three similar patients, were described in a report on early postoperative findings (Ignelzi and Bucy, 1968).

Following BL's delivery by Cesaerian section, right hemiparesis was noted at the age of five months. Seizures developed at the age of four years, and despite anticonvulsant drugs, increased to ten to twelve per day. Preoperative language studies indicated that although verbal comprehension was apparently normal, speech was distorted and difficult to understand. At the age of 5.5 years, he underwent a left hemispherectomy with, as Table I-II shows, the most salutary results. The absence of a right facial paralysis immediately after left hemispherectomy, is especially noteworthy. Speech, which had been almost unintelligible, rapidly improved and became normal. In addition to the cessation of seizures without the use of medication, Table I-II reflects the subsequent development of normal or above normal language, verbal reasoning, visual ideational, and other nonlanguage capacities.

If the transfer of functions from BL's left hemisphere (injured at birth and removed 5.5 years later) to the right hemisphere was "incomplete" (Griffith and Davidson), and/or the lateralization of different functions can *not* "really be reversed with complete impunity" (Teuber, 1967); or if the limitations on residual functions after right or left hemispherectomy "bear particularly heavily upon language as opposed to nonlanguage functions" (McFie, 1961), language and verbal reasoning capacities sixteen years after removal (and 21 years after birth injury) of the left hemisphere should be less well developed than nonlanguage functions.

Special orofacial and language examinations of both BL and PK failed to reveal any suggestion of even a slight defect in speech, auditory comprehension, reading, writing, or orofacial functions.

If conclusions were based only on Wechsler tests, we may note that in contrast to the findings of Griffith and Davidson and of McFie, BL's Verbal IQ (113) was fifteen points higher than his Performance IQ

(98), placing him in the 80th percentile or higher than four of five adults with two intact hemispheres in verbal intelligence. It is also interesting to observe that BL's Verbal IQ (113), Performance IQ (98), and Full Scale IQ (107) sixteen years after *left* hemispherectomy for birth injury are strikingly comparable to those of Griffith and Davidson's first patient (Verbal IQ 121, Performance IQ 91, Full Scale IQ 109) fifteen years after *right* hemispherectomy.

Comparisons of language and nonlanguage test scores of BL with left and PK with right hemispherectomy also reveal consistently higher scores by BL in almost all nonlanguage as well as language tests. (The only measure showing a higher score by PK was the written form of the Symbol Digit Substitution Test (Smith, 1967) in which writing with the left hand handicapped BL by blocking the standard. However, this did not occur in the WAIS Digit Symbol subtest, and comparisons of the *oral* form of the Symbol-Digit test reflected the pattern of superior capacities shown by BL in other measures.)

Comparisons of PK's Verbal and Performance IQ's, however, suggest that nonlanguage functions have not developed as much as language functions four years after right hemispherectomy. (This might suggest that the development of nonlanguage functions was selectively attenuated in cases with right hemispherectomy. However, Performance IQ's were higher than Verbal IQ's in only 3—one aphasic and 2 severely retarded—of 13 cases with left hemispherectomy; and in one of 8 with right hemispherectomy.)

The tests in the neuropsychologic battery were selected or constructed to differentiate impairment in test modalities (i.e. those involved in perceptions of and responses to the presented tasks) from impairment of the "higher" mental functions the tests were designed and are assumed to measure. Although slightly subnormal scores in the Benton Visual Retention and Hooper Visual Organization tests also suggest less development of the specific nonlanguage visual perceptual functions involved, correct responses to thirty-one of the thirty-six problems in the Raven Coloured Progressive Matrices tests indicated normal capacities for nonverbal analagous reasoning, or the ability to abstract in "visual systems of thought."

Time is one of the most important factors in evaluating the effects of brain lesions (Smith, 1962), and Meyers (1958) has emphasized the importance of lifetime studies in efforts to evaluate initial and later effects of hemispherectomy. We may therefore note that PK's preoperative, two-year postoperative, and four-year postoperative performances revealed continuing postoperative increases in Performance IQ's (75 versus 80 and 85) compared to an initial postoperative increase followed by little change in Verbal IQ's (85 versus 95 and 96). Follow-up studies of these and other patients with hemispherectomy for tumour as well as for IH are therefore of special interest with respect to possible changes in the organization or levels of cerebral functions with time.

The pattern of higher Verbal than Performance IQ's following left hemispherectomy was also demonstrated by EK, one of Dr. Joseph Ransohoff's cases with birth injury and surgery at the age of 7.8 years. In addition to cessation of seizures, a Verbal IQ of 98, Performance IQ of 77, Full Scale IQ 88, Peabody Picture Vocabulary of 107 when tested at the age of 15.6 years, normal responses in Double Simultaneous (face-hand) stimulations were shown by only one other patient (BL) among the twenty-three tested.

Thus, consistent with the findings of Basser, Carlson *et al.*, and Wilson, our neuropsychological and language tests revealed no evidence of dysphasia in twenty-three of twenty-four cases with left or right hemispherectomy for IH, and no evidence of significant differences in effects of right or left hemispherectomy on language and nonlanguage tests. In contrast to the findings in Verbal-Performance IQ comparisons, higher Performance IQ's in three of thirteen patients with left and one of nine cases with right hemispherectomy might suggest that effects of removals of either hemisphere are more marked on nonlanguage capacities. Indeed, one of the most striking findings in studies of twenty-four patients thus far was that with only one exception (an aphasic hospitalized for continuing psychotic episodes, examined 3 years after left hemispherectomy), correct grammatical speech had developed in all patients, including four whose intelligence test scores were below the lowest limits.

The consistent findings of subsequent development or improvement of language functions after right or left hemispherectomy for IH in almost all reported studies suggest that, in the reorganization of functions in the drastically reduced neuroanatomical economy resulting from removal of either hemisphere, *there may be a developmental hierarchy in which the development of language functions takes precedence over nonlanguage and verbal reasoning functions.* The suggested priority and independence of language in the development of cerebral functions is indicated by two patients with right and two with left hemispherectomy whose verbal and nonverbal reasoning capacities were below the lowest limits of standardized intelligence tests for children or adults. In addition to similar cases reported in earlier studies of hemispherectomy for IH, priorities for the selective development of speech and verbal comprehension (but *not* of reading and writing) are also evident in the severely mentally retarded. Thus, the findings indicate that the *acqui-*

sition of (or the development, organization, and integration of the complex process involved in) speaking and understanding speech are "no more learned than, say ability to walk is learned" (Chomsky, 1967).

Clearly, then, the biological substrata of language functions, and nonlanguage visual ideational functions that are manifested in normal adults, are duplicated in each hemisphere. In those reported cases in which normal language and other capacities fail to develop after left or right hemispherectomy for IH, such failures may reflect limitations on the residual hemisphere superimposed by insults either concomitant with or subsequent to the initial obvious lesion resulting in infantile hemiplegia.

Although chronic dysphasia in unoperated adults with a history of early right hemiplegia is relatively rare, the development of normal language following early speech difficulties has been interpreted as evidence that language functions had shifted to the presumably intact right hemisphere. However, the proportion of dysphasics in Wilson's (1970) later follow-up studies of fifty cases (including the 34 studied by McFie) was markedly lower than that indicated in the earlier study by McFie (1961). The apparent recovery from early aphasia might therefore be interpreted as evidence that, *in the presence of damage to structures in the remaining hemisphere in which language normally develops in cases without bilateral lesions, other intact structures in the immature brain provided the biological substrata necessary for the development of normal language.*

The development of normal language functions preoperatively or marked improvement in speech after left or right hemispherectomy cannot therefore be interpreted as evidence that the residual hemisphere is intact. Indeed, in view of the usual history of frequent severe and intractable seizures before surgery, it is not surprising that careful analyses of the accumulating data indicate that an intact residual hemisphere after surgery is rare.

Previous studies have reported evidence of damage to the residual hemisphere in the forms of persisting abnormal EEG's and/or aphasia. However, in addition to the obvious contralateral right or left hemiplegia, careful studies of manual motor functions on the side ipsilateral to the hemisphere removed revealed additional evidence of such damage.

Analyses of manual dexterity performance with the supposedly intact hand of 19 patients with left and 13 with right hemispherectomy for IH revealed only 11 (six with right and five with left hemispherectomy) with approximately normal capacities. In 21 others, manual dexterity scores with the presumably intact hand ranged from moderately (10 patients) to markedly (11 patients) subnormal (Costa *et al*, 1963). Comparisons of scores in manual dexterity with scores in language, verbal and nonverbal reasoning and memory tests revealed that with few exceptions, patients with subnormal manual dexterity scores were more markedly impaired in overall intellectual capacities than those with normal scores. Since reduced manual dexterity alone indicated that the residual hemisphere had been handicapped in two of every three patients with right or left hemispherectomy for IH in our population, it is obvious that tacit assumptions in earlier studies that the remaining hemisphere was intact were unwarranted. It is, therefore, not surprising that conclusions on the capacities of a single hemisphere or the functional plasticity of the young brain described in such studies differ (Smith, 1973).

The implications of this finding in studies of children and adults with hemispherectomy for IH for studies of other populations with presumably lateralized lesions were indicated in a study of 100 pre-morbidly right-handed adults with reported left-sided cerebrovascular lesions resulting in chronic aphasia.* Manual dexterity scores with the *left* hand of 58 right hemiplegics and 42 nonhemiplegics who had been tested with the same battery revealed subnormal scores in 31 (31%) consisting of 23 (39.7%) of the 58 hemiplegics and 8 (19.1%) of the 42 nonhemiplegics. Paralleling the findings in studies of our hemisphe-rectomy patients, hemiplegics and nonhemiplegics with subnormal *left* hand dexterity scores also showed greater impairment in language, verbal and nonverbal reasoning, memory and sensory functions than those with normal left hand dexterity scores. Since the mean interval between stroke and examination was 17 months, the findings cannot be readily interpreted as transient early "distance" effects of strokes. Instead they indicate that, as in preoperative and postoperative studies of the IH hemispherectomy cases, assumptions that the functions of the opposite hemisphere are intact are unwarranted. In some cases, the effects of chronic cerebrovascular lesions may radiate to and disrupt the functions of the opposite hemisphere; in others, in addition to evidence of gross language, motor and/or sensory defects indicating apparent involvement of the left or right hemisphere, subnormal functions of the presumably intact hemisphere may be due to unsuspected bilateral lesions.

The marked differences between effects of hemispherectomy for lesions incurred in early or later life also emphasize the marked changes and increasing specialization of each hemisphere in language or non-language functions with normal development of the brain. As noted above, the neuroanatomical substrata for the development of normal or above normal adult language, verbal and nonverbal reasoning capacities are present in both cerebral hemispheres of the infant brain. Thus, the increasing specialization of the left hemisphere in language and verbal reasoning functions and of the right in visual ideational, spatial, and constructional functions indicate a process of mutual reciprocal inhibitions of hemispheric functions. As the brain matures, the left hemisphere gradually assumes a leading role in language and related functions with increasing inhibition of the mechanisms in the right hemisphere capable of such functions; and correspondingly, the right hemisphere assumes a leading role in visual ideational functions with increasing inhibition of left hemisphere mechanisms capable of such functions.

REFERENCES

Basser, L. S.: Hemiplegia of early onset and the faculty of speech with special reference to the effects of hemispherectomy. *Brain, 85:* 427–460, 1962.

Bennett, A. H., and Godlee, R. J.: Case of cerebral tumor. *Br Med J, 1:* 988–989, 1885.

Bogen, J. E.: The other side of the brain. *Bull Los Angeles Neurol Soc, 34:* 73–105, part I(a), 135–161, part II(b), 1969.

Bramwell, B.: On "crossed" aphasias. *Lancet, 1:* 1473–1479, 1899.

Broca, P.: Sur la faculte du langage articule. *Bull Soc D'Anthropologie (Paris),* 6: 493–494, 1865.

Bruell, J. H., and Albee, G. W.: Higher intellectual functions in a patient with hemispherectomy for tumor. *J Consult Psychol, 26:* 90–98, 1962.

Cairns, H., and Davidson, M. A.: Hemispherectomy in the treatment of infantile hemiplegia. *Lancet, 2:* 411–415, 1951.

Carlson, J., Netley, C., Hendrick, E. B., and Prichard, J. S.: A reexamination of intellectual disabilities in hemispherectomized patients. *Trans Am Neurol Assoc, 93:* 198–201, 1968.

Chomsky, N.: In Millikan, C. H., and Darley, F. L. (Eds.): *The General Properties of Language in Brain Mechanisms Underlying Speech and Language.* New York, Grune and Stratton, 1967, pp. 73–88.

Costa, L. D., Vaughan, H. G., Levita, E., and Farber, N.: The Purdue Pegboard as a prediction of the presence and laterality of cerebral lesions. *J Consult Psychol, 27,* 133–137, 1963.

Dandy, W. E.: Physiological studies following extirpation of the right cerebral hemisphere in man. *Johns Hopkins Hosp Bull, 53:* 31–51, 1933.

————: Removal of right cerebral hemisphere for certain tumors with hemiplegia. Preliminary report. *JAMA, 90:* 823–825, 1928.

Falconer, M. A., and Wilson, P. J. E.: Complications related to delayed hemorrhage after hemispherectomy. *J Neurosurg, 30:* 413–426, 1969.

Feld, M.: De L'hemiplegie cerebrale infantile aux encephalapothie catricielles. Place et signification des hemispherectomies, *Vth Int Neurol Congress, 4:* 387–391, 1953.

Flourens, P.: *Recherches Experimentale sur les Proprietes et des Fonctions du Systeme Nerveux dans les Animaus Vertebres.* Paris, Chez Crevot, 1824.

French, L. A., Johnson, D. R., Brown, I. A., and Von Verben, F. B.: Cerebral hemispherectomy for control in intractable convulsive seizures. *J. Neurosurg, 12:* 154–164, 1955.

Gardner, W. J., Karnosh, L. J., McClure, C. C., and Gardner, A. K.: Residual function following hemispherectomy for tumor and for infantile hemiplegia. *Brain, 78:* 487–502, 1955.

Griffith, H., and Davidson, M.: Long-term changes in intellect and behavior after hemispherectomy. *J Neurol Neurosurg Psychiat, 29:* 571–576, 1966.

Gros, C., and Vlahovitch, B.: Etude de la sensibilite dans les hemispherectomies. *Congre Neurologique International, 4:* 320–322, 1953.

Hebb, D. O.: Intelligence in man after large removals of cerebral tissue: Defects following right temporal lobectomy. *J Gen Psychol, 21:* 437–446, 1939.

Hillier, W. F.: Total left cerebral hemispherectomy for malignant glioma. *Neurology, 4:* 718–721, 1954.

Ignelzi, R. J., and Bucy, P. C.: Cerebral hemidecortication in the treatment of infantile cerebral hemiatrophy. *J Nerv Ment Dis, 147:* 14–30, 1968.

Jackson, H.: Case of large cerebral tumor without optic neuritis and with left hemiplegia and imperception. *Roy Lond Ophthalmic Hosp Rep, 8:* 434, 1876.

Kennard, M. A., and Fulton, J. F.: Age and reorganization of the central nervous system. *J Mount Sinai Hosp, 9:* 594–605, 1942.

Kennedy, F.: Stock-brainedness, the causation factor in the so-called "crossed aphasias." *Am J Med Sci, 6:* 849–859, 1916.

Liepman, H. K.: Die linke hemisphere und das handeln. *Med Wochenschr, 52:* 2322–2326, 1905.

Lenneberg, E. H.: *Biological Foundations of Language.* New York, Wiley, 1967.

Lereboullet, J.: Removal of left cerebral hemisphere. *Paris Med, 1:* 358–360, 1936.

Lhermitte, J.: L'ablation complete de l'hemisphere droit dans les cas de tumeur cerebrale localizee compliquee d'hemiplegie: La decerebration supra-thalamique unilaterale chez l'homme. *Encephale, 23:* 314–323, 1928.

McFie, J.: The effects of hemispherectomy on intellectual functioning in cases of infantile hemiplegia. *J Neurol Neurosurg Psychiatry,* 1961.

McHenry, L. C.: *Garrison's History of Neurology.* Springfield, Thomas, 1969.

McKenzie, K. G.: The present status of a patient who had the right cerebral hemisphere removed. *JAMA, 111:* 168, 1938.

Mensh, I. N., Schwartz, H. G., Matarazzo, R. G., and Matarazzo, J. D.: Psychological functioning following cerebral hemispherectomy in man. *Arch Neurol Psychiatry, 67:* 787–796, 1952.

Meyers, R.: Recent advances in the neurosurgery of cerebral palsy. In Illingworth, R. S. (Ed.): *Recent Advances in Cerebral Palsy.* London, Churchill, 1958, pp. 330–386.

Monakow, C. V.: Localization of brain functions. *J fur Psychologie und Neurologie, 17:* 185–200, 1911.

Obrador, S. A.: Hemisferectomia en el tratamiento de las convulsiones de la hemiplegia infantil por hemiatrofia cerebral. *Arq Neuro-psiquiat (S Paulo), 9:* 191–197, 1951.

Pool, J. L.: Answer to question "Would you recommend hemispherectomy for treatment of a cerebral glioma?" *Clin Neurosurg,* 1968, p. 286.

Roberts, L.: Aphasia, apraxia, and agnosia in abnormal states of cerebral dominance. In Vinken, P. J., and Bruyn, G. W. (Eds.): *Handbook of Clinical Neurology.* New York, Wiley, 1969, vol. 4. pp. 312–326.

Rowe, S. N.: Mental changes following the removal of the right cerebral hemisphere for brain tumor. *Am J Psychiatry, 94:* 604–612, 1937.

Smith, A.: Ambiguities in concepts and studies of "brain damage" and "organicity." *J Nerv Ment Dis, 135:* 311–326, 1962.

————: Speech and other functions after left (Dominant) hemispherectomy. *J Neurol Neurosurg Psychiatry, 29:* 467–471, 1966.

————: Nondominant hemispherectomy. *Neurology, 19:* 442–445, 1969.

————: Objective indices of severity of chronic aphasia in stroke patients. *J Speech Hearing Dis, 36:* 167–207, 1971.

————, and Burkland, C. W.: Dominant hemispherectomy, *Science, 153:* 1280–1282, 1966.

————, and Burkland, C. W. B.: Nondominant hemispherectomy: Neuropsychologic implications for human brain factors. *APA, 1967 Convention Proc.,* pp. 103–104.

Smith, A.: *Hemispherectomy and Functional Plasticity of the Human Brain.* Society for Neuroscience Abstracts, 1973, p. 111.

Smith, A.: *Neuropsychological Studies of Stroke Patients with Chronic Aphasia.* International Neuropsychological Society 2nd Annual Meeting, Boston, Feb. 8, 1974.

Strong, O. S., and Elwyn, A.: *Human Neuroanatomy.* Baltimore, Williams and Wilkins, 1943.

Subirana, A.: Handedness and cerebral dominance. In Vinken, P. J., and Bruyn, G. W. (Eds.): *Handbook of Clinical Neurology.* New York, Wiley, 1969, Vol. 4, pp. 248–272.

Terman, L. M., and Merrill, M. A.: *Measuring Intelligence.* Boston, Houghton Mifflin, 1936.

Teuber, H. L.: Lacunae and research approaches to them. In Millikan, C. H., and Darley, F. L. (Eds.): *Brain Mechanisms Underlying Speech and Language.* New York, Grune and Stratton, 1967, pp. 204–216.

Vulpian, A.: Lecons sur la physiologie generale et comparee du systeme nerveux. *Paris Balliere, 6:* 920, 1866.

Weisenburg, T. H., and McBride, K. E.: *Aphasia: A Clinical and Psychological Study.* New York Commonwealth Fund, 1935, p. 322.

————, Roe, A., and McBride, K. E.: *Adult Intelligence.* New York Commonwealth Fund, 1936.

White, H. H.: Cerebral hemispherectomy in the treatment of infantile hemiplegia, *Confin Neurol, 21:* 1–50, 1961.

Williams, D. J., and Scott, J. W.: The functional responses of the sympathetic nervous system of man following hemidecortication. *J Neurol Psychiatry, 2:* 313–322, 1939.

Wilson, P. J. E.: Cerebral hemispherectomy for infantile hemiplegia. *Brain, 93:* 147–180, 1970.

Zangwill, O. L.: *Cerebral Dominance and Its Relation to Psychological Function.* Edinburgh, Oliver and Boyd, 1960.

————: Speech and the minor hemisphere. *Acta Neurologica et Psychiatrica Belgica, 67:* 1013–1020, 1967.

Zollinger, R.: Removal of left cerebral hemisphere. *Arch Neurol Psychiatry, 34:* 1055–1064, 1935.

[CHAPTER II]

PATTERNS OF HEMISPHERIC SPECIALIZATION AFTER HEMIDECORTICATION FOR INFANTILE HEMIPLEGIA

Bruno Kohn and Maureen Dennis

INTRODUCTION

ATTEMPTS TO STUDY THE plasticity of the immature human nervous system have been variously made in comparing the behavioral consequences of early and late brain damage. The issue (e.g. Hebb, 1942; Lashley, 1938; Teuber, 1970; Teuber and Rudel, 1962) relates to the extent of functional compensation following infantile insult: Is it greater than that after similar damage incurred by adults? No simple answer to this question can be given. The effects of early injury are neither uniformly less nor more disruptive; rather, the severity of impairments appears to vary with the functions studied. Possibly related to this diversity of consequences is evidence that functional cerebral organization undergoes changes during the course of maturation (Hebb, 1942). Thus, the logic itself involved in the comparison of early and late lesion effects, interfering, as they may, with differentially organized neural mechanisms, could be questioned (Teuber, 1970).

The notion of a plastic, immature nervous system which, when damaged, compensates through atypical involvement of intact structures has, however, obtained some support from investigations of cerebral asymmetries following infantile brain injury. The development of speech functions and verbal intelligence in individuals who had suffered perinatal pathology of either the left or right cerebral hemisphere appears to justify the assumption that the capacity of the two brain halves for a mediation of language skills may be at least temporarily equivalent. Basser (1962) and McFie (1961) have tested infantile hemiplegics who

This investigation was supported by the Medical Research Council of Canada through grant MA-4134 to the first and a Fellowship to the second author. We are grateful to Drs. P. C. Bucy, E. B. Hendrick and H. J. Hoffman for permission to test their patients and to Drs. J. Arbit and C. T. Netley for making some of the intelligence test scores available.

had undergone left or right hemidecortication for relief of convulsive seizures: the postoperative level of verbal intelligence proved to be unrelated to the laterality of disease and surgery. This absence of speech defects comparable in severity to the consequences of left hemisphere damage in adults led the authors to propose that brain damage during the first year of life is compensated for by a development of verbal abilities in the less affected brain half.

The potential for a compensatory development of language functions appears to diminish during early childhood. Lansdell (1969) found, in a group of patients with right hemisphere control of speech resulting from early pathology of the left hemisphere, an inverse relation between the age at onset of the first symptoms and the verbal intelligence scores.

While cerebral malfunction of early onset can spare verbal competence, it is not clear whether abilities which depend on analyses of spatial relationships are similarly preserved. The present report describes a study of such spatial skills in a group of hemidecorticate infantile hemiplegics.

MATERIALS AND METHODS

Subjects who had undergone left or right hemidecortication were tested. Each group comprised three females and one male. The onset of initial symptoms—hemiplegia in seven, seizures in one case—dated to the first year of life for all the subjects. Three of the subjects had been operated by Dr. P. C. Bucy, the surgery on five of them had been performed by Dr. E. B. Hendrick and Dr. H. J. Hoffman. The mean age at surgery was 14 years for the left hemidecorticate (LH) and 12.2 years for the right hemidecorticate (RH) group. In six of the subjects, the removal of neocortex and hippocampus provided complete relief from convulsive seizures and behavioral disorders, while the intensity of seizures was strongly reduced in the remaining two cases. The mean age at behavioral testing was 21.8 and 20.8 years, respectively, for the two groups. At that time, all subjects evidenced homonymous hemianopsia in the field contralateral to the surgical removal and spasticity, in varying degrees, of the contralateral limbs. None of the subjects showed clinical evidence of speech defects or impaired verbal comprehension. Additional details of the medical histories are reported by Ignelzi and Bucy (1968) and Kohn and Dennis (b).

Tactile form recognition with the hand ipsilateral to the cortical removal was assessed by means of a matching procedure using a variety of shapes (Kohn and Dennis, a). Additional tests of spatial abilities (Kohn and Dennis, b) included the following: a test of visuo-perceptual organization (Street, 1931), which requires the subject to identify by name common objects and situations presented in fragmented pictures; a test of left-right discrimination and directional sense (Weinstein, 1958) on which the subject points to those parts of his own body which are marked on front and back diagrams of a man; the Money Road Map Test (Money, 1965), which requires the subject to state the direction of turns to be made in following a path drawn on a city map; a map reading test (Semmes *et al.*, 1955), on which visual maps instruct the subject as to the path to be walked between nine markers placed on the ground. Lastly, the Porteus and WISC paper-and-pencil mazes were used as measures of the subjects' visually guided route-finding skills. On both tasks, the subject draws a path through a series of mazes of increasing complexity. WISC or WAIS I.Q. scores were obtained from all the subjects.

RESULTS

The mean full scale I.Q. scores were similar for LH and RH groups (83.0 and 79.5, respectively). Neither VIQ (85.3 for LH, 85.8 for RH) nor PIQ scores of the two groups (82.0 for LH, 76.3 for RH) differed reliably. The mean VIQ score of the RH group, however, tended ($t = 2.94$, $p < .10$) to be higher than their PIQ score.

The LH and RH performances, expressed as percentages of the maximum obtainable scores on the various tests, are shown in Figure II-1. Some of the subjects were unavailable for the period of time required to complete all the tests.

The results obtained with the LH and RH groups fall into two distinct patterns: on three of the tests, i.e. tactile form matching, visual closure and personal orientation, the performances of the two groups were indistinguishable. On the remaining four tests, i.e. the WISC and Porteus Mazes, the Money Road Map test and a map reading test of extrapersonal orientation, the LH group proved consistently superior to the RH group.

Normative data allow for a comparison of age levels at which the skills measured by the various tests used develop in normal subject populations. Such a comparison shows that the equivalent performances of the LH and RH groups on three of the tests reflect earlier developing abilities than those required on the tasks where the LH group proved superior. Specifically, six year old normal children perform adequately on tactile form matching tasks (Witelson); the abilities necessary on tests of visual closure develop by the age of eight (Street, 1931), while about 90 percent of the ten year old subjects tested obtain perfect scores on measures of bodily orientation (Poeck and Orgass, 1964; Williams and Jambor, 1964). In consequence, the LH and RH performances

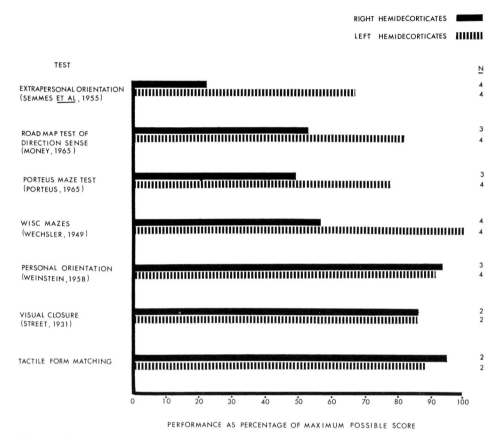

Figure II-1. Test scores of infantile hemiplegics after left or right hemidecortication.

indicate that after infantile brain damage either left or right hemisphere processes can mediate skills based on spatial analyses which are established in a normal developmental sequence by the age of ten years.

Such a functional equivalence of the two hemispheres is not apparent on WISC and Porteus Mazes in which tasks of graded difficulty determine the developmental level of the subject. The clearly superior LH performances point to a better development of the abilities in a right than a left hemisphere. Further evidence for the superiority of spatial skills mediated by a right hemisphere derives from the Money Road Map test. On this task, normal subjects tend to be errorless by about 16 years of age (Money, 1965). As Figure II-1 shows, the corresponding scores of the RH group point once more to less developed spatial abilities than those displayed by the LH subjects.

In summary, those LH and RH performances which suggest a functional equivalence of the left and right hemispheres, relate strictly to

early-maturing spatial skills. In contrast, if spatial tasks require processes which develop in a normal course of events during the second
decade of life, the superior level of right hemisphere functions indicates
a distinct and consistent impairment in such abilities when they are
mediated by a left remaining hemisphere.

The described data bear on two separate issues. One of these arises
in the context of equivalent performances which have been obtained
from the LH and RH groups on some of the tasks. Compensatory developments of the less affected hemisphere following pathology of early
onset might underlie the similar competences. Alternatively, the performances might be indicative of left and right hemisphere functions
which accrue during a normal development. Secondly, the persisting
issue of relative sparing or loss following early and late brain damage
remains to be considered. Are the deficits found in the present study
milder or more severe than those reported after lateralized brain damage
in adults?

Answers to either question require a prior comparison of hemispheric
control of verbal and spatial skills in hemidecorticate subjects on one
hand with, on the other, cerebral organization revealed after late brain
damage on the tasks used in the present study.

EARLY BRAIN DAMAGE AND HEMISPHERIC SPECIALIZATION

It is obvious that the hemispheric control of verbal abilities in hemidecorticate subjects represents a major divergence from cerebral organization in most adult patients. The LH and RH subjects were indistinguishable on tests of verbal intelligence. Thus, within limits of the tests
given, no indication of differing competence with respect to either language comprehension or expression could be obtained. The verbal competence of hemidecorticate subjects, regardless of the side removed,
stands in contrast to that of brain-injured adults where a predominantly
left-hemispheric control of language is well documented.

De Renzi *et al.* (1971), have noted that adults with left brain damage are impaired on a variety of spatial tasks while performances on other
tests of this type are selectively susceptible to injuries of the right hemisphere. According to these authors, the possibility of verbally-mediated
spatial perception should be considered: where aspects of task requirements are amenable to verbalization, either left or right brain damage
disrupts performance. *Pure* spatial tasks which do not lend themselves
to verbal mediation, however, would require largely the integrity of right
hemisphere processes.

To the extent that verbal mediation contributes to the solving of
some of the tests described in the present report, the LH subjects' per-

formances may be determined both by the greater specialization of the remaining right hemisphere for spatial analyses and by the availability of neural mechanisms necessary for verbal encoding. In RH subjects, however, the competence on the same tests could depend on the potential for mediation of purely spatial processes by a remaining left hemisphere.

The first skill for which hemispheric control is to be compared after early and late lesions is tactile form perception. In the absence of somatosensory defects, this ability is impaired after late left as well as right brain damage (Semmes, 1965). Yet, recent evidence points to right hemisphere control for the tactile sense of direction (Carmon and Benton, 1969; Fontenot and Benton, 1971), visual identification of tactually presented forms (De Renzi and Scotti, 1969) and tactile matching of nonsense forms (Milner and Taylor, 1972). In contrast to this hemispheric asymmetry revealed by late brain damage, both early left or right insult in our hemidecorticate subjects spared tactile form recognition.

Performances on tests requiring verbal identification of fragmented visual stimuli are impaired after late right hemisphere injury (De Renzi and Spinnler, 1966; Lansdell, 1968; Newcombe and Russell, 1969), whereas the extent to which verbal resources are drawn upon appears related to the severity of defects after late left hemisphere lesions. When the verbal response is to be selected from an experimenter-presented and strictly limited set of alternatives, left brain damage entails little or no impairment (Lansdell, 1968; Newcombe and Russell, 1969). On the Street test, where the required verbal response must be selected from an unlimited set of options, left injury comes to impair performance, although still not as much as right brain damage (De Renzi and Spinnler, 1966). Additional evidence for right hemisphere control of capacities involved in figural unification stems from a recent study of commissurotomized patients (Nebes, 1972). The adult data differ from those shown for hemidecorticate subjects in Figure II-1; the performances of both LH and RH subjects on the Street test were similar and unimpaired.

Thus it appears that, to a large extent, right hemisphere processes mediate both the perception of tactile direction and form, as well as identification of fragmented figures, whether visually or tactually presented; the degree of the left hemisphere involvement on the latter tasks seems determined by the verbal response requirements. Given the right hemisphere control of such skills in adults, greater deficits might have been expected in the RH than the LH group. Since no differences in the performances of hemidecorticate subjects were found, it is possible that compensatory functions of the left hemisphere mediated the necessary spatial analyses in the RH group. Such a reallocation of functions which are largely right-lateralized in adults is, however, not the only possible explanation of the RH performances. Benton (1973) reported a consistent left hand (and, presumably, right hemisphere superiority) for perception of tactile direction in about 60 percent of the normal subjects tested. Whether or not left hand superiority reflects on problem-solving strategies which differ from those in subjects equally proficient with either hand, remains a question yet to be answered. In consequence, different strategies may have mediated tactile form matching in the LH and RH groups.

The possibility of a genetic predisposition toward a left hemisphere control of spatial abilities in the RH subjects must also be considered. In such a case, their competence on the two tasks would be understandable without reference to an atypical lateralization induced by early brain damage.

Information necessary for a differential prediction of skills related to genetically-determined left hemisphere dominance for spatial abilities, as opposed to a similar control induced by early right hemisphere pathology, is not available at present. An attempt at interpreting the present data in terms of genetic factors, however, would necessarily assume that all RH subjects tested tended genetically toward left hemisphere control of spatial abilities, while in all of the LH subjects this predisposition determined a right hemisphere control for the same skills. In addition, it would follow that all eight hemidecorticate subjects suffered from pathology which affected selectively the brain-half not suited for a control of spatial abilities. While such a constellation of events is possible, its probability of occurrence appears low.

Although the data of the present study could be otherwise interpreted, the most economical account in terms of underlying assumptions would involve the possibility of functional reallocation: following early right hemisphere insult, compensatory developments in the less affected hemisphere might allow for a mediation of those spatial abilities which develop in a normal course of events prior to the age of about ten years. These same processes do not spare spatial skills known to mature during the second decade of life.

A third task on which the LH and RH groups performed equally well was a test of bodily orientation, i.e. discrimination of left and right on the subject's own body and the capacity for left-right transpositional judgments. The extensive literature dealing with disorders of bodily orientation implicates left far more than right hemisphere control for such skills (e.g. McFie and Zangwill, 1960; Orgass and Poeck, 1968; Sauguet *et al.*, 1971; Semmes *et al.*, 1963; Williams and Jambor, 1964). There is, however, considerable disagreement regarding the relationship between speech dysfunctions following left brain damage and the presence or absence of impaired bodily orientation. As a consequence, little can be said about the nature of the underlying mediation: Is it a process codetermined by the laterality of cerebral dominance for speech or is this control independent of language functions? For similar reasons, it remains uncertain what developmental processes promote the equally competent sense of bodily orientation in both groups of hemidecorticate infantile hemiplegics. These abilities may have evolved conjointly with the speech functions in either of the remaining hemispheres, or, alternatively, may have been sustained by independent compensatory processes.

Performances on the Porteus Maze Test, where bodily position of the subject does not represent a reference point relevant to the solution, depend on the integrity of the right hemisphere. Postoperative scores do not differ reliably from those obtained preoperatively in adult patients who had undergone left subthalamotomy, while similar surgery on the right side decreases the scores by over three test years (Meier and Story, 1968). Further, a remarkably high score on the same task has been reported for an adult patient after left hemispherectomy for brain tumour; his test age of 15 years contrasts sharply with that of two patients with right hemispherectomy who scored 5½ and 6 years, respectively (Smith, 1972). The Porteus Maze scores shown in Figure II-1 indicate that, as in adult patients, control of the required skills depends on the integrity of the right hemisphere in infantile hemiplegics. Whether the RH scores $(\overline{X} = 8.4$ test years, as opposed to 13.2 for the LH group) reflect reallocation of function to any extent, remains uncertain.

Directional sense as measured by the Money test is less disordered after late right (parietal) than left (frontal) lesions (Butters *et al.,* 1972). In contrast, three of our four LH subjects obtained high scores on the same test; the deficits in the RH group were uniformly severe. Semmes *et al.,* (1963), using a map reading test, found late left (posterior) lesions to be reliably disruptive while an impairment after right posterior lesions was suggested. On the same task, as on the Money test, it is our RH group which proved severely disabled; again, one of the four subjects depressed the superior performance shown for the LH group in Figure II-1.

The effects of late brain damage suggest, on both of the above tests, some involvement of the right and a clear dependence on the integrity of the left hemisphere processes. The data of the infantile hemiplegics, however, indicate consistently that the development of the skills required on the same tests does not occur with dysfunction of the right brain half although it is largely spared after early left hemisphere disease.

It would appear, then, that the right hemisphere contributes to the maturation of capacities which are conspicuously affected by left hemisphere injuries in adults. Hebb's (1942) suggestion that neural structures involved in the development of certain functions differ from those which mediate the same functions in the adult brain, might apply to the discussed disorders of directional sense.

In conclusion, some evidence has been described, which, although far from unequivocal, nonetheless indicates that the abilities of the right hemidecorticate subjects on tasks deemed spatial can depend on compensatory functions after early right hemisphere damage. It is clear that such reallocation, to the extent that it occurs, spares only the earlier developing and more basic spatial skills. The maturational level of spatial competences shows asymmetries which are related to the laterality of early cerebral pathology. That no such relation has as yet been reported for verbal intelligence might reflect on early hemispheric equivalences for the development of speech; alternatively, it might be due to insufficient sensitivity of the tests used.

SEQUELAE OF EARLY AND LATE BRAIN DAMAGE

That behavioral consequences of late brain injury differ with the side of the hemisphere affected needs no emphasis. Similarly, we found the laterality of early pathology relevant to the developmental level and consequent performances of certain spatial abilities. A comparison of early and late lesion effects on a series of spatial tasks revealed, however, an unexpected pattern of impairments: neither left nor right hemisphere damage results in consistently similar deficits. As the summary in Table II-I shows, the extent of sparing after early damage to the left hemisphere is appreciably different from that apparent after right brain damage.

Considering first the effects of left hemisphere injury, a notably high proficiency on the tests listed in Table II-I is shown for infantile hemiplegics with half of the neocortical mass removed. In contrast, restricted late insult to the left hemisphere impairs, to varying extents, the competence on five out of six tests. Thus, with the question of comparative sparing of spatial abilities after early and late injury raised in the context of left brain damage, early pathology is unequivocally less disruptive than that in adults.

The deficient personal and extrapersonal orientation after late left lesions and sparing of the same functions in the LH group are amenable to a number of interpretations. Three possibilities will be considered, assuming in each instance that successful orientation requires, first, an analysis of the test situation in terms of its spatial features and, sec-

TABLE II-I
RELATIVE IMPAIRMENTS FOLLOWING EARLY AND
LATE BRAIN DAMAGE*

Tests	Left hemisphere injury		Right hemisphere injury	
	Early	Late	Early	Late
Extrapersonal Orientation (Semmes et al., 1955)	Mild†	Severe	Severe	Mild?
Road Map Test of Direction Sense (Money, 1965)	Mild†	Severe	Severe	Mild
Porteus Maze Test (Porteus, 1965)	Mild	None	Severe	Severe
Personal Orientation (Weinstein, 1958)	Mild	Severe	Mild	Mild?
Visual Closure (Street, 1931)	None	Mild	None	Severe
Tactile Form Matching	None	Mild?	None	Severe

* Effects of early injury based on results shown in Figure II-1; effects of late injury based on literature reviewed in the text.
† The depressed mean performance of this group is due entirely to one severely impaired subject; the scores of the other three subjects ranged between 85 to 100 percent.

ondly, a verbal encoding of the information already processed for its directional components.

If the deficient performances after late left brain damage are taken as an indication of impaired capacities for spatial analyses, the conclusion is unavoidable that the right hemisphere of an adult brain analyzes the spatial features of some of the tests (Porteus Maze, visual completion and tactile form recognition) while the left hemisphere performs the same functions in instances of personal and extrapersonal orientation. With such a differentiated bihemispheric participation in the processing of spatial information, however, the contrast of preserved abilities in the LH group with the selective but severe defects after late left brain damage remains to be explained.

A second interpretation, relating the deficient skills to disrupted verbal encoding, finds little support from instances of late left brain damage which result in impaired orientations without concomitant dysphasia (Sauguet et al., 1972; Semmes et al., 1963). A third explanation would account for the latter cases, although it does not provide a basis for preserved orientation in dysphasics with left brain damage. Dependence of spatial capacities on unimpeded interhemispheric transfer might determine impairments after late left brain damage in the absence of speech dysfunctions: the lesions, without affecting structures involved in verbal encoding, could be disruptive of transcommissural communication. Thus, the output of the right hemisphere would not be available for verbal encoding in the left brain half. A disconnection syndrome (Geschwind, 1965) of this type appears more plausible in view of anatomical evidence that forebrain commissures provide heterotopic as well as homotopic links between the hemispheres (e.g. Locke and Yakovlev, 1965; Pandya and Vignolo, 1969). These findings appear to extend the range of behavioral deficits relatable to hemispheric disconnection after discrete cortical damage. Lesions in either hemisphere may, beyond depriving the homologous contralateral areas of interhemispheric input, disrupt the communication between anatomically disparate structures.

Some support for the notion of disconnected spatial and verbal mechanisms as determinants of impaired performances derives from studies of commissurotomized patients. They show more severe impairments on the Street completion test (Bogen *et al.*, 1972) than on the Hooper visual organization test (Nebes, 1972). Regarding the latter results, comments by several of the patients suggest, interestingly, that strategies maximizing left hemisphere participation may have been utilized. Moreover, Bogen (1969) described dysgraphia with the left hand and dyscopia with the right hand in commissurotomized subjects. In some instances, verbal instructions given by the experimenter enabled the subjects to draw geometric figures which they were unable to copy with the right hand (and the left hemisphere). The finding appears to illustrate shortcomings in the left hemisphere analyses of spatial components.

Data regarding the status of commissurotomized patients on tests of personal and extrapersonal orientation would be of considerable interest. Such information might determine whether or not verbal mediation of spatial analyses prevents reverting to solution modes based on spatial information only.

Returning to the comparative effects of early and late left brain damage, it is difficult to conceptualize how left hemidecorticate infantile hemiplegics with a dull normal verbal I.Q. could perform adequately on a battery of spatial tests where restricted late damage results in severe impairments, unless the possibility of disrupted connections between neural mechanisms involved in the processing of spatial information and those subserving verbal mediation is taken into account. Were hemispheric disconnection an established factor in disorders of orientation which occur after late left hemisphere damage, the preserved spatial skills in left hemidecorticate infantile hemiplegics could be ascribed to a joint control of verbal and spatial processes by the remaining right hemisphere.

Some of the spatial abilities tested after right hemidecortication in infantile hemiplegics are, in all probability, spared for entirely different reasons. The unimpaired performances of the RH group prove restricted to three tests listed in Table II-I which, as has been pointed out earlier, measure comparatively early-maturing skills. The behavioral sparing, then, appears determined by the extent to which a potential for compensatory processing of spatial information in the remaining left brain half develops after early right hemisphere disease. Similar left hemisphere mediation is not evident from the performances of subjects with late right brain damage. Early lesions, however, do not spare spatial abilities which improve with age and undergo developments extended into the second decade of life. That the RH group is at least equally and, possibly, more severely impaired on the latter tests than late right brain-damaged subjects, can be ascribed to shortcomings in the left hemisphere mediation of spatial analyses when these exceed a certain level of complexity.

In summary, the status of spatial abilities after early brain damage does not, in itself, provide information regarding the nature of compensatory developments which contribute to a mediation of the preserved skills. After early damage and hemidecortication of the left hemisphere, the processes regulating the analyses of spatial information appear to develop to a remarkably normal extent in the remaining right brain half. It seems, however, that the compensatory element which actually spares the performance of spatial skills involves the reallocation of verbal processes to the right brain half. In contrast, an atypical development of spatial rather than speech functions is more probable in instances of right hemisphere disease and hemidecortication: The subjects' spatial abilities depend on a left hemisphere mediation of processes which are characteristic of right hemisphere functions in the adult brain.

REFERENCES

Basser, L. S.: Hemiplegia of early onset and the faculty of speech with special reference to the effects of hemispherectomy. *Brain, 85:* 427–460, 1962.

Benton, A. L.: Hemispheric participation in the perception of direction. Paper read at the International Neuropsychology Society Meeting, New Orleans, 1973.

Bogen, J. E.: The other side of the brain I: Dysgraphia and dyscopia following cerebral commissurotomy. *Bull Los Angeles Neurol Soc, 34:* 73–105, 1969.

———, DeZure, M., Tenhouten, W. D., and March, J. F.: The other side of the brain IV: The A/P ratio. *Bull Los Angeles Neurol Soc, 37:* 49–61, 1972.

Butters, N., Soeldner, C., and Fedio, P.: Comparison of parietal and frontal lobe spatial deficits in man: extrapersonal vs. personal (egocentric) space. *Percept Mot Skills, 34:* 27–34, 1972.

Carmon, A., and Benton, A. L.: Tactile perception of direction and number in patients with unilateral cerebral disease. *Neurology, 19:* 525–532, 1969.

De Renzi, E., Faglioni, P., and Scotti, G.: Judgment of spatial orientation in patients with focal brain damage. *J Neurol Neurosurg Psychiatry, 34:* 489–495, 1971.

————, and Scotti, G.: The influence of spatial disorders in impairing tactual discrimination of shapes. *Cortex, 5:* 53–62, 1969.

————, and Spinnler, H.: Visual recognition in patients with unilateral disease. *J Nerv Ment Dis, 142:* 515–525, 1966.

Fontenot, D. J., and Benton, A. L.: Tactile perception of direction in relation to hemispheric locus of lesion. *Neuropsychologia, 9:* 83–88, 1971.

Geschwind, N.: Disconnection syndromes in animals and man, Part 2, *Brain, 88:* 585–644, 1965.

Hebb, D. O.: The effect of early and late brain injury upon test scores, and the nature of normal adult intelligence. *Proc Am Phil Soc, 85:* 275–292, 1942.

Ignelzi, R. J., and Bucy, P. C.: Cerebral hemidecortication in the treatment of infantile cerebral hemiatrophy. *J Nerv Ment Dis, 147:* 14–30, 1968.

Kohn, B., and Dennis, M. (a): Somatosensory functions after cerebral hemidecortication for infantile hemiplegia. *Neuropsychologia,* In press.

———— (b): Selective impairments of visuo-spatial abilities in infantile hemiplegics after right cerebral hemidecortication. *Neuropsychologia,* In press.

Lansdell, H.: Effect of extent of temporal lobe ablations on two lateralized deficits. *Physiol Behav, 3:* 271–273, 1968.

————: Verbal and nonverbal factors in right-hemisphere speech: relation to early neurological history. *J Comp Physiol Psychol, 69:* 734–738, 1969.

Lashley, K. S.: Factors limiting recovery after central nervous lesions. *J Nerv Ment Dis, 88:* 733–755, 1938.

Locke, S., and Yakovlev, P. I.: Transcallosal connections of the cingulum of man. *Arch Neurol, 13:* 471–476, 1965.

McFie, J.: The effects of hemispherectomy on intellectual functioning in cases of infantile hemiplegia. *J Neurol Neurosurg Psychiatry, 24:* 240–249, 1961.

————, and Zangwill, O. L.: Visual-constructive disabilities associated with lesions of the left cerebral hemisphere. *Brain, 83:* 243–260, 1960.

Meier, M. J., and Story, J. L.: Selective impairment of Porteus maze test performance after right subthalamotomy. *Neuropsychologia, 5:* 181–189, 1967.

Milner, B., and Taylor, L.: Right-hemisphere superiority in tactile pattern-recognition after cerebral comissurotomy: evidence for nonverbal memory. *Neuropsychologia, 10:* 1–15, 1972.

Money, J.: *A Standardized Road-Map Test of Direction Sense.* Baltimore, Johns Hopkins, 1965.

Nebes, R. D.: Dominance of the minor hemisphere in commissurotomized man on a test of figural unification. *Brain, 95:* 633–638, 1972.

Newcombe, F., and Russell, W. R.: Dissociated visual perceptual and spatial deficits in focal lesions of the right hemisphere. *J Neurol Neurosurg Psychiatry, 32:* 73–81, 1969.

Orgass, B., and Poeck, K.: Rechts-Links Störung oder Aphasie? *Dtsch Z Nervenheilk, 194:* 261–279, 1968.

Pandya, D. N., and Vignolo, L. A.: Interhemispheric projections of the parietal lobe in the rhesus monkey. *Brain Res, 15:* 49–65, 1969.

Poeck, K., und Orgass, B.: Die Entwicklung der Körperschemas bei Kindern im Alter von 4-10 Jahren. *Neuropsychologia, 2:* 109–130, 1964.

Porteus, S. D.: *Porteus Maze Tests: Fifty Years Application.* Palo Alto, Pacific Bks, 1965.

Sauguet, J., Benton, A. L., and Hecaen, H.: Disturbances of the body schema in relation to language impairment and hemispheric locus of lesion. *J Neurol Neurosurg Psychiatry, 34:* 496–501, 1971.

Semmes, J.: A non-tactual factor in astereognosis. *Neuropsychologia, 3:* 295–315, 1965.

————, Weinstein, S., Ghent, L., and Teuber, H.-L.: Spatial orientation in man after cerebral injury: analysis by locus of lesion. *J Psychol, 39:* 227–244, 1955.

————: Correlates of impaired orientation in personal and extrapersonal space. *Brain, 86:* 747–772, 1963.

Smith, A.: Dominant and nondominant hemispherectomy. In Smith, W. L. (Ed.): *Drugs, Development and Cerebral Function.* Springfield, Thomas, 1972, pp. 37–68.

Street, R. F.: *A Gestalt Completion Test.* Teachers College, Columbia University Thesis, 1931, No. 4.

Teuber, H.-L.: Mental retardation after early trauma to the brain: some issues in search of facts. In Angle, C. R., and Bering, E. A. (Eds.): *Physical Trauma as an Etiological Agent in Mental Retardation.* Washington, U. S. Govt. Printing Office, 1970, pp. 7–28.

————, and Rudel, R. G.: Behaviour after cerebral lesions in children and adults. *Dev Med Child Neurol, 4:* 3–20, 1962.

Wechsler, D.: *Wechsler Intelligence Scale for Children.* New York, The Psychological Corporation, 1949.

Weinstein, S.: Body image: the psychophysical approach. Paper read at symposium on body image and brain damage: a critical evaluation. Washington, D. C., APA Meeting, 1958.

Williams, M., and Jambor, K.: Disorders of topographical and right-left orientation in adults compared with its acquisition in children. *Neuropsychologia, 2:* 55–69, 1964.

Witelson, S. F.: Left-right asymmetry in the perception of dichotomous tactual stimulation. In preparation.

[CHAPTER III]

HEMISPHERECTOMY AND THE PLACING REACTION IN CATS

J. E. Bogen

INTRODUCTION

THIS CHAPTER BEGINS WITH a brief review of experimental hemispherectomy, including the available literature and the author's personal
experience. Next are reported the author's experiments using hemispherectomized cats to investigate the compensatory capabilities of the
nervous system, focusing on the placing reaction as a specific example of
a behavioral deficiency following a cerebral lesion. The concluding discussion considers some implications for several historical issues in
neurophysiology.

The main lesson learned from experimental hemispherectomy has
been that so long as the ablation is confined to one side, there is remarkably little effect in the long term on either instinctive or learned behavior.
As early as 1824, Flourens hemispherectomized pigeons, ducks, and chick-
ens; he concluded that they retained "all senses and intellectual faculties
except for vision with the opposite eye." Vulpian confirmed these results
in 1866; he noted that a contralateral weakness dissipated after a few days
so that, "one can hardly see a difference between the operated and a normal pigeon."

Experimental hemispherectomy in mammals was pioneered by Goltz
(1953, 1888) in an investigation whose importance he fully appreciated:

> I will begin by relating an experiment which I hope will be acclaimed by
> all true friends of science. I succeeded in observing for 15 months an animal
> in which I had taken away the whole left hemisphere.

Goltz then described at some length the behavior of this preparation,
concluding:

> We have seen that a dog without a left hemisphere can still move volun-
> tarily all parts of his body and that from all parts of his body, action can
> be induced which can only be the consequence of conscious sensation. This
> is incompatible with that construction of centers which assumes that each
> side of the brain can serve only those conscious movements and sensations
> which concern the opposite half of the body.

Subsequent experimental hemispherectomy has provided no contradiction of Goltz, only the addition of details whose brief recapitulation is one purpose of the present essay.

HEMISPHERECTOMY: TERMINOLOGY

Hemispherectomy has been carried out to varying degrees of completeness. The terms "hemidecortication" or "hemicorticectomy" are probably more appropriate than "hemispherectomy" for the operation employed by some writers who have deliberately spared the basal ganglia (and sometimes the hippocampus). More commonly some amount of basal ganglia is removed, leaving medial remnants. When the basal ganglia including thalamus are totally removed, the section through the brain stem usually traverses the subthalamus immediately in front of the colliculi; for this procedure the terms "hemidecerebration," "semidecerebration," "total hemispherectomy" and "hemicerebrectomy" have been proposed. The latter two terms are used interchangeably in this paper and a cat having such an operation is referred to as an "H cat." The term "total hemispherectomy" has also been used when striatum as well as cortex is removed but the thalamus remains (Austin and Grant, 1955); from the functional standpoint this seems reasonable, since following such an operation there is nearly complete degeneration of the thalamus except in the midline and intralaminar nuclei (Austin and Grant, 1955; Lassek, 1954; Lassek and Evans, 1945; LeGros and Russell, 1940; Locke *et al.*, 1964; Mettler, 1943; Powell, 1952; Walker, 1935, 1938a and b). Age makes little difference in the degeneration; similar studies in infant animals gave much the same result (Peacock and Combs, 1965).

The effects of staged removal were specifically studied by Kennard (1938, 1944, 1942) who removed precentral cortex from monkeys and, after recovery from this, completed the unilateral decortication. There was a reappearance of awkwardness in the arm and a tendency to forced grasping. There was also the appearance of new symptoms including hemianopia and tendency of the head and eyes to deflect toward the side of the lesion and of the animal to circle toward that side. However, recovery from the second operation on the same side followed a course at least as rapid as recovery from a hemispherectomy done in a single operation. Kennard noted that inclusion of the corpus striatum in the removal did not produce much difference (cf Mettler, 1943, 1967).

FELINE BEHAVIOR AFTER TOTAL HEMISPHERECTOMY

Before considering certain selected aspects in the light of the literature, our own experience will be briefly reviewed.

TABLE III-I

Cat	Operation	First Op. Follow-up (Weeks)	Termination	Second (or Third) Follow-up in Weeks
59-1	Hemicerebellectomy	5	Wasted away	
59-2	Hemicerebellectomy	3	In coma to death	
59-3	Hemicerebrectomy	1	In coma to death	
59-4	Hemicerebrectomy	50	Run over by car	
59-5	Hemicerebrectomy	7	Hemicerebellectomy	4
59-6	Carotid Ligation	2	Hemicerebellectomy	0
59-7	Hemicerebrectomy	0		
59-8	Hemicerebellectomy	3	Hemicerebrectomy	24
59-9	Hemicerebrectomy	1	In coma to death	
59-10	Occipital lobectomy	6	Hemicerebellectomy	4
59-11	Hemicerebrectomy	7	Frontal lobectomy	30
59-12	Hemicerebrectomy	2	Frontal lobectomy	0
59-13	Occipital lobectomy	4	Loaned out and lost	
59-14	Hemicerebrectomy	0		
59-14	Hemicerebrectomy	0		
59-16	Frontal lobectomy	4	Second frontal lobectomy	8
			Hemicerebellectomy	4
59-17	Hemicerebrectomy	0		
59-18	Hemicerebrectomy	8	Specimen	
60-1	Hemicerebrectomy	13	Loaned out and lost	
60-2	Hemicerebrectomy	8	Hemicerebellectomy	0
60-3	Hemicerebrectomy	1	Decerebrate	
60-4	Hemicerebrectomy	0		
60-5	Frontal lobectomy	12	Hemicerebrectomy	0
60-6	Hemicerebrectomy	2	Sudden "distemper"	
60-7	Hemicerebrectomy	20	Frontal lobectomy	8
60-8	Hemicerebrectomy	6	Loaned out and lost	
60-9	Hemicerebrectomy	0		
60-10	Hemicerebrectomy	30	Frontal lobectomy	1
60-11	Hemicerebrectomy	100	Loaned; sporadic reports	
60-12	Hemicerebrectomy	0		
60-13	Frontal lobectomy	14	Hemicerebrectomy	0
60-14	Hemicerebrectomy	0		
60-15	Hemicerebrectomy	0		
60-16	Hemicerebrectomy	1	Decerebrate	
60-17	Hemicerebrectomy	2	Sudden "distemper"	
60-18	Hemicerebrectomy	126	Subacute illness with anemia	
60-19	Hemicerebrectomy	8	Hemicerebellectomy	0
60-20	Hemicerebrectomy	6	Specimen	
60-21	Hemicerebrectomy	14	Frontal lobectomy	12
60-22	Hemicerebrectomy	6	Wasted away	
60-23	Hemicerebrectomy	1	In coma to death	
60-24	Hemicerebrectomy	24	Frontal lobectomy	4
61-1	Hemicerebrectomy	218	Given away	
61-2	Hemicerebrectomy	2	Wasted away	
61-3	Hemicerebrectomy	0		
61-4	Hemicerebrectomy	16	Frontal lobectomy	10
61-5	Hemicerebrectomy	20	Stolen	
61-6	Hemicerebrectomy	22	Hemicerebellectomy	9
			Frontal lobectomy	2
61-7	Frontal lobectomy	11	Hemicerebellectomy	0
61-8	Frontal lobectomy	25	Hemicerebellectomy	2
61-9	Frontal lobectomy	14	Hemicerebellectomy	0
61-10	Frontal lobectomy	8	Hemicerebellectomy	0
61-11	Hemicerebrectomy	0		

Cat	Operation	First Op. Follow-up (Weeks)	Termination	Second (or Third) Follow-up in Weeks
61-12	Hemicerebrectomy	12	Given away	
61-13	Cord Section	10	Hemicerebrectomy	0
61-14	Hemicerebrectomy	0	Given away	
61-15	Hemicerebrectomy	4	Wasted away	
61-16	Hemicerebrectomy	1	Hemicerebrectomy	0
61-17	Frontal lobectomy	15	Specimen	
61-18	Hemicerebrectomy	22	Frontal lobectomy	10
61-19	Hemicerebrectomy	4	Specimen	
61-20	Hemicerebrectomy	21		
62-1	Hemicerebrectomy	22	Given away	
62-2	Frontal lobectomy	40	Specimen	
62-3	Quartering	1	Woundn't eat	
62-4	Hemicerebrectomy and Frontal lobectomy	0		
62-5	Hemicerebrectomy and Frontal lobectomy	0		
62-6	Hemicerebrectomy and Frontal lobectomy	0		
62-7	Hemicerebrectomy and Frontal lobectomy	4	Specimen	

Of 69 adult cats having massive cerebral ablations, 48 had total hemispherectomy (hemicerebrectomy) as the primary operation. Of these 48, there were 17 operative deaths. Of the 31 H cats in good condition there were seven who subsequently died of an intercurrent illness. Eight healthy H cats were given away or lost. Four animals were sacrificed for photographic specimens. Four animals surviving hemicerebrectomy in good condition had a hemicerebellectomy, two of them surviving this operation in good condition. Eight H cats had contralateral frontal lobectomy as a secondary operation; seven of these were followed long enough to obtain data on the placing reactions.

Under the supervision of Professor Berry Campbell, adult cats were totally hemispherectomized (see Table III-I). It was our aim to obtain as complete a removal of the right hemisphere as possible, beginning with a section exactly in the mid-line. Injury therefore commonly occurred on the medial aspect, including hypothalamus, of the remaining hemisphere. There was a high mortality rate; but the surviving animals had very clean ablations with no residual cerebrum on the operated side (see Fig. III-1). The operation, under pentobarbital anesthesia, included a mid-line section with a spatula which was then brought out laterally in front of the colliculi. Following this the hemisphere (the *right* hemisphere in all cases) was scooped out *in toto*.

During the first few weeks there was usually a large nonreactive pupil on the right. All animals when suspended by the pelvis had a severe counterclockwise rotation of the spine; when lying on the left side they had difficulty righting; when standing they showed a marked rotation of the head with the right ear uppermost (see Fig. III-2). When jumping down from a table they often fell onto the left shoulder. All ignored vis-

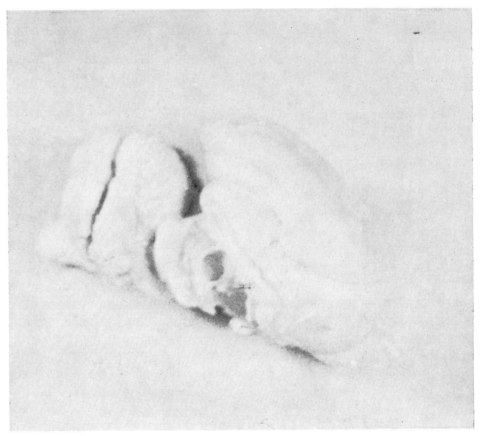

Figure III-1. Brain of an H cat (61-18) shows a slight amount of herniation across the midline. The colliculi and third ventricle are easily seen; the basal ganglia are absent on the operated side.

ual stimuli to the left and all circled to the right when walking.* Successful walking first appeared from 2 to 16 days after operation (see Fig. III-3). These difficulties, except the hemianopia, subsided to varying de-

---

* Bazett and Penfield did what they called "semi-decerebration" which consisted of scooping out the entire right hemisphere down to the midbrain. Their results were essentially the same as those of others except that they noted the animals circled *toward the intact* left hemisphere; this is such a remarkable exception to the findings of all others that it may even be a typographical error, particularly since they noted that the forced rotation of the head was of the type noted by all others, that is the occiput rotated down to the left and the chin up toward the right. Kennard did secondary contralateral operations in several instances; removal of cortex from the remaining side produced a dramatic new loss of function and was of particular interest because the deviation of the animals in circling was toward the original side rather than toward the side of the second lesion. H. C. Bazett, and W. C. Penfield, "A Study of the Sherringtonian decerebrate animal in Chronic as Well as the Acute Condition," *Brain* 45: 185–265 (1922).

Figure III-2. Cat #61-19, 3 days post-op. For a week or so after total hemispherectomy, the cat eats poorly if at all from a dish placed on a horizontal surface because of the persistent twist of the entire body and especially of the head. Such a cat placed on its right side (so the snout points downwards), rarely eats well because of persistent attempts to stand. This may be attributable to body-on-body righting tendency being stronger than head-on-body.

grees. In those H cats which showed the best recovery, use of the affected forelimb was impressive; one commonly used the affected limb to lift food to his mouth. A few H cats remained filthy and quite indiscriminate in their toilet habits; but several others were extremely fastidious, and these devoted as much time to licking the left limb as the right. Most H cats showed partial return of forelimb hopping by the fourth week; certain placing reactions often showed good return and are further discussed below.

It is worth emphasizing that the H animal is extremely disabled immediately after operation, requiring very careful post-operative care for several weeks. Return to the "near-normal" state requires many months. Kellogg (1949) wrote:

So great is the difference in the behavior of these animals [immediately

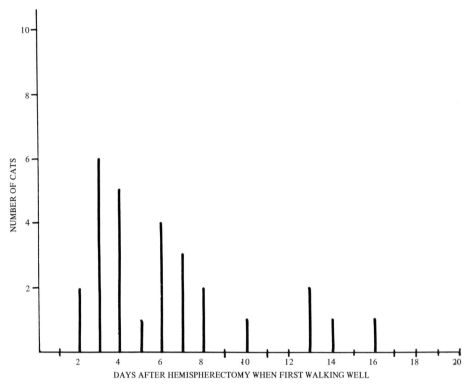

Figure III-3. Shown here is the number of cats first walking well on each day subsequent to total hemispherectomy. Of 48 adult cats having a right mid-line-hemispherectomy (hemicerebectomy) as the primary operation, 17 succumbed before return of independent ambulation. The remaining 31 first walked well from two to sixteen days after operation. Of the 31 cats who survived, data was inadequate on three of them so this graph shows data for only 28 cats.

post-op and some months later] that they would appear, in fact, to be entirely different individuals.

According to Young and Horner (1971), movies of their H cats showed essentially equal use of the limbs on each side. In our experience the H cats, even after a year of progressive recovery, showed asymmetric behavior: unusual sounds usually caused turning to the right, no matter where the source. Long after the cats were able to run and climb with grossly normal agility they would circle to the right several times when released from their cages. The cat (60-11, see Table III-I) which ate with its left paw was completely baffled on one occasion by a mouse which clung to its left shoulder. Several H cats, however, were very adept at catching mice in the laboratory. Long-term asymmeric behavior was also observed in cats operated when quite young (see below). No asymmetry was observed in the clinging of H cats made catatonic with bulbocapnine (Van Harreveld and Bogen, 1961).

One of our laboratory cats (60-10, see Table III-I) gave birth three weeks following hemispherectomy to a live litter of kittens. Both Dr. Campbell and I kept H cats as house pets for several years. He has described one of these (59-4) in a previous report (Campbell, 1960). The one (60-18) kept at our home over two years was practically indistinguishable from a normal cat by many visitors. When told that the cat had only half a brain, they often said, "Oh yes . . . it seems a little strange." When they were then asked to decide which hemisphere had been removed, most were reduced to guessing, being correct about half of the time. Only those visitors who looked for the hemianopia were consistently correct.

In sum, our own extended experience has confirmed in its essentials the conclusion of Goltz that an animal after extirpation of an entire hemisphere can still have an intact personality and voluntary control of both sides of its body.

LEARNING AFTER HEMISPHERECTOMY

The nearly normal behavior of recovered H animals has been analyzed more closely by the use of quantitative psychological tests. Earlier work (Blagoveshchenskaya, 1929; Bromily, 1948; Kellogg and Bashore, 1950; Melka, 1965; Rosenthal, 1936) had as its principal result that conditioned reflexes reappeared after a temporary loss following hemispherectomy. Serkov *et al.* concluded that the remarkable compensatory possibilities should be ascribed to "bilateral cortical representation."

Tsang (1937) tested the ability of hemidecorticate rats to learn a maze and concluded that hemispherectomy caused only slight impairment (even when no allowance was made for the visual loss). Of greatest interest was the finding that removal of an entire hemisphere was less detrimental than removal of both frontal lobes, and much less detrimental than removal of both occipital lobes even though considerably less tissue was removed than in the hemispherectomy. As compared with removal of the anterior half on one side and the posterior half on the other, hemispherectomy was remarkably less detrimental. These results are particularly significant since Tsang was a student of Lashley and favored the "principle of mass action." The results, in my opinion, afford a very strong argument against the mass action point of view. In particular, they illustrate that so long as one hemisphere remains intact, the behavioral loss is relatively small. A very large behavioral loss is produced, however, when smaller injuries are inflicted on both hemispheres.

Although H monkeys are capable of learning quite complex problems, they may have difficulties when there are long delays between trials (Thompson and Bucy, 1969). They may learn more slowly than normal but can attain comparable levels (Kruper, *et al.*, 1961a; 1961b). Patton (139) observed:

> Perhaps the most striking finding was that the hemicerebrectomized monkey can achieve a level of performance on a complex learning task which equals that of the normal animal.

Following more recent, extensive studies (1971, 1971) Kruper, Patton and Koskoff concluded:

> showing clear learning deficits when comparing the performance of these animals to the performance of normal monkeys continues to be a compelling challenge.

One might suppose this would be even more true if the removal were done at an early age. Wenzel *et al.* (1962) decorticated nine-day-old kittens. When teaching a T-maze, they made specific efforts to avoid the pitfall of testing for vision rather than learning, by closing off one limb and permitting the animal to explore. These special learning situations, including the maze, were introduced after several months; the H cats did not differ significantly from their litter mate controls. These authors agreed with the impressions of others (Berman *et al.*, 1958; Hicks and D'Amato, 1970; Kellogg and Bashore, 1950; Kruper, *et al.*, 1961a, 1961b, 1971a, 1971b; Poltyreff and Alexejeff, 1936; Ramirez de Arellano, 1961; Thompson and Bucy, 1969; White, 1962; White and MacCarty, 1959; White *et al.*, 1961, 1959a, 1958, 1959b) that in spite of removal of massive amounts of brain (nearly one-half), "the behavioral loss is extremely small or even undetectable."

ELECTROGRAPHIC STUDIES

In the absence of any systematic personal experience with EEG of H cats, I will only mention that a principal finding has been a slowing over the remaining hemisphere which gradually returns to normal. Some controversy revolves around the extent to which activity of the brain stem reticular formation is affected by the absence of the usual descending influences from the ablated hemisphere (Adey and Lindsley, 1959; Lindsley *et al.*, 1949; Serkov and Makulkin, 1963; Zernicki *et al.*, 1970).

An interesting approach related to hemispherectomy is the preparation of an isolated hemisphere which is deprived of its neuronal connections to the rest of the brain but retains its circulation (and sometimes its optic and olfactory input). This has most commonly been accomplished by combining a mid-line bisection with a rostral hemisection of the brain stem. The behavior of such animals is essentially the same as that of a hemispherectomized animal (Berlucchi, 1966). Observation of the isolated hemisphere has mainly been electrical; the EEG shows almost continuous synchronization typical of sleep or coma, at least in the first weeks after operation (Baldwin and Mejia, 1969; Berlucchi, 1966; Frost, *et al.*, 1966; Harner, 1970; Kellaway, *et al.*, 1966; Rinaldi and Himwich, 1955; Villablanca, 1967; Voneida, 1966). Shortly after operation the electrical activity of cortical units is depressed, especially during the occasional periods of EEG silence (Frost *et al.*, 1966). After a recovery period, there may be brief periods of desynchronization during behavioral sleep, and brief periods of desynchronization can be produced by olfactory stimuli. One cat which was kept for more than two years was reported (Harner, 1970) to show alternating episodes of sleep, "desynchronized sleep," and apparent EEG arousal which were simultaneous with (or starting before) the other hemisphere. There is a good deal more to be learned from such preparations; at the present time they furnish a further illustration of the remarkable differences between the acute postoperative condition and the stabilized, chronic state.

FORELIMB PLACING DEFICIT AS AN EXPERIMENTAL MODEL FOR "PARALYTIC STROKE"

Following partial hemispheric injury in the adult human, there is often a severe, long-lasting contralateral hemiplegia. One might suppose that further ablation, including removal of the entire hemisphere, would increase the deficit. As a matter of fact, further removal of tissue may in some cases actually improve the function (Welch and Penfield, 1950). Hemispherectomy in the infantile hemiplegic is often followed by improvement (Ignelzi and Bucy, 1968; Jacobs, 1961). These results complicate considerably our understanding of the pathophysiology of paralysis, including any attempt to utilize cerebral injury in the laboratory animal as a model for "strokes" in humans.

Hitzig and Fritsch (1870) are best remembered for using stimulation to localize a "motor center"; when they ablated the same area and observed a "debility" of the contralateral forelimb, they explicitly avoided comparing it with "human pathology." These early probings were followed, however, by the extensive researches of Ferrier (1886), at least one of whose animals was considered by Charcot to be the very model of a hemiplegic human (Clarke and O'Malley, 1968). But subsequent experience with hemispherectomy (as described above) makes clear that remarkable recovery can occur in the experimental animal. This result seems at odds with the commonly persistent uselessness of the human hand. As long ago as 1830, Bouillaud said:

It is certain that after the ablation of the cerebral hemispheres, an animal may walk, run, move its jaws, eyelids, eyes, etc.; and it is not less certain that an alteration of the cerebral hemispheres in man gives rise to a paralysis more or less complete of voluntary motion on the opposite side of the body. Can we refute the one set of facts by the other? No, certainly not, for facts equally positive are not susceptible of refutation. A time will come when new light will dispel the apparent contradiction which exists between them.

The discrepancies between experimental brain injury and what Hughlings Jackson called "the cruel experiment made on man by nature" are sometimes ascribed to species differences. This can be overemphasized. Some of the discrepancies are certainly attributable to differences in the nature of the lesion; a surgical excision has more distinct boundaries and it is usually made in an animal brain otherwise healthy (rather than with generalized arteriosclerosis, for example.) But I should like to emphasize that the discrepancies are at least in part illusory and result from testing human beings in a manner different from cats or monkeys. In the former we worry about the loss of dexterity in the hand, whereas in the latter we marvel at the return of motility in the entire limb. Therefore, in approaching the question of an animal model for paralytic strokes, it can be crucial as to what behavior should be used as a criterion.

Although many aspects of behavioral deficit in the affected forelimb or a cat or a monkey can be difficult to demontrate after cortical injury, this is not true of the placing reaction. The impairment in placing is easily demonstrated following cortical injury in the experimental animal and this is in marked contrast to the great regularity of placing in a normal animal. Even when placing returns under some conditions (described below) it is never as delicately performed as by the normal animal.

There is an additional point which has impressed me over some years of experience with both cats and humans: in both the placing deficit of a cat's paw and the paralyzed human hand, there is an excess of flexor tone which prevents function. In both cases, removal or balancing of the excessive flexor tendency permits the return of function which was previously absent. Since placing can be shown, indeed can be *made* to recover after what was once thought to be a "complete and permanent" loss, the extent to which it can be homologized with human palsy is clearly of interest.

How and why placing recovers is the main concern of what follows.

PLACING REACTIONS: TERMINOLOGY

The placing reaction in the forelimb of a cat typically consists of a distinct movement sequence: there is flexion, cephalad displacement and then extension of the limb with placement of the volar surface of the forepaw on a surface. Placing can also be elicited under conditions in which the limb displacement is lateral, medial or caudad, but these have not been extensively studied.[*]

When Magnus (1924) and Rademaker (1931) discussed placing, they used the term "Stehbereitschaft" (preparation to stand), emphasizing the apparent purpose of the movement-sequence. Bard (1933) preferred to describe the circumstances in which the placing appeared—an approach more cumbersome but less open to misinterpretation.

Some authors have referred to "tactile" or "proprioceptive" or "visual" placing. The last seems reasonable, since one can imagine no other stimulus than visual when placing occurs as a cat is being brought up to (but not against) a table edge. If vision is excluded, as by section of the optic nerves, a cat will not place until contact is made with the edge of the table. If, in addition to vision, touch is excluded (by section of radial, median and ulnar nerves and circumcision of the skin at the elbow), any placing which is produced when the paw dorsum contacts the table edge can probably be ascribed to proprioception. The experiment of excluding proprioception and vision has apparently never been done; the term "tactile placing" describes those instances in which placing is elicited by minimal touch insufficient to cause joint displacement. It is preferable to use the term "contactual placing" (Gilman and Marco, 1971).

To describe placing in terms of a single sensory modality can be misleading because the reaction is usually elicited by a combination of stimuli. A cat which is hungry will "visually place" on a table edge more dependably if there is food on the table; this seems to be the case (though never systematically tested) even when the food is not visible and can only be smelled. There are various facilitating and inhibitory factors. For example, a cat which is slow to place for any reason, when its paw dorsa contact the table edge, will often place quickly if a slight pinch is applied to its abdomen. "Visual placing" is distinctly less apt to occur if a rod or a bar is used instead of a table edge beyond which stretches a surface to receive the foot.[†] When attempts are made to test the placing with vision excluded, a blindfold may be used; but this introduces another complication since a blindfold not only excludes vision but also exerts a more general inhibitory influence via scalp afferents (Bogen and Campbell, 1962a,

---

[*] The term "vestibular placing" is sometimes used for a distinctly different behavior which Magnus called the "Sprungbereitschaft." This is a cephalad extension of the forelimb accompanied by spreading of the toes. It can be regularly elicited by suddenly lowering a (correct-side-up) cat toward the ground; it is eliminated by labyrinthectomy. R. Magnus, *Körpstellung* (Berlin Springer, 1924).

[†] Paw contact placing habituates rapidly if there is water beyond the edge rather than a solid surface (Wertenbaker, *et al,* 1972).

and Van Harreveld and Bogen, 1961). A cat which will place with neither visual nor contact stimuli may do so with both together, as I have observed on numerous occasions and as was recently reported for the rat (Hicks and D'Amato, 1970).

The tendency to use such terms as "tactile placing" or "proprioceptive placing" may reflect an "S→R" reflexologic view of central nervous system organization, which is no longer in the favor which it once enjoyed. In contrast, one can consider "placing" to be a unified motor pattern which can be elicited by a variety of stimuli and facilitating circumstances; neither its form nor occurrence is dependent on any one of these stimuli. Following an experimental ablation, one asks, "how can placing now be elicited?" rather than asking "is placing present or lost?"

In our researches, only three circumstances were considered and only the latter two of them in detail. These are the presentation of a table edge without contact (visual placing), bringing the paw dorsa into contact with the table edge while vision is excluded (paw-contact placing) and bringing the under surface of the jaw into contact with the table edge while excluding vision as well as other body contact (chin-contact placing). Variations in these were determined principally as a function of cerebral ablations and time of recovery therefrom. With respect to these experiments (as with all others reported to date), the reader must have faith that there has been adequate control of olfaction, pain, arousal, satiation and feline feelings toward the experimenter.

TRIGEMINOCERVICAL (HALTER) INHIBITION OF PLACING REACTIONS

Before describing the recovery of placing which has been suppressed as a consequence of cortical ablation, a specific point in testing methods deserves emphasis. This concerns the complexities of using a blindfold to exclude vision.

A blindfold not only occludes vision but also exerts a variety of other effects. These effects result from pressure on the scalp and they can be eliminated by combined trigeminal and cervical neurotomies, denervating the areas shown in Figure III-4a (adapted from Van Harreveld and Bogen).

If a normal cat is blindfolded, it commonly attempts to remove the eye covering with its forepaws, so that the blindfold is more irritating than it is sedative. But if the head is wrapped so as to avoid the eyes (as iin Fig. III-4b), many cats will manifest a loss of muscle tone and may remain motionless on the tabletop, sometimes for minutes at a time. If the headwrap is quickly whisked off, the cat becomes suddenly more alert, the change sometimes being quite dramatic.

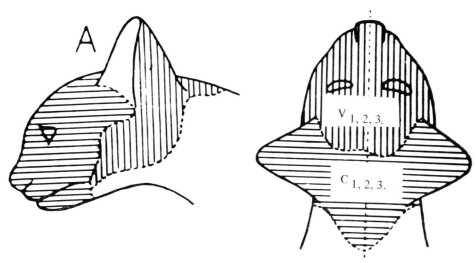

Figure III-4a. The diagram shows the skin areas responsible for the nonvisual effects of applying a blindfold.

Bandaging the head in such a way as to avoid the eyes affects the contact placing reactions. The inhibitory effect on placing reactions is most evident when placing is unstable as a result of cortical ablation (Fig. III-4c, III-4d). The same effect can be demonstrated, less consistently, on the intact (normal) cat, as shown in Figure III-4e.

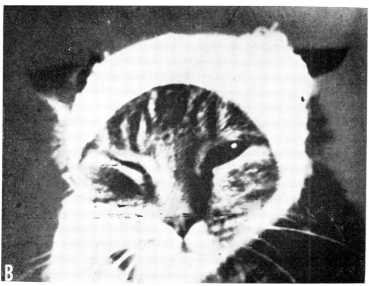

Figure III-4b. The photo shows how a headwrap (a 10-inch length of 3-inch roller gauze) can be applied to produce inhibition of a variety of postural reactions, without interfering with vision (see text for discussion).

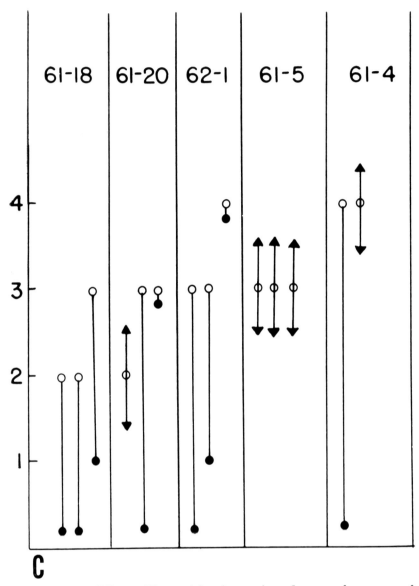

Figure III-4c. Five different H cats (showing various degrees of recovery of chin-contact placing) were tested on several occasions before and after wrapping the head. Inhibition was sometimes quite dramatic (drop from open circle to dot); at other times (arrows) the cats were uncooperative.

These results accord with the inhibitory effects of placing a halter on a horse; and they are probably related to the soothing effect of rubbing housepets about the scalp. Whatever its significance to the animal, this phenomenon is important to the investigator in two ways: first, it illus-

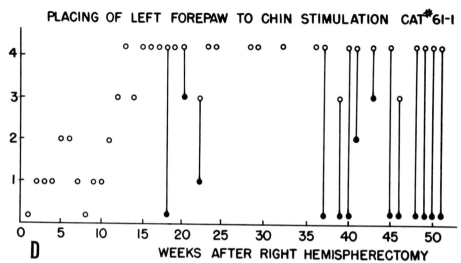

Figure III-4d. This cat was tested on a number of occasions over an 8-month period, beginning at 18 weeks at which time chin-contact placing had recovered to essentially normal. On each occasion, application of the head wrap (shown in Fig. III-4b) caused a diminution or disappearance of the recovered functions.

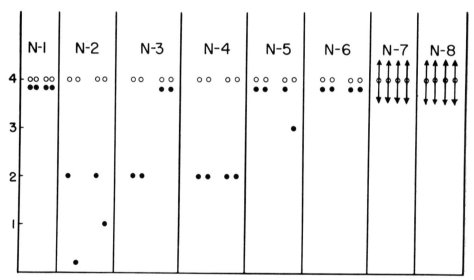

Figure III-4e. 8 different unoperated cats were tested, each on two occasions. The open circles show chin-contact placing before head-wrap, the black dots after head-wrap was applied. In two cats (7 & 8) struggling invalidated the results. In three cats (1, 5 and 6) the head-wrap had no effect. In one cat (3) both paws were inhibited on one occasion and not on another. In one cat (4) both paws were inhibited equally on both occasions. In one cat (2) the right paw was inhibited more than the left on both occasions.

trates the pitfalls of using a blindfold to eliminate vision in the testing of postural reflexes. Second, it affords a partial explanation of inconsistencies in reports on the recovery of placing reactions after placing has been suppressed by cerebral ablation.

SPONTANEOUS RECOVERY OF PLACING REACTIONS

Sherrington's investigations into the *Integrative action of the nervous system* were partly concerned with the analysis of certain postural reflexes. After spending some time with him, Magnus then undertook the study of body posture or *Körperstellung*, including those reactions related to the standing position. Following in Magnus' footsteps, Rademaker studied standing or *Das Stehen*, including a variety of changes both in muscle tone and in limb position. The limb position changes included the Stehberitschaft (placing) and Hinkebein (hopping) reactions, which are easily elicited in the normal animal. Bard (1931, 1932a, 1932b, 1933) restricted himself to placing and hopping in their various forms. Following this familiar historical pattern of ever-increasing depth and narrowness, we have concentrated on forelimb placing, and the factors favoring its recovery.

Rademaker found that placing was lost in the forelimb contralateral to a hemispherectomy. Bard found just as severe a deficit when only the sensorimotor cortex was removed; and he further found that placing was *not* lost if the entire hemisphere was removed *except* for the sensorimotor cortex. He thus clearly established a special significance with respect to placing of a relatively local area of cortex. This result was considered a particularly striking example of cortical localization; nearly 40 years later it was still cited as the best example of a behavior pattern strictly dependent upon a specific cortical locus (Lenneberg, 1967).

It seemed that the loss of placing from sensorimotor cortecectomy was "complete and permanent" (Woolsey and Bard, 1936) and that it was identical with the loss from ablation of the entire hemisphere. These conclusions were widely published by Bard and his school (Bard, 1931, 1932a, 1932b, 1933, 1938b, 1961; Bard and Brooks, 1932; Bard *et al.*, 1932; Bard and Macht, 1958; Bard and Mountcastle, 1948; Bard and Orias, 1933; Brooks, 1933; Brooks and Peck, 1940; Brooks and Woolsey, 1936; Woolsey, 1933) with the result that placing came to be understood as being impossible without cortex (Brooks and Peck, 1940). This impression was repeatedly reinforced by its repetition in almost all physiology textbooks.[‡]

[‡] Placing reactions can occur when the cerebral cortex has lost the sensorimotor areas or indeed when cortex is totally absent. This fact can serve as an example of how long it sometimes takes for information to creep into the textbooks.

It was originally believed, on grounds reasonable at the time, that following sensori-motor corticectomy, the placing reactions are completely and permanently lost." This assertion appeared (p. 378) in the 1949 edition of Fulton's *Physiology of the Nervous System,* where it was concluded that these reactions "depend upon the integrity of the motor area of the frontal lobe" (p. 190). When Ruch entered the picture to edit a 1960 text together with Fulton, the situation was described with more precision and some reservation:

> According to Bard contact placing is focally localized in the post-Central gyrus, but others believe that some ability returns unless posterior parietal lobe is also removed. (p. 344)

When Ruch and Patton wrote their text of 1965, the matter was dropped alto-gether (perhaps because it had become somewhat complex by this time). Others such as Houssay (1955) merely stated the known facts without interpretation:

> Extirpation of the cortex suppresses placing reactions on the opposite side of the body (p. 108)

Bard's own text retained as late as 1961 the original assertion saying, ". . . re-moval of all cortex lying behind the central sulcus completely eliminates the placing reaction . . ." (p. 1159). He also pointed out that this phenomenon is "an example of strict localization of function" (p. 1069). However, he qualified this by pointing out that "a proprioceptive correcting or placing allied to hopping remains and may become quite prominent." Although others supposed that these facts showed that placing re-quires the cortex, Bard offered elsewhere (p. 1129) a more subtle and sophisticated in-terpretation which continues to fit facts appearing subsequently:

> It is in accord with our general conception of cortical functions that these cor-tically managed reactions have to do with the finer adjustments of postures which are developed by subcortical levels of integration.

Bard's statements remained unchanged in a subsequent (12th) edition of 1968, edited by Mountcastle.

As an example of the impression received by those somewhat farther from the scene, we can quote Davson and Eggleton (1962):

> . . . tactile placing reactions were no longer possible after ablation of post-central cortex . . . this response depends upon the integrity of both the pre- and post-central foot areas (p. 1045).

This is an amplified version of the incorrect statement in the earlier edition edited by Evans, who probably adopted Fulton's phrase:

> This is called a 'placing reaction.' It is dependent on the integrity of the cerebral cortex (p. 287).

Chatfield (1957) may have used Fulton as his source:

> Placing reactions depend, as mentioned, on the integrity of the sensorimotor cortex (p. 208).

Ochs (1965) also retained the older view:

> These reflexes (hopping and placing) require that the sensorimotor portion of the cerebral cortex be intact (p. 300).

In this same vein, Best and Taylor (1966) not only stated the matter more strongly than necessary but misinterpreted it:

> Bard and Brooks found that removal of this region (the sensorimotor area of the cortex) from both cerebral hemispheres abolished the placing reactions . . .

This last statement was published about six years after an account by Denny-Brown in the Handbook of Physiology:

> The coarse reaction called proprioceptive placing . . . emerges as a subcortical coordination that eventually becomes very facile in long-term survival after (bi-lateral) removal of the pre- and post-central gyri (p. 792).

Some persons were so misled as to suppose that if a drug (De Risio and Tonini, 1956) or radiation (Sikou *et al.*, 1962) affected placing, that this was in itself evidence of a cortical site of drug action or of radiation injury.

A number of investigators (Denny-Brown and Chamber, 1955; Evans and Ingram, 1939; Peele, 1944; Ruch and Fulton, 1935; Travis and Woolsey, 1956) have reported some recovery of placing after its initial disappearance. Our results are quite different for paw-contact placing than for chin-contact placing. The former returns sporadically if at all. The latter seems almost invariably to recover following a frontal lobectomy (including all cortex anterior to the ansate sulcus) and this recovery is relatively rapid (see Fig. III-5). Following hemispherectomy, the recovery is quite variable from one cat to the next, and takes longer (see Fig. III-6).

With respect to chin-contact placing, we found that sensorimotor (or frontal) ablation produces as profound an initial deficit as total hemispherectomy; but the likelihood of an eventual recovery is greater with the lesser ablation. The differences among the H cats are as yet unexplained; it is possible that very slight discrepancies in the posterior encroachment upon the mid-brain are responsible, or at least contributory.

Visual placing in the affected limb was not systematically followed in

---

In contrast to some other authors, Ganong was up to date; he wrote in 1963, in 1965, and in a third edition of 1967:

> These various placing reactions are abolished on one side by unilateral decortication, but it has recently been claimed that some of them reappear after subsequent removal of the other hemisphere. This casts doubt on the claim that they are entirely dependent upon intact motor cortex, but this portion of the brain is certainly important in their regulation (p. 149).

In spite of the wide availability of Denny-Brown's work, and although Ganong kept up to date, others have continued in the old vein. For example, Roberts (1967) wrote:

> It has already been explained that the placing reactions are learned responses and it is therefore not surprising that their successful execution depends upon the integrity of the motor areas of the cortex (p. 251).

Eyzaguirre (1969) wrote:

> The central site of some postural reflexes, such as the hopping and placing reactions, is located in the cerebral cortex . . . these reflexes can be elicited only when the sensorimotor cortex is intact (p. 162).

Rushworth (1969) wrote:

> The (placing) reaction is destroyed by a lesion which involves either the primary sensory area of the cortex or the primary motor area (p. 69).

And according to Monnier (1970):

> The (placing) reaction is abolished when the frontal pole or the contralateral hemisphere has been removed (p. 421).

If, as Bard believed and we agree, placing is a particularly instructive example of central nervous organization, the readers of textbooks will hopefully be better served in the future.

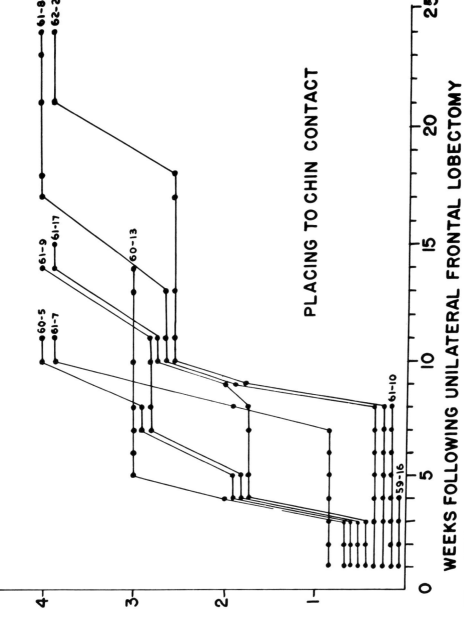

PLACING TO CHIN CONTACT

WEEKS FOLLOWING UNILATERAL FRONTAL LOBECTOMY

Figure III-5. The complete loss of chin-contact placing which follows a contralateral frontal lobe removal is succeeded by gradual reacquisition, so that in 8 to 16 weeks the majority showed responses hardly distinguishable from that of the unaffected limb. The Y-axis shows the quality of chin-contact placing on a scale from 0 to 4. The number at the end of each line identifies the cat and also indicates the time at which a second operation was done, terminating the initial experiment.

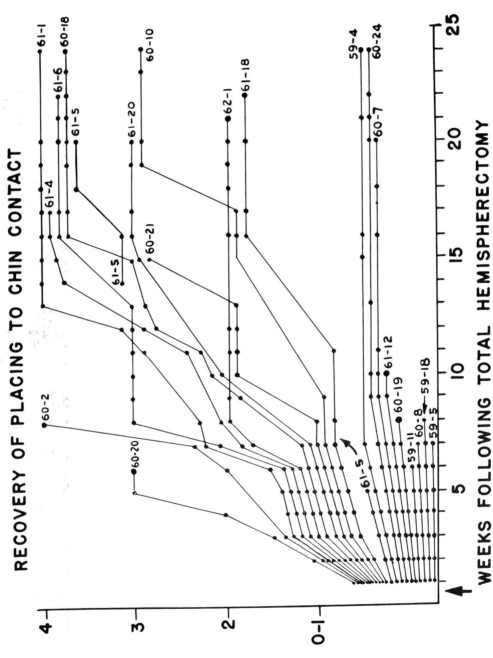

Figure III-6. Recovery of chin-contact placing following total hemispherectomy. As compared with frontal lobectomy, the reaction reappears in fewer animals and requires a longer time. (Compare with Fig. III-5).

all of our experiments. However, excellent visual placing was observed on several occasions in two H cats: 61-1 at eight months postoperatively and in 61-4, first appearing at four months postoperatively. In contrast, no visual placing was ever observed in six other H cats where it was explicitly tested (61-5, 61-6, 61-12, 61-18, 61-20, and 62-1).

DESCENDING INFLUENCES ON PAW-CONTACT PLACING

Although chin-contact placing returns after unilateral frontal lobectomy, paw-contact placing continues in abeyance except for rare occasions, about 1 to 2 percent of trials. The fact that it occurs at all seems to suggest that sensorimotor cortex is not absolutely required. It has sometimes been suggested that the rare occasions on which paw-contact placing appears are attributable to a less-than-complete sensorimotor ablation. However, approximately the same result (paw-contact placing in 1 to 2% of trials) obtains with the H-cat. We therefore concluded that the placing was not "destroyed" by the cortical ablation but that its capacity was still present somewhere within the nervous system. Professor Campbell and I were originally led to this interpretation by our belief that all placing was of a similar nature, rather than supposing that chin-contact placing (which commonly returns) is an altogether different "reflex." A second and more direct source of encouragement was to find, when we went into the literature looking for it, that return of paw-contact placing after a second ablation was mentioned in passing by several investigators (Tower, 1935; Denny-Brown and Chambers, 1958; Travis and Woolsey, 1956). We set about testing this phenomenon in a systematic way, using H-cats to avoid any "vicarious" function of cortex spared by a restricted sensorimotor ablation.

Our first experiment with the sequence of hemispherectomy followed by contralateral frontal ablation (59-11) resulted in a dramatic reappearance of paw-contact placing as shown in Figure III-7a. In subsequent experiments, various intervals were maintained between the two operations. In one experiment (Fig. III-7b), the animal was followed for less than a week after the second operation; but in spite of this short follow-up it was clear that there was return of a capacity which had been suppressed for a long time. Other animals were followed for various times after surgery and showed the same return; three of these results (60-7, 60-21, 60-24) have been published previously (Bogen and Campbell, 1962b).

In some normal animals the placing behavior is more labile than others; this lability of placing is markedly increased by the secondary removal of cortex so that such a cat may have spontaneous alternating movements of the fore-limbs whenever it is lifted from the ground. This

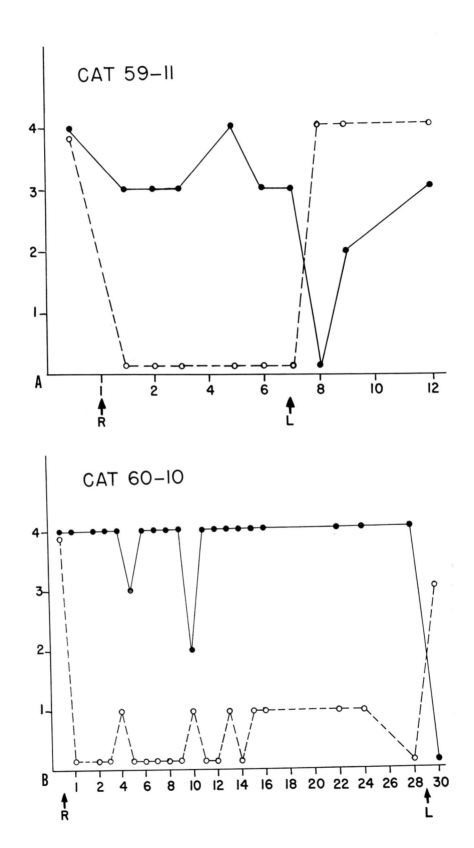

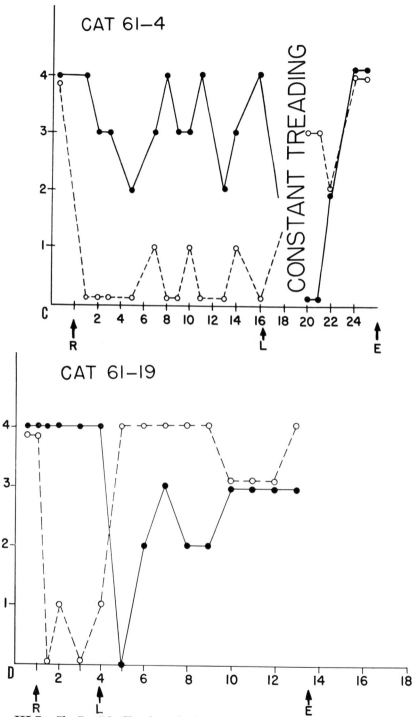

Figure III-7a, 7b, 7c, 7d. Foreleg placing to contact of paw dorsum with a table edge. The right-sided operation (R) was hemicerebrectomy. The left-sided operation (L) was removal of the remaining frontal lobe. The ordinate shows the level of performance in arbitrary units. The abscissa shows elapsed time in weeks. The solid dots show the performance of the right fore-leg. The open circles show the performance of the left foreleg.

results in a treading action whose appearance also seems dependent on how hungry or frightened the cat is. In one cat (Fig. III-7c), there was almost constant treading whenever the cat was picked up following the second operation. However, the threshold of the treading behavior eventually rose so the cat reached a stable state in which no movement occurred until a specific stimulus was applied. After this recovery of stability, placing was regularly elicited to paw-contact on both sides.

The question could be asked as to how long an interval between operations is necessary for the appearance of the phenomenon. The shortest interval between hemispherectomy and contralateral frontal lobectomy was four weeks (Fig. III-7d).

As a general rule, bilateral injury causes a more profound loss when it is simultaneous rather than sequential (Ades and Raab, 1946; Braun, 1966; Ettlinger and Kalsbeck, 1962; Rosen *et al.*, 1971; Travis and Woolsey, 1956). In particular, bilateral frontal lobectomy in the cat is said to be followed by a loss of placing, bilaterally, which does not recover (Bard, 1933; Magoun, 1938). It is conceivable, however, that the simultaneous combination of one frontal lobe and the other entire hemisphere could give a different result. Four such operations were attempted; one cat (62-7) did well, ambulating independently on the third day. This cat was kept for three weeks during which time no fore-limb placing of any kind could be elicited.

It is still widely believed that placing is lost after cortical ablation because the cortex is essential to this behavior (see footnote*). The return after a second operation clearly invalidates this explanation. The best explanation presently available is that sensorimotor cortex (more than other parts of the cortex) has a facilitating influence on a contralateral reaction organized within the brain stem and spinal cord. Removal of this contralateral facilitation is poorly compensated because of an excess of tonic inhibition from ipsilateral sensorimotor cortex. This explanation leads us to expect that there may be a large number of facilitatory and inhibitory influences whose balance can be upset or redressed in any number of ways. This conclusion is consonant with the observations that chronic decerebrate cats (Bazett, 1922) and decerebrate newborn kittens (Langworthy, 1929) show alternate progression movements, that placing can be seen in most newborn humans in spite of the poor development of cortex (Paine, 1964, Zapella, 1967) that placing has been observed in an infant with hydranencephaly (Barnet *et al.*, 1966, Zapella, 1963, 1967), that placing can be elicited in decorticate cats given amphetamine (Meyer *et al.*, 1963), and paw-contact placing occurs even in hypothalamic cats after they are given caffeine (Bogen, *et al.* in press). Related are the observations that placing can be lost with stereotaxic lesions near the red nucleus (Evans and Ingram, 1939) and in the cerebellum (Chambers and Sprague, 1955); and that placing can be increased by electrical stimulation of the cerebellum (Sprague and Chambers, 1954) and the caudate nucleus (Davis, 1958).

The interdependence of cerebrum and cerebellum has interested many investigators (Adrian, 1943; Fulton, 1936; Schneider and Crosby, 1963; Schoolman and Delgado, 1958; Snider and Eldred, 1952; Sprague and Chambers, 1959), some of whom have specifically considered making a lesion in one to relieve symptoms produced by a prior lesion in the other. We considered this with specific reference to placing, particularly because when hemicerebellectomy depresses ipsilateral fore-limb placing, the affected limb has an excess of extensor tone. This contrasts with the excess

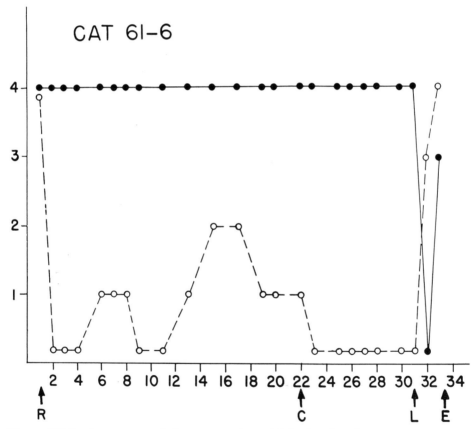

Figure III-8. A sequence of three operations (right hemicerebrectomy, left hemicerebellectomy and left frontal lobectomy) was carried out. Some tendency for return of paw-contact placing after the first operation was eliminated by the second operation. After the third operation, the paw-contact placing promptly returned. The symbolism is the same as in Figure III-7.

of flexor tone seen after cerebral ablations. One can suppose that balancing the flexor and extensor tendencies would permit placing to reappear after a second operation.

Four cats (59-5, 60-2, 60-19, 61-6) had hemicerebrectomy with minimal return of paw-contact placing; they then had a contralateral hemicerebellectomy. Only two (59-5, 61-6) survived the second operation and in these what placing had reappeared was suppressed. These results indicate that so far as placing is concerned, hemicerebellectomy does not "balance" a contralateral hemispherectomy.

One cat with previous hemispherectomy and hemicerebellectomy survived a third operation (removal of the remaining frontal lobe) following which there was a prompt return of the placing on the side ipsilateral to the third operation (see Fig. III-8). In this case, the disinhibition of paw-contact placing by ipsilateral frontal lobectomy was sufficiently pronounced to overcome the *combined* suppressive effects of the first two operations.

Several other experiments were done on the question of cerebro-cerebellar relations. One cat (59-16) had two frontal ablations four weeks apart and never had return of placing until after a third operation, a hemicerebellectomy which was followed by the appearance of excellent paw-contact placing in the fore-limb contralateral to the second (left) lobectomy and the (left) hemicerebellectomy. One cat (61-8) had good return of right fore-limb placing to chin-contact (but not to paw-contact) following a left frontal lobectomy; a subsequent *left* hemicerebellectomy did not suppress placing in the *left* fore-limb, as would ordinarily be expected after a primary hemicerebellectomy.

Our experiments in cerebello-cerebral interaction were of the probing type and insufficient in number to permit any firm conclusions. They do provide, however, some glimpses into the extent to which the cerebellum participates in the overall imbalance which is responsible for loss of placing after a cerebral ablation.

ONTOGENY OF CORTICOFUGAL INFLUENCES

Introduction

In addition to the adult cats described above and listed in Table III-I, we also did hemicerebrectomy on a number of kittens. This work with kittens was mainly concerned with the placing reactions. We supposed that if operation were sufficiently early, there would be less long-term effect on placing (particularly the most labile, paw-contact placing). This is apparently not the case. But the kitten experiments were quite enlightening because of the serendipitous discovery that *total hemisphe-*

rectomy in a kitten is not immediately followed by loss of contralateral placing, as it is in the adult.

The first observations made on kittens were to determine the usual times of appearance of paw-contact, chin-contact and visual placing. Subsequent litters were subjected to operation.

Results

1. A litter of four kittens was first observed on the ninth post-partum day at which time all had their eyes open and all but one placed fairly well to paw-contact. Placing to chin-contact was absent in three of these kittens and questionable in one. None of them placed visually

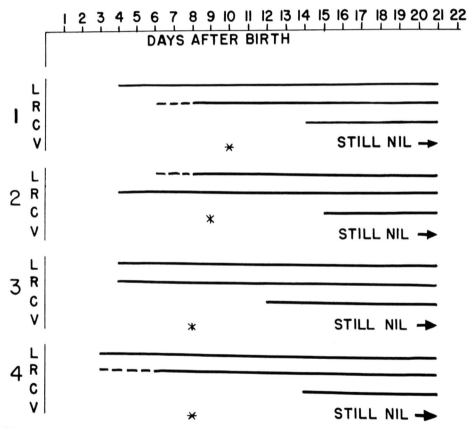

Figure III-9. Appearance of placing in the four kittens (numbered in order of birth) of litter number three. Each kitten was tested daily for paw-contact placing (left and right paws separately with the other paw held), chin-contact placing and visual placing. Definite placing of each type first appeared with the origin of the solid line. The asterisk indicates the first day of widely opened eyes. L means paw-contact placing for the left paw, R for the right paw. C means chin-contact placing with both paws. V means visual placing.

at this time. When the kittens were re-examined on the twentieth day, all placed well to paw-contact and all placed well to chin-contact; but none of them placed visually. Visual placing was fully in evidence when they were re-tested on the fortieth day.

2. A second litter of three kittens was followed several times per week. They all had good placing to paw-contact by the end of the first week. By the end of the second week (at which time all of them had their eyes open), they all had fairly good chin placing, although with some struggling. There was still no visual placing by the end of the third week, but it appeared by the end of a month.

3. A third litter of four kittens was observed daily for three weeks. The results are shown in Figure III-9 where it can be seen that paw-contact placing appeared about the 4th to 6th day (before the eyes opened). Placing to chin-contact appeared about the 12th to 14th day. Visual placing had not appeared by the end of the third week.

4. A fourth litter of three kittens was operated on the seventh day at which time they had good placing to paw-contact but had no placing to chin-contact or to visual stimulus (the eyes were still closed). All of them died shortly after hemicerebrectomy.

5. A fifth litter consisted of four kittens, one of which died early. The remaining three were first tested at the age of eight weeks. All of them had active placing to paw-contact, to chin-contact and to visual stimulus. All three became adept at catching moths fluttering near a light put out to attract insects to the cat's play yard. All three of them had a right hemicerebrectomy at the age of four months; one died. The other two were walking fairly well on the second post-operative day in spite of the marked head rotation (chin up to the right) and tendency to circle which is typical of the hemispherectomized cat. These kittens had also been trained previously to come for food to a whistle. One week after operation they were first tested for retention of this habit. Both kittens became excited and began circling toward the right (clockwise) and one of them required several more weeks to overcome this tendency. The other kitten was less affected and was able to find its way to the food within a few days although circling several times (after hearing the whistle) before starting on a straight path. Both of these hemispherectomized kittens included the left forelimb in their bathing by the end of the fourth week. By the eighth week after operation the better kitten was able to catch moths with either forelimb. There was no sign of placing of any kind with the left forelimb at this time although hopping had partially returned. By the end of the fourth month, both of these kittens were climbing trees well, coming

when whistled for and were able to catch moths with either forepaw although using the right forelimb much more frequently (perhaps because of the left hemianopia). When a sudden loud noise (a motorized lawnmower) appeared at this time both kittens circled wildly to the right for the first time in many weeks. This tendency to circle to the right still reappeared with sudden loud noises as long as a year after operation. Also by a year after operation, there was still no evidence of paw-contact placing in the affected limbs.

6. From a sixth litter, two kittens were operated on the eighth post-partum day at which time the eyes were closed but there was good placing to paw-contact. One kitten survived a week during which repeated observation showed that the placing reaction had not been significantly affected by the operation.

7. A seventh litter (of three kittens) was operated on the tenth post-partum day at which time all still had closed eyes but all had good placing to paw-contact. Two of them succumbed shortly after operation. The third was nursing well the next day at which time there was excellent placing bilaterally. Paw-contact placing was also excellent bilaterally when tested the second post-operative day. The mother cat and the surviving kitten were then removed from the laboratory and data on the interim was not obtained. When the kitten was tested three weeks later (post-operative day 23) all three types of placing were markedly impaired in the left forelimb.

8. An eighth litter of four kittens all had right hemicerebrectomy on the twelfth post-partum day. One of them survived and was tested daily for two months. Placing to paw-contact was brisk bilaterally throughout the immediate post-operative period. Chin placing first began to appear on the 22nd day after birth and was good by the 27th day. Visual placing first appeared on the 28th day of life and was definite on the 29th day although less brisk in the left forelimb than the right. On the 32nd day of life there appeared an asymmetry in the left forelimb for chin-contact placing but not yet for paw contact placing. This condition persisted for a week. By the 40th day a diminution of left fore-limb placing to paw-contact became quite evident. Left paw-contact placing progressively diminished throughout the next few days; from the 45th to 60th days on every occasion there was excellent placing in the right forelimb in all three respects whereas only traces of placing in all three respects could be obtained from the left forelimb. When two months old, the kitten contracted a febrile illness and succumbed in several days. The results of daily testing for placing are shown in Figure III-10 (Days 53 through 60 were the same as day 52).

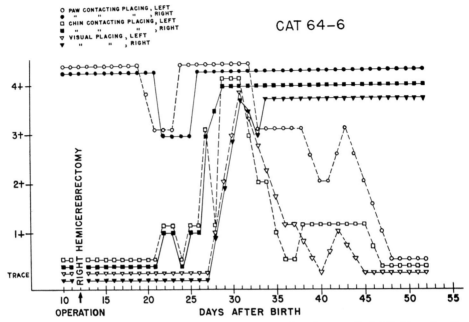

Figure III-10. Development of corticofugal facilitation and inhibition in the hemicerebrectomized kitten 64-6. At the time of operation (twelfth post-partum day) paw-contact placing was well established bilaterally but there was no placing to chin-contact or visually. Toward the end of the fourth week both of the latter appeared bilaterally and between the 30th and 33rd days all three forms of placing were brisk bilaterally. All three forms of placing then progressively disappeared from the affected limb, reflecting the development of ipsilateral descending inhibition from the maturing cortex (M. Suzuki assisted in these observations).

Discussion

Results from the unoperated litters suggest that, in round numbers: paw-contact placing appears during the first week (before opening of the eyes), chin-contact placing appears by the end of the second week, and visual placing requires nearly four weeks to become firmly established[§] (see Fig. III-9). *If a kitten is hemispherectomized during the second week, at which time there is paw-contact placing but no chin-contact or visual placing, the result is surprising: the paw-contact placing is unaffected.* A similar result was recently reported in the rat; placing did not disappear until 17 days after hemidecortication (Hicks and D'Amato, 1970; Amassian, 1971).

_____

[§] These findings are the same as those of others (Warkentin and Smith 1937) although these authors used the term "tactual placing" to indicate what we have called "chin contact placing," as can be seen from their definition of "tactual placing" on page 383.

In retrospect this result is understandable—it means that the ipsilateral corticofugal inhibition has not yet developed. By following the operated kitten one can determine when this inhibition develops; this turns out to be about a week after the appearance of visual placing. There is, therefore, a time when the completely hemispherectomized kitten places bilaterally in all three respects, subsequently losing all three reactions in the affected paw during the fifth and sixth weeks. Figure III-10 illustrates how this experiment unmasks the progressive development of facilitatory and inhibitory influences descending from the cortex.[‖]

Wenzel, Tschirgi and Taylor (1962) followed two kittens, decorticated at the age of one week, for three subsequent years. When these authors were kind enough to permit my examination of their two kittens about a year following operation, both kittens placed bilaterally to chin-contact, but no paw-contact placing could be elicited.

CONCLUDING DISCUSSION

Recovery from hemispherectomy is steadily progressive so that dividing the recovery period into acute and chronic phases is rather arbitrary. It is useful to make the distinction, however, because of the disabling asymmetries which are characteristic of the immediate post-operative period and only appear in the chronic state when there is some unusual stress.

Unilateral ablation of a paired part of the nervous system typically causes an asymmetry, sometimes more disabling than a bilateral removal. Since the rabbit experiments of Magnus (1924) it is well known that unilateral labyrinthectomy causes much greater postural disability than a bilateral operation. With Van Harreveld, I have seen this confirmed repeatedly in the cat (1961). The comparison between labyrinthectomy and hemispherectomy is limited, however, because the hemispherectomized animal has a better recovery.

In the short term, the H cat is severly crippled, worse in some respects than a cat with no cerebrum at all. A cat can walk well within an hour after removal of all brain above the hypothalamus (Bard and Rioch, 1937; Bogen *et al.*, In preparation; Guzman-F and Del Pozo, 1953; Hinsey 1940; Hinsey and Ranson, 1928) as can a decorticate monkey (Travis and Woolsey, 1956). In contrast, the H cat rarely walks or even stands

---

[‖] Possibly related to this finding is the recent report that a baboon with forelimb deafferentation at birth switched at the age of 4 months from the more normal palmar placement to walking on the dorsum of the manus. E. Taub, P. Perrella, and G. Barro, "Behavioral Development After Forelimb Deafferentation on Day of Birth in Monkeys with and Without Blinding," *Science, 181:* 959–960 (1973).

in less than a day or two (Fig. III-3). But in the long term, a single remaining hemisphere provides a behavioral repertoire which is not halfway between having two hemispheres and having none. Instead, the behavior in the chronic H cat is most of the time indistinguishable from the intact condition.

The reappearance in an H animal of most of its normal behavioral repertoire is partly ascribable to a duality of representation in the cerebral hemispheres, the implications of which I have discussed at some length elsewhere (Bogen, 1969a, 1969b; Bogen and Bogen, 1969). But most of the postural recovery has a different origin.

The immediate source of motor output is not the cerebrum, but the neuraxis (brain stem and spinal cord). The patterns of motor expression within the neuraxis suffer a transient disorganization after disconnection from overlying parts, but eventually resume their usual status. This probably is ascribable in part to the subsidence of previously ongoing inhibition, and may also be attributable to the appearance of inhibition previously latent. An everyday example of this in neurological practice is the rapid return of normal eye movements following a stroke which temporarily produces a complete inability to gaze away from the injured hemisphere. The readjustments in the oculomotor system are but a fraction of the total readjustment which occurs after total hemispherectomy.

It is now established (Bogen *et al.*, In Preparation; Macht, 1942; Maling and Acheson, 1946; Meyer *et al.*, 1963) that certain stimulant drugs can elicit postural reactions ordinarily absent from the truncated neuraxis. This fact supports the view that the neural assemblies of the spinal cord and brain stem have not lost their capacity to function as more brain has accumulated above, with the evolution of a primitive walking amphibian into a piano-playing man. Rather, the neuraxis has retained the same capacity for integrated response, the cerebro-cerebellar development providing a more precise initiation, termination and fractionation of action patterns already present in even the lowest vertebrate forms. In this view, phylogenetic development is not seen as a progressive "encephalization" with higher levels *assuming* tasks once located more caudally. Rather, the total pattern of activity inherent in the lower centers is differentiated into new, partial patterns of greater precision and flexibility (Coghill, 1929, 1933, 1936, 1943).

We might say that the machinery is still in the basement where it always was, and that there have been added upstairs a larger number of computers to control the machinery. Seen from this vantage, it would not be surprising to find the machinery out of order should there be damage to specific parts of an upstairs computer (e.g. frontal lobe on one side). But proper disconnection (such as removing the other frontal lobe) results in a resumption of function because the disturbing imbalance of descending influences has been eliminated. Of course, the restituted function might be expected to be less finely adjusted and less appropriate than before.

Since motor capacity in the neuraxis can be freed of inhibition by removal of ipsilateral cerebral cortex, one may naturally ask if there is somewhere here a possibility of clinical application. When hemiplegia follows unilateral damage, a lesion to the other side might restore some function. But there will simultaneously be a removal of facilitation (and with it the capacity for precise, purposeful movement) for the remaining side. Therefore such a procedure would be disastrous in its overall effect. However, the experiments on kittens (Fig. III-10) make it clear that the ipsilateral inhibition is separable from the contralateral facilitation.

There is a need for further experiments in which placing is released by a secondary ipsilateral operation which does not de-facilitate contralaterally; such experiments could reasonably begin with caudate lesions, pyramidal section or orbital corticectomy. There may well be an operation, or a drug, which eliminates ipsilateral inhibition without disturbing contralateral facilitation. The knowledge that such inhibition exists must make easier the search for its location and nature.

Some further comment is appropriate regarding the once popular concept of "encephalization." By "encephalization" was meant that in the course of phylogenesis, the neural structures subserving certain functions come to be located higher in the neuraxis. Or alternatively expressed, a particular function cannot be performed in the absence of certain structures which, as evolution proceeds, are added on higher in the neuraxis. This generalization may once have seemed reasonable; but most of the evidence for it can now be otherwise interpreted.

An argument for "encephalization" was offered by Walker and Fulton (1938) when they observed that carnivores (dogs and cats) walk soon after a hemispherectomy, that a macaque uses its affected forelimbs to grasp a bar a week after operation, that baboons did not do this for a month and that "a chimpanzee never regained a volitional grasp." (These authors reported only one chimpanzee which they followed for only 28 days.) On the basis of their observations they concluded:

> It is obvious from the above account that the neurological disturbances following hemidecortication become progressively greater as the phylogenic scale is ascended.

The idea that a cat recovers function of its distal limb parts faster than does a monkey is probably a misconception based on the more rigorous criteria which are used for recovery in primates. If one examines the more delicate paw motions of a cat, one sees that they recover no better than finger motions are reputed to recover in monkeys. The placing reaction to chin-contact requires months to reappear (as shown in Fig. III-6); and the placing reaction to paw-contact appears after hemispherectomy only on rare occasions. The complementary idea that after hemispherectomy a human is worse than a chimpanzee which is worse than a monkey, etc. is also a misconception. Even if the single chimpanzee of Walker and Fulton is representative of that species, there is no doubt that the human can do better than the baboons reported by those authors. I have seen two patients with hemispherectomy, operated in adulthood for tumour, who subsequently had a useful grasp enabling them to hold onto a bar or a valise handle with the affected hand (Bogen, 1969a). Voluntary flexion and even voluntary extension of the fingers may occasionally appear following hemispherectomy for infantile hemiplegia (Ignelzi and Bucy, 1968 and White, 1961); particularly good examples were reported by French and Johnson (1955) and by Ueki (1966). A result nearly as good can occur even after hemispherectomy for a tumour first appearing in adulthood (Burklund, 1972).

Another supposed example of encephalization is the plantar reflex or great toe sign of Babinski (1896); this consists of an upward motion of the hallux (great toe) when the planta (sole) is stimulated in a person with CNS injury, instead of the downward motion typically found in the normal adult.

In human development during gestation and infancy there is a cyclic alternation between the upward and downward responses to plantar stimulation (Hooker, 1952; Humphrey, 1969). In the newborn, the response is usually down according to some (Hogan and Milligan, 1971), whereas most investigators (Brain and Wilkinson, 1959; Collier, 1899; Leri, 1903; McGraw, 1941) have found upward motion of the hallux to be prominent through infancy. During the second year as the child's walking progresses, there is an increasing tendency to downward motion, usually quite consistent by the second or third birthday. This stability may be ascribable to tonic descending influences in the pyramidal (corticospinal) tract which becomes myelinated during this time. Subsequent interruption of the descending influences (by injury to brain or spinal cord) restores the more primitive condition of upgoing toe.

It is now generally accepted that the plantar reflex is part of an overall flexor or withdrawal reflex of the limb (Brain and Wilkinson, 1959; Collier, 1899; Landau and Clare, 1959; Walshe, 1956; Wartenberg, 1947). In general, a painful stimulus causes withdrawal of the stimulated surface (Hagbarth, 1960). As a result, the pattern of muscular coordination changes as the painful stimulus is moved up and down or around the extremity (Grimby, 1963). If one stimulates, in a normal human adult, the surface under the head of the first metatarsal, the great toe commonly goes up along with the other toes (Dosuzkov, 1932; Grimby, 1963; Dohrmann and Nowack, 1973).

Fulton and Keller (1932) noted a greater prominence of the Babinski sign in the gibbon and the chimpanzee than in the baboon, and a much greater prominence in the two higher primates than in the monkey. When they summarized their conclusions at the end of their book, they asserted that:

> during the process of encephalization the cortex has *taken over* functions normally carried out in lower forms by the older reflex mechanisms of the medulla and cord (italics mine).

They do not include in this summary an important observation which they mentioned earlier (page 65): the gibbon has bipedal, plantigrade locomotion and thus "runs dexterously on two feet giving the appearance of a human midget." The chimpanzee also commonly walks in a bipedal, plantigrade fashion.

In the four-legged animal (such as a carnivore or monkey) a noxious stimulus to the bottom of the foot produces a withdrawal of the entire limb including upward flexion and abduction of all the toes. In the two-legged animal this would throw the animal off-balance. Therefore, instead of withdrawal of the entire limb, the leg is partly flexed while at the same time the toes move *downward* thus bearing the weight which was previously distributed on the entire sole including the stimulated area. The difference found in the various animals with respect to the plantar reflex can thus be seen as an adjustment to bipedal, plantigrade locomotion rather than the result of a bigger brain or "encephalization."

One of the arguments for encephalization was that removal of visual cortex caused progressively greater deficits in higher animals; and so the cortex was said to have "taken over" functions "at the expense" of more caudal structures (Marquis and Hilgard, 1937). Subsequent experiments (Black and Myers, 1968; Schneider, 1969; Sprague, 1966; Trevarthen, 1968; Trevarthen and Sperry, In preparation) have shown this to be overly simplistic, and have reinforced the view that lower levels retain their functions, being overlain rather than replaced, as neocortex is progressively added.

The evolution of theory with more information can be seen in two quotations. In 1935, Ruch joined Fulton (1935) in his belief in a "vertical migration of function." In 1965, Ruch and his co-authors wrote (1965)

> In the course of evolution, the forebrain has come to dominate lower midbrain and spinal centers more and more, the domination being most complete in man and other higher primates. This evolutionary process is generally referred to as "encephalization."

Some comment is in order as to the directions of future research. It is unlikely that important information will come from extending hemispherectomy to other species, although no one has yet reported hemispherectomy in an orang or a gorilla. More complex psychological testing of the hemispherectomized animal may be productive; but such testing of humans is more apt to be rewarding, and hemispherectomized humans are not excessively rare. There is much more to be done in the matter of secondary lesions. Although the chronically recovered H animal is in most respects a "whole person," there is very little redundancy or safety factor remaining; almost any lesion of the remaining hemisphere produces a dramatic change. In the H animal, therefore, almost every structure of the cerebrum can be studied by either ablation or stimulation with the expectation of a definite result.

As discussed earlier, there is probably a good deal more to be learned from the "isolated hemisphere." Furthermore, a variety of interesting experiments have been based on completely disconnecting a hemisphere *except* for part or all of the corpus callosum (Hossman, 1969a; 1969b).

Mention should also be made of the restriction of input to a single hemisphere of the split-brain, as well as the various means of "temporary hemispherectomy" such as intracarotid amytal, unilateral spreading depression and unilateral electrical anesthesia. In sum, many opportunities remain for increasing our understanding of the double-brained animal by examining one brain at a time.

REFERENCES

Ades, H. W., and Raab, D. H.: Recovery of motor function after two-stage extirpation of area 4 in monkeys. *J Neurophysiol, 9:* 55–60, 1946.

Adey, W. R., and Lindsley, D. F.: On the role of subthalamic areas in the maintenance of brain-stem reticular excitability. *Exp Neurol, 1:* 407–426, 1959.

Adrian, E. D.: Afferent areas in the cerebellum connected with the limbs. *Brain, 66:* 289–315, 1943.

Amassian, V. E., Ross, R., and Donat, J.: Development of contact placing and thalamocortical organization in kittens. *Fed Proc, 30:* 434, 1971.

———, Weiner, H., and Rosenblum, M.: Neural systems subserving the tactile placing reaction: A model for the study of higher level control of movement. *Brain Res, 4:* 171–178, 1972.

Baldwin, M., and Mejia, R.: Effects of unilateral section of the brainstem after mesial cerebral incision. *Ann NY Acad Sci, 162:* 459–471, 1969.

Bard, P.: Some postural deficiencies following certain cortical ablations. *Am J Physiol, 97:* 503, 1931.

———: The cortical representation of certain postural reactions and the normal functioning of cortical remnants. *Arch Neurol Psychiatry, 28:* 745–747, 1932a.

———: The cortical representation of certain postural reactions and the normal functioning of cortical remnants. *J Nerv Ment Dis, 76:* 56–69, 1932b.

———: Studies on the cerebral cortex. 1. Localized control of placing and hopping reactions in the cat and their normal management by small cortical remnants. *Arch Neurol Psychiatry, 30:* 40–74, 1933.

———: Studies on cortical representation of somatic sensibility. *Harvey Lect, 33:* 143–169, 1938a.

———: Studies on the cortical representation of somatic sensibility. *Bull NY Acad Med, 14:* 585–607, 1938b.

——— (Ed.): *Medical Physiology,* 11th ed. St. Louis, Mosby, 1961.

———, and Brooks, C. M.: Localized cortical control of some postural reactions in the cat and rat together with evidence that small cortical remnants may function normally. *Assoc Res Nerv Ment Dis 13:* 107–157, 1932.

———, Brooks, C. M., and Lowry, T.: Cerebral localization of "hopping" and "placing" reactions in cats, rats and alligators. *Am J Physiol, 101:* 3–4, 1932.

———, and Macht, M. B.: The behaviour of chronically decerebrate cats. *Ciba Foundation Symposium on the Neurological Basis of Behaviour,* London, Churchill, 1958, pp. 55–71.

———, and Mountcastle, V. B.: Some forebrain mechanisms involved in expression of rage with special reference to suppression of angry behavior. *Assoc Res Nerv Ment Dis, 27:* 362–404, 1948.

———, and Orias, O.: Localized cortical management of visual and labyrinthine placing reactions. *Am J Physiol, 105:* 2–3, 1933.

———, and Rioch, D. McK.: A study of four cats deprived of neocortex and additional portions of the forebrain. *Bull Johns Hopkins Hosp, 60:* 65–147, 1937.

Barnet, A., Bazelon, M., and Zappella, M.: Visual and auditory function in an hydranencephalic infant. *Brain Res, 2:* 351–360, 1966.

Bazett, H. C., and Penfield, W. C.: A study of the Sherringtonian decerebrate animal in the chronic as well as the acute condition. *Brain, 45:* 185–265, 1922.

Berlucchi, G.: Electroencephalographic activity of the isolated hemicerebrum of the cat. *Ex Neurol, 15:* 220–228, 1966.

———, Sprague, J. M., Levy, J., and DiBerardino, A. C.: Pretectum and superior colliculus in visually guided behavior and in flux and form discrimination in the cat. *J Comp Physiol Psychol, 78:* 123–171, 1972.

Berman, A. J., Knapp, H. D., and Rabiner, A. M.: Recovery of function following massive unilateral cerebral ablations in the monkey. *Trans Am Neurol Assoc, 82:* 82–84, 1958.

Best, C. H., and Taylor, N. B.: *The physiological basis of medical practice,* 8th ed. Baltimore, Williams and Wilkins, 1966.

Black, P., Cianci, S. N., and Markowitz, R. S.: Differential recovery of proximal and distal motor power after cortical lesions. *Trans Am Neurol Assoc, 96:* 173–177, 1971.

———, and Myers, R. E.: Brainstem mediation of visual perception in a higher primate. *Trans Am Neurol Assoc, 93:* 191–193, 1968.

Blagoveshchenskaya, W.: Formation of associations in animals with but one hemisphere. *Nov Refl Fiziol Nerv Sist, 3:* 333–378, 1929 (cited by Kellogg & Bashore, 1950).

Bogen, J. E.: The other side of the brain I: Dysgraphia and dyscopia following cerebral commissurotomy. *Bull Los Angeles Neurol Soc, 34:* 73–105, 1969a.

———: The other side of the brain II: An appositional mind. *Bull Los Angeles Neurol Soc, 34:* 135–162, 1969 b.

————, and Bogen, G. M.: The other side of the brain III: The corpus callosum and creativity. *Bull Los Angeles Neurol Soc, 34:* 191–220, 1969.

————: Concluding discussion. In Smith, W. L. (Ed.): *Drugs, Development and Cerebral Function.* Springfield, Thomas, 1971.

————, and Campbell, B.: Total hemispherectomy in the cat. *Surg Forum, 11:* 381–3, 1960.

————, and Campbell, B.: Trigeminocervical (halter) inhibition of placing reactions. *Fed Proc, 21:* 368, 1962a.

————, and Campbell, B.: Recovery of foreleg placing after ipsilateral frontal lobectomy in the hemicerebrectomized cat. *Science, 135:* 309–310, 1962b.

————, and Campbell, B.: Recovery time for placing following unilateral ablations in cats. *Fed Proc, 22:* 456, 1963.

Bogen, J. E., Suzuki, M., and Campbell, B.: Paw-contact placing reactions in hypothalamic cats given caffeine. (In preparation)

Bonin, G. von (tr.): *Some papers on the Cerebral Cortex.* Springfield, Thomas, 1960.

Bouillaud, J.: Recherches expérimentales sur les fonctions du cerveau (lobes cerebraux) en général, et sur celles de sa portion antérieure en particulier. *J hebd de méd, 6:* 527, 1830. (quoted by Dandy, W.: *Surgery of the Brain,* 1945)

Bradford, F. K.: Ablations of frontal cortex in cats with special reference to enhancement of the scratch reflex. *J Neurophysiol, 2:* 192–201, 1939.

Brain, R., and Wilkinson, M.: Observations on the extensor plantar reflex and its relationship to the functions of the pyramidal tract. *Brain, 82:* 297–320, 1959.

Braun, J. J.: The neocortex and visual placing in rats. *Brain Res, 1:* 381–394, 1966.

Bromiley, R. B.: The development of conditioned responses in cats after unilateral decortication. *J Comp Physiol Psychol, 41:* 155–164, 1948.

Brooks, C. M.: Studies on the cerebral cortex II: Localized representation of hopping and placing reactions in the rat. *Am J Physiol, 105:* 162–171, 1933.

————, and Peck, M. E.: Effect of various cortical lesions on development of placing and hopping reactions in rats. *J Neurophysiol, 3:* 66–73, 1940.

————, and Woolsey, C. N.: Relation in the rabbit of electrically excitable areas of cortex to placing and hopping reactions. *Am J Physiol, 116:* 17–18, 1936.

Brown, T. G.: On the nature of the fundamental activity of the nervous centers together with an analysis of the conditioning of rhythmic activity in progression, and a theory of the evolution of function in the nervous system. *J Physiol* (Lond), *48:* 18–46, 1914.

Bucy, P. C., and Fulton, J. F.: Ipsilateral representation in the motor and premotor cortex of monkeys. *Brain, 56:* 318–342, 1933.

Buresova, O., and Nadel, L.: Interhemispheric transfer in the rat. *Physiol Behav, 5:* 849–853, 1970.

Burklund, C. W.: Cerebral hemisphere function in the human: fact versus tradition. In, Smith, W. L. (Ed.): *Drugs, Development and Cerebral Function.* Springfield, Thomas, 1972.

Campbell, B.: The factor of safety in the nervous system. *Bull Los Angeles Neurol Soc, 25:* 109–117, 1960.

Chambers, W. W., and Liu, C-N.: Cortico-spinal tract of the cat. An attempt to correlate the pattern of degeneration with deficits in reflex activity following neocortical lesions. *J Comp Neurol, 108:* 23–55, 1957.

Chambers, W. W., and Sprague, J. M.: Functional localization in the cerebellum. I. Organization in longitudinal cortico-nuclear zones and their contribution to the control of posture, both extrapyramidal and pyramidal. *J Comp Neurol, 103:* 105–129, 1955.

Chatfield, P. O.: *Fundamentals of Clinical Neurophysiology.* Springfield, Thomas, 1957.

Clarke, E., and O'Malley, C. D.: *The human brain and spinal cord.* Berkeley, U of Cal Pr, 1968, p. 516.

Coghill, G. E.: *Anatomy and the problem of behavior.* Cambridge, Cambridge U Pr, 1929.

————: The neuroembryologic study of behavior. *Science, 78:* 131–138, 1933.

————: Correlated anatomical and physiological studies of the growth of the nervous system of amphibia. *J Comp Neurol, 64:* 135–167, 1936.

Coghill: Flexion spasms and mass reflexes in relation to the ontogenetic development of behavior. *J Comp Neurol, 79:* 463–486, 1943.

Collier, J.: An investigation upon the plantar reflex, with reference to the significance of its variations under pathological conditions, including an enquiry into the etiology of acquired pes cavus. *Brain, 22:* 71–99, 1899.

Davis, G. D.: Caudate lesions and spontaneous locomotion in the monkey. *Neurology, 8:* 135–139, 1958.

Davson, H., and Eggleton, M. G.: *Principles of Human Physiology.* Philadelphia, Lea and Febiger, 1962.

Denny-Brown, D.: The general principles of motor integration. In Field, J. (Ed.): *Handbook of Physiology:* Neurophysiology Vol. II. Washington, Am Physiol Soc, 1960.

Denny-Brown, D.: *The Cerebral Control of Movement.* Springfield, Thomas, 1966.

Denny-Brown, D., and Chambers, R. A.: Visuo-motor function in the cerebral cortex. *J Nerv Ment Dis, 121:* 288–289, 1955.

Denny-Brown, D., and Chambers, R. A.: The parietal lobe and behavior. *Assoc Res Nerv Ment Dis, 36:* 35–117, 1958.

De Risio, C., and Tonini, G.: Azione della bulbocapnina su alcuni reflessi posturali del gatto. *Boll Soc Ital Biol Speri, 32:* 66–67, 1956.

Dohrmann, G. J., and Nowack, W. J.: The upgoing great toe: optimal method of elicitation. *Lancet,* 339–341, February 17, 1973.

Dosuzkov, T.: The plantar reflex, its signification, the methods of its examination and the causes of some diagnostic errors. *J Nerv Ment Dis, 75:* 374–383, 1932.

Doty, R. W.: Modulation of visual input by brain-stem systems. *In Young, F. A.,* and Lindsley, D. B. (Eds.): *Early experience and visual information processing in perceptual and reading disorders.* Washington, Nat Acad Sci, 1970.

Ettlinger, G., and Kalsbeck, J. E.: Changes in tactile discrimination and in visual reaching after successive and simultaneous bilateral posterior parietal ablations in the monkey. *J Neurol Neurosurg Psychiatry, 25:* 256–270, 1962.

Evans, B. H., and Ingram, W. R.: The effects of combined red nucleus and pyramidal lesions in cats. *J Comp Neurol, 70:* 461-476, 1939.

Evans, Sir C. L.: *Starling's Principles of Human Physiology.* Philadelphia, Lea & Febiger, 1952.

Eyzaguirre, C.: *Physiology of the Nervous System.* Chicago, Yearbk Med, 1969.

Ferrier, D.: *The Functions of the Brain.* New York, Putnam's, 1886.

Flourens, P.: *Recherches expérimentales sur les propriétés et les fonctions du système nerveux dans les animaux vertébrés.* Paris, Crevot, 1824.

French, L. A., and Johnson, D. R.: Observations on the motor system following cerebral hemispherectomy. *Neurology, 5:* 11–14, 1955.

Frost, J. D., Kellaway, P., and Gol, A.: Single-unit discharges in isolated cerebral cortex. *Exp Neurol, 14:* 305–316, 1966.

Fulton, J. F.: The inter-relation of cerebrum and cerebellum in the regulation of somatic and autonomic functions. *Medicine, 15:* 247–306 (1936).

Fulton, J. F.: *Physiology of the nervous system, 3rd ed.* New York, Oxford U Pr, 1949.

Fulton, J. F., and Keller, A. D.: *The sign of Babinski: a study of the evolution of cortical dominance in primates.* Springfield, Thomas, 1932.

Ganong, W. F.: *Review of Medical Physiology.* Los Altos, Lange, 1967.

Gilman, S., and Marco, L. A.: Effects of medullary pyramidotomy in the monkey. *Brain, 94:* 495–514, 1971.

Goltz, F.: Uber die Verrichtungen des Grosshirns. *Pflügers Arch, 42:* 419–467, 1888. (English trans. in Bonin, 1960).

Goltz, F. L.: In Anderson, E., and Haymaker, W. (Eds.): *The Founders of Neurology.* Springfield, Thomas, 1953.

Grimby, L.: Normal plantar response: integration of flexor and extensor reflex components. *J Neurol Neurosurg Psychiatry, 26:* 39–50, 1963.

Guzman-F., C., and Del Pozo, E. C.: Jump reflex in hypothalamic cat. *J Neurophysiol, 16:* 376–380, 1953.

Hagbarth, K. E.: Spinal withdrawal reflexes in the human lower limbs. *J Neurol Neurosurg Psychiatry, 23:* 222–227, 1960.

Harner, R. N.: Hemi-cerveau isolé: a model for study of spontaneous EEG activity. *EEG Clin Neurophysiol, 28:* 97, 1970.

Hein, A., and Held, R.: Dissociation of the Visual Placing Response into elicited and guided components. *Science, 158:* 390–392, 1967.

Hicks, S. P., and D'Amato, C. J.: Motor-sensory and visual behavior after hemispherectomy in newborn and mature rats. *Exp Neurol, 29:* 416–438, 1970.

Hicks, S. P., and D'Amato, C. J.: Effects of ablation of motor-sensory cortex are different in newborn and mature rats. *Proc Soc Neurosci,* p. 255, 1973.

Hinsey, J. C.: The hypothalamus and somatic responses. *Assoc Res Nerv Ment Dis, 20:* 657–685, 1940.

Hinsey, J. C., and Ranson, S. W.: A note on the significance of the hypothalamus for locomotion. *J Comp Neurol, 46:* 461–463, 1928.

Hitzig, E., and Fritsch, G. T.: Uber die elektrische Erregbarkeit des Grosshirns, *Arch Anat Physiol,* 300–332, 1870.
    English translation in Bonin, 73–96, 1960; and H. Wilkins, Neurosurgical classics XII, *J Neurosurg, 20:* 904–916, 1963.

Hogan, G. R., and Milligan, J. E.: The plantar reflex of the newborn. *New Engl J Med, 285:* 502–503, 1971.

Hooker, D.: *The prenatal origin of behavior.* Lawrence, U of Kansas Pr, 1952.

Hossmann, K.-A.: Untersuchungen uber transcallosale Potentiale an der akuten Corpus Callosum-Katze. *Dtsch Z Nervenheilk, 195:* 79–102, 1969.

Hossman, K. A.: Midline Section of the Cat Brain with sparing of the Corpus Callosum. *EEG Clin Neurophysiol, 26:* 627–629, 1969.

Houssay, B. A.: *Human Physiology* 2nd ed. New York, McGraw-Hill, 1955.

Humphrey, T.: Postnatal repetition of human prenatal activity sequences with some suggestions of their neuroanatomical basis. In Robinson, R. J. (ed.): *Brain and Early Behavior,* London, Acad Pr, 1969.

Ignelzi, R. J., and Bucy, P. C.: Cerebral hemidecortication in the treatment of infantile cerebral hemiatrophy. *J Nerv Ment Dis, 147:* 14–30, 1968.

Jacobs, M.: *Cerebral Hemispherectomy—A survey of the Literature, 1926–1957.* Unpublished doctor's dissertation, University of Pittsburgh, 1958. (Cited by Patton, 1961)

Kellaway, P., Gol, A., and Proler, M.: Electrical activity of the isolated cerebral hemisphere and isolated thalamus. *Exp Neurol, 14:* 281–304, 1966.

Kellogg, W. N.: Locomotor and other disturbances following hemidecortication in the dog. *J Comp Physiol Psychol, 42:* 506–16, 1949.

———, and Bashore, W. D.: Influence of hemidecortication upon bilateral avoidance conditioning in dogs. *J Comp Physiol Psychol, 43:* 49–61, 1950.

Kennard, M. A.: Reorganization of motor function in the cerebral cortex of monkeys deprived of motor and premotor areas in infancy. *J Neurophysiol, 1:* 477–496, 1938.

———: Reactions of monkeys of various ages to partial and complete decortication. *J Neuropathol Exp Neurol, 3:* 289–310, 1944.

———, and Fulton, J. F.: Age and Reorganization of the Central Nervous System. *J Mt Sinai Hosp, 9:* 594–605, 1942.

———, and Kessler, M. M.: Studies of motor performance after parietal ablations in monkeys. *J Neurophysiol, 3:* 248–257, 1940.

Koskoff, Y. D., Patton, R., Migler, B., and Kruper, D.: Hemicerebrectomy in the rhesus monkey: surgical technique and preliminary behavioral observations. *Cerebral Palsy Review,* Sept.–Oct., 1959.

Kruper, D. C., Boyle, B., and Patton, R. A.: Eye preference in hemicerebrectomized monkeys. *Psychon Sci, 7:* 105–106, 1967.

———, Koskoff, Y. D., and Patton, R. A.: Delayed alternation in hemicerebrectomized monkeys. *Science, 133:* 701–702, 1961a.

———, Patton, R. A., and Koskoff, Y. D.: Delayed object-quality discrimination in hemicerebrectomized monkeys. *J Comp Physiol Psychol, 54:* 619–624, 1961b.

———: Visual Discrimination in hemicerebrectomized monkeys. *Physiol Behav, 7:* 173–179, 1971a.

———: Hand and eye preference in unilaterally brain ablated monkeys. *Physiol Behav, 7:* 181–185, 1971b.

Kugelberg, E., Eklund, K., and Grimby, L.: An electromyographic study of the nociceptive reflexes of the lower limb. *Brain, 83:* 394–409, 1960.

Landau, W. M., and Clare, M. H.: The plantar reflex in man. With special reference to some conditions where the extensor response is unexpectedly absent. *Brain, 82:* 321–335, 1959.

Langworthy, O. R.: *A correlated study of development of reflex activity in fetal and young kittens. Contributions to Embryology, #114.* Washington, Carnegie Inst., 1929.

Larsell, O., and Coghill, G. E.: In Haymaker, W. (Ed.): *The Founders of Neurology,* Springfield, Thomas, 1953.

Lassek, A. M.: *The pyramidal tract.* Springfield, Thomas, 1954.

———, and Evans, J. P.: The human pyramidal tract. XII. The effect of hemispherectomies on the fiber components of the pyramids. *J Comp Neurol, 83:* 113–119, 1945.

LeGros Clark, W. E., and Russell, D. S.: Atrophy of the thalamus in a case of acquired hemiplegia associated with diffuse porencephaly and sclerosis of the left cerebral hemisphere. *J Neurol Neurosurg Psychiatry, 3:* 123–140, 1940.

Lenneberg, E. H.: *Biological Foundations of Language.* New York, Wiley, 1967, p. 214.

Léri, A.: Le réflexe des orteils chez les enfants. *Rev Neurol, 11:* 689–692, 1903.

Lindsley, D. B., Bowden, J. W., and Magoun, H. W.: Effect upon the EEG of acute injury to the brain stem activating systems. *EEG Clin Neurophysiol, 1:* 475–486, 1949.

Locke, S., and Kruper, D. C.: Transcallosal connections of the cingulate gyrus in monkey. *Anat Rec, 153:* 377–382, 1965.

Locke, S., Kruper, D. C., and Yakovlev, P. I.: Limbic nuclei of the thalamus and connections of limbic cortex. *Arch Neurol, 11:* 571–582, 1964.

Longmire, W. P.: The central control of postural reactions in the lizard. *Am J Physiol, 119:* 362, 1937.

Lundberg, A., and Norsell, U.: Spinal afferent pathway of the tactile placing reaction. *Experientia, 16:* 123, 1960.

Macht, M. B.: *The general behavior of decerebrate cats in the chronic state with particular reference to the expression of emotions.* Doctoral Dissertation, Johns Hopkins University, Baltimore, 1942.

Macht: Effects of d-amphetamine on hemi-decorticate, decorticate and decerebrate rats. *Fed Proc, 63:* 731–732, 1950.

Magnus, R.: *Körperstellung.* Berlin, Springer, 1924.

Magoun, H. W., and Ranson, S. W.: The behavior of cats following bilateral removal of the rostral portion of cerebral hemispheres. *J Neurophysiol, 1:* 39–44, 1938.

Maling, H. M., and Acheson, G. H.: Righting and other postural activity in low decerebrate and in spinal cats after d-amphetamine. *J Neurophysiol, 9:* 379–386, 1946.

Marquis, D. G., and Hilgard, E. R.: Conditioned responses to light in monkeys after removal of the occipital lobes. *Brain, 60:* 1–12, 1937.

McGraw, M. B.: Development of the plantar response in healthy infants. *Am J Dis Child, 61:* 1215–1221, 1941.

Megirian, D., and Bures, J.: Unilateral cortical spreading depression and conditional eyeblink responses in the rabbit. *Exp Neurol, 27:* 34–45, 1970.

Melka, J.: Connecting function of rat brain after resection of one hemisphere (Czech). *Sb ved praci lek fak Karlovy, 8:* 383–393, 1965. (Summary in Biol. Abstracts 17796, 1967)

Mettler, F. A.: Reflexes and recovery of motor capacity in the monkey after extensive chronic unilateral cerebral removals. *Anat Rec, 85:* 328–329, 1943a.

———: Extensive unilateral cerebral removals in the primate. *J Comp Neurol, 79:* 185–245, 1943b.

———: On the origin of the fibers in the pyramid of the primate brain. *Proc Soc Biol Med, 57:* 111–113, 1944.

———: Cortical subcortical relations in abnormal motor functions. In Yahr, M. D., and Purpura, D. P. (Eds.): *Neurophysiological Basis of Normal and Abnormal Motor Activities.* Hewlett, Raven, 1967.

Meyer, P. M., Horel, J. A., and Meyer, D. R.: Effects of DL-amphetamine upon placing responses in neodecorticate cats. *J Comp Physiol Psychol, 56:* 402–404, 1963.

Monnier, M.: *Functions of the nervous system II. Motor and psychomotor functions.* Amsterdam, Elsevier, 1970, p. 421.

Mountcastle, V. B. (Ed.): *Medical physiology,* 12th ed. St. Louis, Mosby, 1968, Vol. II.

Nadel, L., and Buresova, O.: Interocular transfer in the hooded rat. *Physiol Behav, 4:* 613–619, 1969.

Ochs, S.: *Elements of Neurophysiology.* New York, Wiley, 1965.

Osawa, K.: Long term observations of hemispherectomized dogs (Eng. summary). *Brain and Nerve,* (Tokyo), *18:* 805–811, 1966.

Paine, R. S. *et al.*: Evolution of postural reflexes in normal infants and in the presence of chronic brain syndromes. *Neurology, 14:* 1036–1048, 1964.

Pasik, P., Pasik, T., and Bender, M. B.: Oculomotor function following cerebral hemidecortication in the monkey. *Arch Neurol, 3:* 298–305, 1960.

Patton, R. A.: Hemicerebrectomy and adaptive behavior in the rhesus monkey. In Brosin, H. W. (Ed.): *Experimental Psychiatry.* Pittsburgh, U of Pittsburgh Pr, 1961.

Peacock, J. H., and Combs, C. M.: Retrograde cell degeneration in diencephalic and other structures after hemidecortication of rhesus monkeys. *Exp Neurol, 11:* 367–399, 1965.

Peele, T. L.: Acute and Chronic parietal lobe ablations in monkeys. *J Neurophysiol, 7:* 269–286, 1944.

Plotkin, H. C., and Russell, I. S.: The hemidecorticate learning deficit: evidence for a quantitative impairment. *Physiol Behav, 4:* 49–55, 1969.

Poltyreff, S. S., and Alexejeff, W. A.: Über die Möglichkeit der Bildung bedingte Reflexe bei Hunden mit exstirpierter Hirnrinde von der Hemisphäre gegenüberliegenden Köperoberfläche aus. *Z Biol, 97:* 297–305, 1936.

Powell, T. P. S.: Residual neurons in the human thalamus following hemidecortication. *Brain, 75:* 571–584, 1952.

Rademaker, G. G. J.: *Das Stehen* Berlin, Springer, 1931. (Review, in English, by A. T. Mussen in *Arch Neurol Psychiatry, 28:* 679–701, 1932)

Ramirez de Arellano, M.: Hemidecortication in monkeys. Comparison of rate and degree of recovery of neurological deficit as related to age at time of operation. *Excerpta Med Inter Congr Ser, 38:* 150–151, 1961.

Riesen, A. H.: Studying perceptual development using the technique of sensory deprivation. *J Nerv Ment Dis, 132:* 21–25, 1961.

Rinaldi, F., and Himwich, H. E.: Cholinergic mechanism involved in junction of mesodiencephalic activating system. *Arch Neurol Psychiatry, 73:* 396–402, 1955.

Roberts, T. D. M.: *Neurophysiology of postural mechanisms.* London, Butterworth's, 1967.

Rosen, J., Stein, D., and Butters, N.: Recovery of function after serial ablation of prefrontal cortex in the Rhesus monkey. *Science, 173:* 353–356, 1971.

Rosenthal, J. S.: (Conditioned reflexes in dogs lacking one cerebral hemisphere). *Arch Sci biol,* (St. Petersburg), *42:* 287, 1936. (Cited by Kellogg and Bashore, 1950).

Ruch, T. C., and Fulton, J. F.: Cortical localization of somatic sensibility. *Assoc Res Nerv Ment Dis, 15:* 289–330, 1935.

———, and Fulton, J. F.: *Medical Physiology and Biophysics.* Philadelphia, Saunders, 1960.

———, Patton, H. D., Woodbury, J. W., and Towe, A. L.: *Neurophysiology,* 2nd ed. Philadelphia, Saunders, 1965.

Rushworth, G.: Some general considerations on the functions and functional capacity of the central nervous system. In Vinken, P. J., and Bruyn, G. W. (Eds.): *Handbook of Clinical Neurology.* Amsterdam, North-Holland Pub., 1969, ch. 2.

———: On postural and righting reflexes. *Cerebral Palsy Bull, 3:* 535–543, 1961.

Scheibel, M. E., and Scheibel, A. B.: Developmental Relationship Between Spinal Motoneuron Dendrite Bundles and Patterned Activity in the Hind Limb of Cats. *Exp Neurol, 29:* 328–335, 1970.

Schneider, G. E.: Two visual systems. *Science, 163:* 895–902, 1969.

Schneider, R. C., and Crosby, E. C.: The interplay between cerebral hemispheres and cerebellum in relation to tonus and movements. *J Neurosurg, 20:* 188–197, 1963.

Schoolman, A., and Delgado, J. M. R. Cerebro-cerebellar relations in the awake cat. *J Neurophysiol, 21:* 1–16, 1958.

Sechzer, J. A. *et al.*: Developmental behaviors: delayed appearance in monkeys asphyxiated at birth. *Science, 171:* 1173–1175, 1970.

———, Ervin, G. N., and Smith, G. P.: Suppression of the visual placing response by 6 hydroxydopamine: Restoration with amphetamine. *Soc for Neurosciences Abstracts,* 1972, p. 117.

Serkov, F. N., and Makulkin, R. F. Electrical activity of the brain after hemispherectomy (Russian with English summary). *Zh Wyshej Nerv Dyatelnosty, 13:* 891–903, 1963.

———, Makulkin, R. F., and Federovich, G. I.: (Conditional defensive motor reflexes in dogs after complete hemispherectomy). *Zh Vyssh Nerv Deyat Pavlova,* (Summary in Biol. abstracts 37048, 1967).

Sherrington, C. S.: Remarks on the reflex mechanism of the step. *Brain, 33:* 1–25, 1910.

Sikov, M. R., Resta, C. F., Lofstrom, J. E., and Meyer, J. S.: Neurological deficits in the rat resulting from X-irradiation in utero. *Exp Neurol, 5:* 131–138, 1962.

Smith, K. U.: The effects of removal of the striate cortex upon certain unlearned visually controlled reactions in the cat. *J Genet Psychol, 50:* 137–156, 1937.

Snider, R. S., and Eldred, E.: Cerebro-cerebellar relationships in the monkey. *J Neurophysiol, 15:* 27–40, 1952.

Sprague, J. M.: Interaction of cortex and superior colliculus in mediation of visually guided behavior in the cat. *Science, 153:* 1544–1547, 1966.

———, and Chambers, W. W.: Control of posture by reticular formation and cerebellum in the intact, anesthetized and unanesthetized and in the decerebrate cat. *Am J Physiol, 176:* 52–64, 1954.

———: An analysis of cerebellar function in the cat, as revealed by its partial and complete destruction, and its interaction with the cerebral cortex. *Arch Ital Biol, 97:* 68–88, 1959.

Taub, E., Perrella, P., and Barro, G.: Behavioral development after forelimb deafferentation on day of birth in monkeys with and without blinding. *Science, 181:* 959–960, 1973.

Ter Braak, J. W. G., Schenk, V. W. D., and Van Vliet, A. G. M.: Visual reactions in a case of long-lasting cortical blindness. *J Neurol Neurosurg Psychiatry, 34:* 140–147, 1971.

Thompson, V. E., and Bucy, P. C.: Learning after cerebral hemidecortication in monkeys. *Physiol Behav, 4:* 455–459, 1969.

Tower, S. S.: The dissociation of cortical excitation from cortical inhibition by pyramid section, and syndrome of that lesion in the cat. *Brain, 58:* 238–255, 1935.

————: Pyramidal lesion in the monkey. *Brain, 63:* 36–90, 1940.

Travis, A.M.: Neurological deficiences after ablation of the precentral motor area in Macaca mulatta. *Brain, 78:* 155–173, 1955.

————, and Woolsey, C. N.: Motor performance of monkeys after bilateral partial and total cerebral decortications. *Am J Phys Med, 35:* 273–310, 1956.

Trevarthen, C. B.: Two mechanisms of vision in primates. *Psychol Forsch, 31:* 299–337, 1968.

————, and Sperry, R. W.: The unity of ambient visual field in man after disconnection of the cerebral hemispheres (In preparation).

Tsang, Y. C.: Maze learning in rats hemidecorticated in infancy. *J Comp Psychol, 24:* 221–254, 1937.

Ueki, K.: Hemispherectomy in the human with special reference to the preservation of function. In Tokizane, R., and Schade, J. P. (Eds.): *Progress in Brain Research.* Amsterdam, Elsevier, 1966, Vol. 21B.

Van Harreveld, A., and Bogen, J. E.: The clinging position of the bulbocapninized cat. *Exper Neurol, 4:* 241–261, 1961.

Villablanca, J.: Electrocorticogram in the chronic "isolated hemisphere" of the cat. Effect of atropine and eserine. *Brain Res, 3:* 287–291, 1967.

Voneida, T. J.: Neuronal isolation by combined midline and transverse section of the cat brain. *Life Sci, 5:* 1277–1282, 1966.

Vulpian, A.: *Leçons sur la physiologie générale et comparée du système nerveux.* Paris, Bailliere, 1866, p. 707.

Walker, A. E.: The retrograde cell degeneration in the thalamus of Macacus rhesus following hemidecortication. *J Comp Neurol, 62:* 407–419, 1935.

————: *The primate thalamus.* Chicago, U of Chicago Pr, 1938a.

————: The thalamus of the chimpanzee: II. Its nuclear structure, normal and following hemidecortication. *J Comp Neurol, 69:* 487–507, 1938b.

————, and Fulton, J. F.: Hemidecortication in chimpanzee, baboon, macaque, potto, cat and coati: a study in encephalization. *J Nerv Ment Dis, 87:* 677–700, 1938.

Walshe, F.: The Babinski plantar response, its forms and its physiological and pathological significance. *Brain, 79:* 529–556, 1956.

Wang, G-H., and Lu, T-W.: Development of swimming and righting reflexes in frog. *J Neurophysiol, 4:* 137–146, 1941.

Warkentin, J., and Smith, K. U.: The development of visual acuity in the cat. *J Genet Psychol, 50:* 371–399, 1937.

Wartenberg, R.: The Babinski reflex after fifty years. *JAMA, 135:* 763–767, 1947.

Weiss, T., and Fifkova, E.: Bioelectric activity in the thalamus and hypothalamus of rats during cortical spreading EEG depression. *EEG Clin Neurophysiol,* *13*: 734–744, 1961.

Welch, K., and Penfield, W.: Paradoxical improvement in hemiplegia following cortical excision. *J Neurosurg, 7*: 414–420, 1950.

———, and Stuteville, P.: Experimental production of unilateral neglect in monkeys. *Brain, 81*: 341–347, 1958.

Wenzel, B. M., Tschirgi, R. D., and Taylor, J. L.: Effects of early postnatal hemidecortication on spatial discrimination in cats. *Exp Neurol, 6*: 332–339, 1962.

Wertenbaker, C. T., Ross, R. J., and Amassian, V. E.: Aversive conditioning of contact placing in cats and its developmental aspects. *Neuroscience Abstracts,* 1972.

White, H. H.: Cerebral hemispherectomy in the treatment of infantile hemiplegia. *Confin Neurol, 21*: 1–50, 1961.

White, R. J.: The clinical implications of cerebral hemispherectomy in the monkey. *Rocky Mt Med J, 59*: 40–43, 1962.

———, and MacCarty, C. S.: Cranial nerve function following total cerebral hemispherectomy in the monkey (macaca rhesus). *Proc Mayo Clin, 34*: 22–29, 1959.

———, MacCarty, C. S., and Bickford, R. G.: Electroencephalographic and clinical study of the totally hemispherectomized monkey during normal and induced convulsive activity. *Fed Proc* 20/1 (March) Part I: 1 page, 1961.

———, MacCarty, C. S., Grindlay, J. H., and Schreiner, L. H.: Operative technics and principles utilized in total hemispherectomy in the monkey and the dog. *Proc Mayo Clin, 34*: 13–22, 1959a.

———, Schreiner, L. H., Hughes, R. A., MacCarty, C. S., and Grindlay, J. H.: The operative method and physiologic consequences of total hemispherectomy in the monkey. *Surg Forum, 8*: 532–537, 1958.

———, Schreiner, L. H., Hughes, R. A., MacCarty, C. S., and Grindlay, J. H.: Physiologic consequences of total hemispherectomy in the monkey. *Neurology, 9*: 149–159, 1959b.

Woods, J. W.: Behavior of chronic decerebrate rats. *J Neurophysiol, 27*: 635–644, 1964.

Woolsey, C. N.: Postural relations of the frontal and motor cortex in the dog. *Brain, 56*: 353–370, 1933.

———, and Bard, P.: Cortical control of placing and hopping reactions in Macaca mulatta. *Am J Physiol, 116*: 165, 1936.

Young, I. J., and Horner, G.: Mild hemiatrophy in chronically hemispherectomized cats. *Proc Soc Biol Psychiatry*, April 30, 1971.

———, and Rauley, W. F.: Histochemical alterations of ventral horn cells resulting from chronic hemispherectomy or chronic dorsal root section. *Exp Neurol, 26*: 460–481, 1970.

Zappella, M.: The placing reaction in the newborn. *Dev Med Child Neurol, 5*: 497–503, 1963.

———: Clinico-pathologic correlations regarding the central mechanism of the placing reflex in infancy and childhood. *Act Nerv Sup* (Praha), *9*: 19–24, 1967.

Zelazo, P. R., Zelazo, N. A., and Kolb, S.: "Walking" in the newborn. *Science, 176*: 314–315, 1972.

Zernicki, B., Doty, R. W., and Santibañez-H. G.: Isolated midbrain in cats. *EEG Clin Neurophysiol, 28*: 221–235, 1970.

[CHAPTER IV]

A NOTE ON THE PROBLEM OF CONSCIOUS MAN AND CEREBRAL DISCONNECTION BY HEMISPHERECTOMY

George Austin, William Hayward, and Stanley Rouhe

INTRODUCTION

CURRENT INTEREST IN DEVELOPING improved models of conscious man stimulates us to inquire more deeply into the problems of some of the interlocking anatomic physiologic, and philosophic implications which must be considered. It is no longer useful to refute the existence of certain questions as to whether qualitative values of thought such as joy, envy, sadness, hate, love, etc. can be quantitated, nor to deny the critical nature of awareness of inductive thought and ideational thinking as important in distinguishing the mentation of conscious man from that of our more sophisticated models (Pask, 1961; Amosov, 1967; Arbib, 1964; Weinberg, 1959; Lansdell, 1968; Eccles, 1953; Gunther, 1971).

Conscious man in the normal range has awareness or knowledge of knowing multiple perceptions at any instant; a form of second order knowing (Weinberg, 1959). This is in contradistinction to the usual automatisms of psychomotor seizures, types of daydreaming, sleepwalking, and altered states of consciousness (ASC) in which perception occurs but for which there is usually no volitional recall (Tart 1972). It is assumed that speech is an observable form of behavior, and that perception or discrimination by descriptive vocalization, presupposes knowledge of perception of an event. Most importantly we assume that descriptive communication of knowing, and awareness of knowing perception of an event by introspection, are different exclusive aspects of the same thing. We can then approximate a function of awareness of knowing, by descriptive communication of a discrimination based on language probing, and on the additional condition that there should exist no motor or sensory dysphasia (Austin and Hayward, 1969; Cherry, 1957).

In this approach, human speech is assumed man's most sensitive form of language (Cherry, 1957). This supposes that the level of awareness of knowing at a given time is proportional to the recalled communicated description of the external world. Certain further operational or descriptive meanings of some of the terms used seem important at this point of discussion.

Meaning can be operationally described as the selective function of a "message" or description relative to the recipient. By an event, we mean anything that happens. Sensation is the part of the total experience which is due to the stimulus alone independently of past history. Perception, as opposed to sensation involves habit based on past experience (Russell, 1960, 1959).

Knowing a perception, means the act of making an appropriate perceptive response to an event, with recall for the event and response. Awareness of knowing a perception is the introspective knowledge of knowing perceptions; a shared process of the mind and of the events perceived (Hintz, 1960; Whitehead, 1953).

Such an approach permits us the convenience of grading depressed conscious man into testable levels of confusion and stupor for purposes of clinical evaluation (Austin and Grant, 1955; Austin *et al.*, 1963, Austin and Hayward, 1969). To some extent these levels of states may be further related to brain anatomy and physiology as observed and studied under pathologic conditions. This type of approach to the problem of conscious man has been of considerable clinical use in the study of neurosurgical patients following head injury, or with intracranial lesions (Austin *et al.*, 1963, Austin and Hayward, 1969; Whitty and Zangwill, 1966). It should be obvious that the grading of depressed conscious patients into arbitrary levels of confusion or stupor indicates that there are many states in each level. These run, for example, from a state of slight confusion to a state of delirium, from a state of drowsiness to a state of deep coma. Understandably, there will be a slight overlap with the normal conscious states, and between slight confusion and stupor.

But what of the many ancillary factors that we seem to ignore such as attention focusing, and duration, the role of volitional response, the case of knowing and wanting to respond, but being unable to signal any response? We have encountered cases in whom there appeared to be no response to verbal stimuli, but who have recovered and ten to fourteen days later told us that they understood all that was said previously but were unable to respond. Throughout this brief note on the problem of conscious man, therefore, we have recourse to Occams' razor, since reducing the number of premises to as few as possible will reduce the error. Perhaps this is almost a necessity due to the vast ignorance that still exists about the problem of consciousness.

We have studied certain observed features of man's brain function under pathological conditions which may serve as guideposts in developing hypotheses and future brain models:

    a. From head injury patients with uncomplicated concussions we observe that, associated with the transient loss of consciousness, there follows a limited period (varying from days to seconds) of gradually decaying retrograde and post-traumatic amnesia, demonstrated by the patient's communicating to us inability to recall just prior and just after events. This implies that the recall memory mechanisms are more sensitive than the filing of perceptions. The best theory of concussion in our opinion postulates the role of sudden brief axonal stretching as the main causation factor, according to Stritch (Shapiro and Smith, 1969; Stritch, 1961; Whitty and Zangwill, 1966; Plum and Posner, 1966).

    b. Interruption, by bilateral chemical leucotomy of the frontal ideational cortex (Areas 9, 10, & 11 of Brodmann) connections to the thalmus (medialis dorsalis nuclei) shows a significant depression of all modalities of described intensity discrimination including time perception, touch, pain and click interval, (Austin *et al.* 1963) as well as loss of drug addiction without withdrawal signs.

    c. Electrical stimulation of the dominant thalamus (ventralis lateralis nucleus) during stereotactic surgery under local anesthesia can produce complete mutism for periods of more than two minutes, but as shown by appropriate verbal testing, this does not block the patient's filing and recall of information received during the period of mutism. Electrocoagulation of the ventralis posterior nuclei (primary sensory nuclei) or of the centre median nucleus, although transiently altering pain perception, has no effect on consciousness (either dominant or nondominant).

    d. The effects of progressively decreasing brain functions, by diffuse neuronal impairment observed following general anesthesia, cerebral edema (Bour and Ledingham, 1967; Carter *et al.*, 1961; Shapiro and Smith, 1969; Kety, 1967; Chance, 1967) diffuse hyponatremia, barbiturate poisoning, CO poisoning, cyanide poisoning, and forms of anoxia or asphyxia, etc. gradually induce confusion, stupor, and coma in that order. (Confusion being arbitrarily described as a state of responsiveness in which there is an abnormally prolonged latency in response to verbal stimulation, or where the communicated response shows inaccuracy and poor orientation; stupor being a condition in which the patient either tends to fall asleep or is in a sleep-like condition from which he may usually be aroused by appropriate stimuli except conditions of coma, in which the patient cannot be stimulated to respond for communication, no matter how strongly the stimuli are applied.) Again, when recovery occurs it is the memory recall mechanism which recovers last, with more recent events the last and least likely to recover. Studies of time perception during conditions of mild stupor show a consistent underestimation during the emergence from prolonged stupor, similar to that encountered in long-term experimental cave dwellers (Austin and Hayward, 1969). This is opposite to the time perception of patients with Parkinson's disease who experience an overestimation and exaggerated time sense.

SUMMARY OF CEREBRAL LOBECTOMY AND FUNCTION

Some of the earlier studies of problems of consciousness have been done in neurosurgical patients following areas of brain destruction.

These consisted of infarctions of entire lobes, bullet wounds involving different regions, head injuries destroying certain areas, and surgical ablation for tumors or seizures at the time of operation. More recently investigative studies of effects of toxic anoxia have also been important (Kety, 1967; Chance, 1967; Davies and Bronk, 1957; Shalit *et al.*, 1972; Kety, 1963; Thews, 1963; Bakay and Bendixen, 1963; Longmuir and McCabe, 1965).

Frontal Lobectomy

It has been shown that complete ablation of the frontal lobe on either side in the human, when it remains anterior to the motor area, has virtually no effect on the state of conscious response, although it modifies the conscious response in terms of producing a degree of euphoria. This is considerably more so when on the dominant side. Bilateral frontal lobectomies back to the anterior horn of the ventricle have also been described in which there have not been any significant changes in consciousness as long as an adequate blood pressure was maintained during the surgical ablation. All results may be grossly modified, if there are drops of blood pressure below the critical level of mean pressure of approximately 65 mm of mercury. This causes loss of autoregulation and may lead to a critical decrease in cerebral blood flow (CBF) and hypoxia, if continued for more than a few minutes, depending on the patient's age. If decreased CBF continues longer it may lead to thrombosis of the anterior cerebral arteries with extension to the Circle of Willis.

Although originally cerebral dominance for speech was thought to reside in the hemisphere opposite that of handedness, it is now fairly well documented that the dominant hemisphere tends to be the left, regardless of handedness, unless there has been some damage in earlier life to the left hemisphere, in which case, the right hemisphere is able to take over and assume the speech dominance (Roberts, 1966). It is extremely rare that there exists bilateral speech areas. In our present use of speech to describe perception or discriminative events, the presence of both Broca's area and Wernicke's area are necessary prerequisites. However, other forms of language communication (tongue, finger, eyelid movement, etc.) can be established so that only the sensory speech area (Wernicke's) would be necessary.

Temporal Lobectomy

From the work of Penfield (1958, 1952); Walker (1960); Falconer (1955); and the present authors (Austin *et al.*, 1963), it can be stated that temporal lobectomy on either side, for a distance of 8 cm back from the temporal tip, produces no change in the state of consciousness in terms of descriptive communication of perception. These operations are characteristically done under local anesthesia. In the occasional situation which arises when one temporal lobe has been extensively damaged, and the other temporal lobe has been surgically extirpated, it is usual to have a marked change in personality with some rage reactions and extreme emotional liability. In addition, it has been shown that bilateral temporal lobectomy can lead to severe memory deficit, mainly for recall of recent events in the human. Even in these cases, except for the above symptoms and a slight grade of confusion, there is no depression of gross or crude consciousness. Factors that we have at our disposal following lobectomy suggest that recent memory is a diffuse process probably including both temporal lobes acting in parallel on deeper gray matter structures bilaterally, since unilateral temporal lobectomy causes virtually no memory impairment. Another important feature of the temporal lobe and its memory structure has to do with the aura and automatisms of psycho-motor seizure which characteristically result from temporal lobe lesions. Typically these seizures may produce bizarre memory patterns including deja vue phenomena, jamais vue phenomena, etc., as well as varied automatisms. In the great majority of these automatisms, patients behave in a manner which shows them to be perceptive to environment, but usually with no recall for the events during the automatism and unable to communicate or respond to observers. In a small minority of cases, this is not the case.

Occipital Lobes

Since World War I a number of cases have been reported of bilateral occipital lobectomy, with the result of cortical blindness, but with no change in the state of consciousness. In the dominant hemisphere we have previously reported occipital lobectomies for 7 cm forward from the occipital pole (Austin *et al.*, 1949) with no alteration in state of consciousness, although there was the usual homonymous hemianopia and a slight degree of macular sparing. Perhaps equally significant, however, was the loss of normal alpha rhythm by EEG and its re-establishment more anteriorly in the posterior temporal and parietal regions (Masland *et al.*, 1949).

Parietal Lobes

With damage to the nondominant parietal lobe, there have been reported changes in gnostic phenomena and of body symmetry. Characteristically, there has been the tendency to ignore the opposite half of the body, particularly when the right-sided nondominant parietal lobe has been seriously damaged. The left parietal lobe (dominant) causes a similar change with respect to the right half of the body, plus agraphesthesia, asterognosis, decreased sensory perception, and some degree of intellectual impairment (dyscalculia, etc.) depending on the degree of damage. If we consider the angular gyrus to be at the posterior temporo-parietal junction, then damage to this sensory speech area (Wernicke's area) leads to inability to communicate due to total loss of recognition of the spoken or written word. Under such circumstances, it is virtually impossible to test for any state of consciousness, since the lack of verbal and written comprehension or sensory aphasia obviates the testing technique (Roberts, 1966).

SUMMARY OF BRAIN STEM LESIONS

Sprague (1967) in his excellent review of the effects of chronic brain stem lesions in animals has concluded that, the more caudal the brain stem transaction (midbrain-pons) in animals, the greater the neurological behavior deficit. In general, the more caudal the lesion, the shorter the percentage of time in sleep-like states. Thus, midpontine lesions showed the lowest percentage of sleep-like states, which agrees with the picture of vigilant coma in man with ventral pontine destructive lesions. EEG and behavior studies done in midpontine hemisection likewise revealed a bilaterally activated EEG pattern, and the animals appeared awake but showed marked hypokinesia and lack of motor initiative.

In summarizing the effects of hypothalamic lesions reported in the literature Sprague concluded that:

1. Bilateral lesions just caudal or rostral to the mammillary nuclei through the caudal hypothalamus produced the most profound effect on the waking capacity of all species often resulting in permanent somnolence.
2. The above lesions were not associated with a cataleptic posture, and arousal by painful stimuli was often possible.
3. Rostral and lateral hypothalamic lesions not extending past the mammillary nuclei produced only slight drowsiness and docility.
4. There is a downstream neural pathway mediating impulses from the caudal and lateral hypothalamus to the rostral midbrain tegmentum. There is also evidence of a reverse pathway going upward from the rostral midbrain tegmentum via the medial forebrain bundle to the lateral hypothalamus (Clemente and Sterman, 1967). It has been suggested that this is commensurate with a so-called waking center in the rostral midbrain tegmentum.

Animals (monkeys and cats) with bilateral midbrain lesions, eradicating the ventro-medial tegmentum produced a profound coma or deep somnolence. However, lesions of the midbrain, sparing the ventral and medial tegmentum usually produced very little somnolence. Importantly however, if the ventromedial tegmentum was destroyed in two or more stages, no marked somnolence occurred. From this one may conclude that unilateral lesions in this region do not produce coma.

Large lesions in the periaqueductal gray matter produce severe and long lasting mutism, inattention, hypokinesia and flaccidity. Even unilateral lesions result in prolonged or permanent mutism.

Lesions in the colliculi lead to general lack of 'awareness' to all visual stimuli, with loss of facial and vocal expression. However, there appeared to be no change in general wakefulness.

In summarizing, Sprague suggests the importance of the overall integrative activity of the brain stem in maintaining wakefulness, rather than a concept of a wakeful center. Nevertheless, large ventromedial midbrain lesions, he concluded, have the most marked effect on wakefulness, probably by virtue of interrupting hypothalamic influences. Deep somnolence and some degree of catatonia, followed bilateral lesions of the caudal subthalamus in animals. This review of brain stem lesions in animals is helpful in analyzing consciousness in man. The known size and exact positioning of the lesion, the lack of increased intracranial pressure as a disturbing feature, and the fact that animals can be studied with multiple lesions made in two or more stages all provide considerable insight into the problem in man.

In general, the findings of depressed consciousness with brain stem lesions in man have been somewhat similar to those in animals (Barrett, 1967). The difficulty of course, has been the lack of sufficiently well demarked lesions in the human brain stem. From the original work of Cairns (1952) it has become apparent that large lesions throughout the lower brain stem (medulla, pons, and midbrain) are capable of producing prolonged stupor. The degree of the stupor appears to be related to the size of the lesion and the abruptness with which it is produced. Cairns also observed that the more caudal the lesion in the brain stem, the more profound the disturbance of consciousness. Other authors, notably French (1952) and Jefferson (1952) have confirmed that lesions located in the midbrain tegmentum similar to those in animals, produced a prolonged coma (Lindsley, 1960). In spite of the numerous case records and postmortems, it still is impossible to determine whether or not destruction of the dominant thalamus results in prolonged coma. It is the authors' opinion that it probably either results in long coma or makes the testing of consciousness an impossibility due to destruction of the integration of the speech mechanisms. Further cases are needed with destruction of dominant thalamus, which would test this point.

Coma and sleep wake cycles may have some relationship, but should not be directly compared with each other. In most cases of stupor of all degrees there is evidence of sleep cycles. At present the theories of sleep do not account for coma. Deafferentation of the cerebrum, long a popular theory of sleep, loses much of its attractiveness when viewed after the findings of total nondominant hemispherectomy. Similarly, the theory of active brain stem inhibition of the cerebrum becomes dulled when one considers the ineffectiveness of loss of one entire hemisphere. Whether an inherent intra brainstem cycling mechanism of a multiple state system (Rosen, 1972) will develop validity remains to be further investigated. This would infer a system for gross consciousness with multiple stabilities. From the evidence of brain stem damage in lower animals and man, it would be inherent in the ventral pontine tegmentum, the ventro medial mid-brain tegmentum and the postero-lateral hypothalamus. Adherents to the special sanctity of the cortex in maintaining the wakeful stage of gross consciousness in man are becoming fewer. At present, it seems from the evidence that the cortex probably mediates mainly the subtle nuances of higher level consciousness, memory, and speech, and that gross consciousness or wakefulness remains a special poorly understood ventral tegmental function.

CEREBRAL DISCONNECTION BY NONDOMINANT
HEMISPHERECTOMY

At this time we review our results with hemispherectomy to re-evaluate their role in studying conscious man. Four cases of total right sided (nondominant) hemispherectomy were done in adults under local anesthesia for the purpose of attempting to completely extirpate proven hemisphere gliomas. All patients had a left hemiparesis or hemiplegia at the time of operation and the tumor had been verified by previous craniotomy. Survival time postoperatively was three and one-half months to two years (Austin and Grant, 1955). These four cases, originally reported sixteen years ago, may be analyzed with more relevance now. Preoperatively all were within the normal conscious range.

A brief description of the operative technique, not previously described, seems pertinent. The problem is to completely remove the entire hemisphere, leaving only the thalamus and hypothalamus. The former rapidly degenerates, as described previously, leaving only the hypothalamus, septum pellucidum and lower brain stem (LBST) consisting of midbrain, pons, and medulla intact. The operation is begun using a curved midline scalp incision extending from one inch above the nasion, to one inch posterior to the mastoid tip. Going down the sphenoid ridge, the middle cerebral artery is clipped approximately 1 cm distal to the anterior cerebral artery bifurcation. The distal anterior cerebral artery is clipped approximately 1.5 cm distal to the anterior communicating artery. During this part of the operation, the mean blood pressure is maintained around 90 mm of Hg. to avoid retrograde thrombosis. Any small arterial side branches are clipped or coagulated several mm from the main trunks. The larger veins from the frontal lobe into the longitudinal sinus are coagulated and then the frontal lobe gradually removed down through the frontal horn of the ventricle by first using fine subpial sutures on reversed needles in order to minimize bleeding. Next, the temporal lobe is removed for a distance of about 9 cm back from the tip and through the temporal horn by a similar technique after first coagulating the petrosal veins and the inferior vein of Labbe. Following this the under surface of the parieto-occipital junction is retracted and the distal post cerebral artery coagulated or clipped approximately 0.5 to 1.0 cm from the post communicating artery. Finally the parieto-occipital lobe is removed, again utilizing the subpial reversed suture technique. The midline of excision goes through the lateral ventricle at the basal ganglia-thalamic junction. Conversation with the patients was carried on throughout the operations without any significant change in conscious state. The results were as follows:

1. No significant change in sleep-awake cycle, tested qualitatively.
2. Significant increase in touch and position sense threshold, with the threshold opposite the removed hemisphere being approximately five times that of the normal side, measured three months after the hemispherectomy.
3. Initially an increase in pain (needle algesimeter) threshold to three times that of normal on the side opposite hemispherectomy, followed by gradual return to normal over a three month period.
4. No marked changes in conscious state with the possible (not quantitated) exception of:
   a. Slightly prolonged latency of response to questions.
   b. Decrease of interpersonal relationship with decrease in emotional affect.
   c. Slight euphoria.

In all cases the cortex, basal ganglia and white matter were completely removed.

The autopsy specimen of one patient obtained three and one-half months following the hemispherectomy showed that grossly the entire thalamus had also degenerated on the side of the operation. Certain questions now deserve reappraisal:

1. Does this operation mean that an acute hemispherectomy, done without previous existing pathology and without a severe preexisting hemiparesis, would produce no alteration of consciousness?

The fact that there was not any observable change in the level of consciousness in our four patients, either during or following the procedure is in favor of the interpretation that the operation done without prior hemispheric damage would not affect conscious behavior, at least at the rather gross level we have studied. The only reported adult hemispherectomy on the left side, reported by Zollinger (1935) was also done on a damaged hemisphere. Similarly, the many reported hemispherectomies on children were done in cases of severely damaged hemispheres with seizures. In many of these the seizures were alleviated. In our four reported cases there appeared to be a more normal EEG rhythm or at least an increase in normal electrical activity apparent in the remaining hemisphere, recorded six weeks after the operation.

> 2. How does one explain the gradual recovery of normal pain sensation on the side opposite the hemispherectomy?

This suggests that pain sensation has a bilateral thalamic representation to some degree. It also points out the ineffectiveness of a unilateral thalamic lesion to alleviate intractable pain. To understand the gradual recovery, one may consider the possibility of sprouting new synaptic terminals from an ipsilateral afferent pain source to fill in the gaps left by degenerated afferent terminals from the hemispherectomy. It has now been demonstrated that sprouting of new synaptic terminals occurs in the brain (Raisman, 1969) as well as the spinal cord (McCouch *et al.*, 1958). Although there were no long range studies of a psychological nature done on our patients beyond three months, it would appear that some of the chronic changes in personality associated with post concussion syndrome could be explained by sprouting of new synaptic terminals following degeneration of some afferents due to head injury. As of this moment the problem of developing a sensitization to the synaptic transmitter by the denuded subsynaptic membrane can not be ruled out. Previously we have given evidence that this appears unlikely at a spinal cord level (McCouch *et al.*, 1958), but the two factors are not mutually exclusive. Synaptic rearrangement also remains a possibility, as does plasticity (Eccles, 1953).

> 3. Since nondominant hemispherectomy does not cause observable changes in the level of consciousness, what is the function of the nondominant hemisphere other than motor, sensory, and visual control on the contralateral side?

Possible functions are that it may act as an amplifier or facilitation mechanism for events such as short term memory, in conjunction with the opposite temporal and frontal lobes. This is suggested by the loss of short term memory and the change in emotional liability following bilateral temporal lobectomy (Lansdell, 1968).

The nondominant hemisphere may also act as a tremendous neuronal reserve available for the development and filing of imaginative and ideational thinking, as well as fresh memory patterns. Although these sensitive factors were not studied in our patients, the fact that we observed a loss of interpersonal relationships, a flattened affect, and generalized blunting of personality suggest this possibility. Indeed at present, the lack of more delicate tests of this type is a major drawback. Characteristic of the loss of affect, however, was the following question and answer with one of our patients, six weeks after the operation:

"Al, how do you feel?"

"With me hands," the reply was given without any change in voice tone or facial expression.

It may also act in attention amplification or focusing, a factor difficult to assess. This is suggested in a way by the findings of a short attention span in all of our patients, when tested by the clinical psychologist. Certainly more subtle testing of this function is needed.

DISCUSSION

We may consider consciousness as the set of all states of knowledge of immediate experience, without any necessary intervening process. Operationally, this can be defined in the human as descriptive communication to an observer of qualitative degrees of knowing. This omits discussion of the term "mind," commonly supposed as the individual intellectual content of brain function. It also omits to a large extent the complicated question of lower animal consciousness, which could be construed as possibly existing in the communication of apes, bees, dogs, etc. For the purpose of useful clinical evaluation, we have divided the total state of consciousness into three main levels, slightly overlapping each other as described above.

Although the cultural changes of our social period indicate the importance of so-called altered states of consciousness (ASC) as described by Tart (1972), in this presentation we merely admit their presence and importance without stressing or studying mechanisms.

Higher levels of consciousness include awareness of degrees of imaginative and ideational concepts. In fact, if there is anything that distinguishes conscious thought of humans from the behavior of intelligent machines and lower animals, it is this awareness of degree of creative imagination and ideational knowledge, with the ability to recall and describe to an observer (Hook, 1960).

Originally in the behaviorist's philosophy, operationally, consciousness was discriminative behavior. This implied that the act of discrimination itself constituted knowledge of discrimination. This is not sufficient, for knowing a perception or discrimination can only be assumed if the individual has recall, and describes it in some form of language to an observer.

In the study of lower animals it may conceivably suffice to consider the discriminative act itself in terms of conditioned reflex at the brain level, as evidence for primitive knowledge of that act. The prerequisites then, for investigating some of the anatomic bases for normal and depressed states of consciousness, have been the human patient with the ability to communicate to an observer the patient's knowledge of events in response to applied stimuli. It should be reiterated that what we study is evidence of consciousness rather than the introspective mechanism itself.

This preliminary study of nondominant hemispherectomy emphasizes that clinical testing fails to show any change in gross consciousness when all cortex, white matter, basal ganglion and thalamus are gone. The role of hypothalamus (nondominant) remains to be evaluated. The septal region on the basis of destruction of the septum pellucidum by tumors appears to be relatively unimportant, but this is not a final answer to the ventral septal region. From our point of view, it would appear that only the partial dominant hemisphere with sensory motor cortex, plus speech areas and their thalamic, basal ganglia and brain stem connections are prerequisites for a normal level of gross consciousness as we evaluate it clinically. We would reiterate that the role of nondominant hypothalamus and septal region is still to be fully evaluated and that the integrity of the ventro-rostral reticular formation of the lower brain stem (midbrain, pons, and medulla) appears to be a vital necessity. Although we discuss the problem of hemispherectomy on the basis of four cases in the nondominant hemisphere, this remains the largest adult series of complete hemispherectomy.

In this note on the problem of conscious man, we have mentioned clinical usefulness of the current method of evaluation. That is, we suppose that given an examiner in a supposedly normal state of consciousness, then a state of consciousness (SOC) may be grossly evaluated, provided the sensory speech area is intact (or at least some form of motor communication is available—eyelid, tongue, finger movement, etc.). However, given a deeply stuporous patient or a condition of mutism, it may be impossible to determine whether the lack of responsiveness is due to brain stem damage, damage to the sensory speech area, or its integrative connection or both. Throughout the entire postulate of such an examination runs an apparent but ever present paradox. This is made evident by the examiner-patient relationship as follows:

> In a clinical environment one person, an examiner, evaluates the state of consciousness of those who can not accurately evaluate their own state of consciousness. This is necessary because of known errors of accurate introspective evaluation. We now know that the brain plays tricks, and illusions of being or seeing are not uncommon. Similarly, faulty imagination, "day dreams," deja vue phenomena, and confusion on emerging from anesthesia

or head injury, etc. all can lead to falsity of introspective analysis. From this background develops the necessity of external evaluation of the accuracy of tested responsiveness by an examiner or observer. Yet how can this be judged a valid condition, when it involves the untested, prejudged, introspective normalcy of the examiner? We readily see the paradoxical nature of this problem. It is all too similar to the well known story of the barber who in a certain town shaves all those who cannot shave themselves; but who shaves the barber? And although we can avoid such paradoxes by the insertion of "some men," the question arises as to who will judge who are the "some men"? Obviously in our clinical testing of patients for levels of consciousness, we can only admit the necessary and seeming paradox of the situation as due to the known fallacies of introspective judgement.

Certain forms of deep stupor involve no speech, or perhaps not even language responsiveness, yet they can be useful in the gradation of the severity of the stupor. Cairns (1952) was the first to describe the condition known as akinetic mutism or vigilant coma. In the pure form of this condition, the patient retains the "eyes open" appearance of alertness and even will occasionally appear to follow the examiner, yet fails to obey commands or to communicate. This condition may be temporary, but usually is permanent. It has been described with bilateral lesions throughout the reticular formation, as well as with combined thalamic and basal ganglion lesions, and with lesions of the septum-hypothalamic junction. Pathologic factors include midline tumors, head injury, CO poisoning, or bilateral anterior cerebral artery occlusion, as well as damage from III or IV ventricle dilatation on the basis of obstructive or even so-called normal pressure hydrocephalus (Freemon, 1971; Ojemann, 1969). In bilateral anterior cerebral artery occlusion, Freemon (1971) describes the lesions as bilateral destruction of the caudate head associated with destruction of medial putamen, septum, medial frontal cortex, and cingulate cortex. It is important to note the bilaterality of the lesions. In contradistinction to akinetic mutism or vigilant coma, Segarra (1970) has described the condition of "somnolent mutism" in which the patient briefly has the eyes open but only during stimulation, and in which there is commonly paralysis of upward gaze with some oculomotor paralysis and loss of light reflexes. The lesion is bilateral in the region of the junction of median zone of midbrain tegmentum, and with the median zone of the dorsal thalamus and subthalamus. This region is the main territory supplied by the perforating branch of the mesencephalic artery which arises unilaterally but supplies the midbrain bilaterally. Mainly, one is impressed that varied conditions of deep stupor or mutism can be produced by widespread bilateral lesions throughout the brain stem. Exceptional cases of seeming mutism due to lesions of the ventral pons have also been described in which the patient could only communicate by eye movements. These can appear following basilar artery occlusion, as described

TABLE IV-I CLASSICAL SYNDROMES OF STUPOR (BRAINSTEM)

Syndrome	Responsiveness	Eyes	Limbs	Reflexes	EEG	Causes and Site of Lesion
Akinetic Mutism or *Vigilant coma (trueform)**,†,‡,§	Eyes open; appears alert and follows examiner with eyes. Unable to communicate with examiner in any way	Pupils equal Normal EOM Corneal reflexes intact	Plastic rigidity Withdraws to pain	Hyperactive tendon reflexes. (+) Babinski (+) Snout (+) grasp	Low voltage 2-4/sec	Usually *bilateral,* junction of septal area and hypothalamus, with some involvement of orbito-medial frontal lobes. Caused by bilateral ant. cerebral artery occlusion, brain stem hemorrhage or tumors; hydrocephalus
Apathetic. Akinetic mutism, or somnolent Mutism†,‖,¶	Eyes open only when stimulated by name calling or pinching; fluctuates with picture of mumbling words on stimulation and limb movement on request	Loss of upward gaze or complete loss of EOM Absent pupillary light reflex; pupillary inequality or bilaterally dilated.	Random movements of extremities. Withdraw to pain	Normal tendon reflexes (+) Babinski	4/sec. medium voltage with frequent theta spikes	Bilateral lesion of posterior periventricular gray extending laterally in butterfly shape to involve the midline thalamic nuclei; reticular nuclei of the thalamus, parafascicularis, and medial portion of centrum medianum nuclei of thalamus. Due to vascular infarction from occlusion of a perforating branch of the mesencephalic artery with a bilateral supply, called the posterior thalamo-subthalamic paramedian artery
Pseudo akinetic Mutism, or so-called "locked-in syndrome"**	Eyes open and appear awake, and alert. Unable to speak, move extremities or respond, except by codified up and down eye movements	Gross visual recognition preserved. No lateral movement of eyes on command or head turning. Corneal reflexes present	Flaccid with no voluntary movement	Hyperactive tendon reflexes (+) Babinski	Normal bilaterally, with 8/sec alpha activity	Bilateral destruction of upper 2/3 of ventral pons with sparing of the mesencephalic tegmentum and part of periventricular pontine tegmentum. Lower pons and medulla not involved. Caused by infarction following basilar artery occlusion approx. 1 cm above origin.
Decerebrate state**,††,¶,‡‡	Deep but rarely reversible stupor. Eyes closed or half open with dysconjugate movement or fixed straight ahead. No volitional response. Picture of	Pupils slightly dilated; respond poorly or absent to light. Usually decreased EOM with some divergent squint.	Opisthotonus with arms and hands extended and hyperpronated. Legs stiff and hyperextended. May occur in spasms and alternate with random	Hyperactive tendon reflexes (+) Babinski	Medium voltage 2-4/sec. Slow waves with spindles	Rostral midbrain lesions below N. Ruber, through the mid brain tegmentum. Caused by hemorrhage, tumors, infarction, anoxia or tentorial herniation. Due to separation of mid brain and pontine reticular formation from more rostral control, allowing excessive vistibulo spinal influence to the spinal cord.

	Tone / General	Pupils / Eyes	Motor	Reflexes	EEG	Pathology / Etiology
	opisthotonus and rigidity exaggerated by stimuli; may occur in spasms. Abolished by dorsal root section or medullary transection		movements. May appear in fragments with waves of shivering and hyperpnea or Cheyne-Stokes respiration			
Decorticate state§§,††,‡‡	Reversible but usually increasing stupor. Noxious stimuli bring out flexion of arms, wrists, and fingers. Adduction of arms and extension with internal rotation of legs. Spontaneous spasms. Often have early Cheyne-Stokes type respirations.	Pupils small and equal. React to light Slight divergent squint.	Usually dense hemiplegia approaching quadriplegia Spontaneous spasms of complete picture	Hyperactive tendon reflexes (+) Babinski	Low voltage Fast activity	Large bilateral lesions of the diencephalon destroying int. capsule and rostral peduncle. So-called high diencephalic decerebration
Apallic state or French-Kretschner-Jellinger syndrome‡,‖	Eyes closed except for spontaneous opening and roaming. Unresponsive to external stimuli. Completely mute and akinetic.	Pupillary abnormalities often present. No EOM paralysis	Akinetic with some purposeless spontaneous limb movement	Hyperactive tendon reflexes (+) grasp reflex (+) Babinski	Diffuse high voltage slow waves, predominantly frontal	Diffuse and widespread destruction of the pallium or hemispheric cortical mantle with relative preservation of brain stem. Caused by anoxia, CO poisoning, chronic viral encephalitis, meningovascular syphilis, or closed head injury

* Frank R. Freemon, "Akinetic Mutism and Bilateral Anterior Cerebral Artery Occlusion," *Journal of Neurology, Neurosurgery, and Psychiatry*, 34: 693, 1971.

† Jose M. Segarra, "Cerebral Vascular Disease and Behavior," *Archives of Neurology*, 22: 408–418, May, 1970.

‡ H. Cairns, "Disturbances of Consciousness with Lesions of the Brain Stem and Diencephalon," *Brain*, 75: 109, 1952.

§ F. Skultety, "Clinical and Experimental Aspects of Akinetic Mutism," *Archives of Neurology*, 19: 1–14, 1968.

‖ J. French, "Brain Lesions Associated with Prolonged Unconsciousness," *Archives of Neurology and Psychiatry*, 68: 727, 1952.

¶ R. Barrett, H. Merritt, and A. Wolf, "Depression of Consciousness as a Result of Cerebral Lesions," in Seymour S. Kety *et al.*, eds., *Sleep and The Altered States of Consciousness* (Baltimore, The Williams and Wilkins Co., 1967) pp. 241–276.

** Fred Plum, and Jerome B. Posner, *Diagnosis of Stupor and Coma* (Philadelphia, F. A. Davis Co., 1966).

†† J. Sprague, "The Effects of Chronic Brainstem Lesions on Wakefulness, Sleep and Behavior," in Seymour S. Kety *et al*, eds, *Sleep and the Altered States and Consciousness* (Baltimore, The Williams and Wilkins Co., 1967) pp. 148–194.

‡‡ E. Kahn, E. Corsby, R. Schneider, and J. Taren, *Correlative Neurosurgery*, 2nd ed. (Springfield, Charles C Thomas, Publisher, 1969).

§§ J. French, "Brain Lesions Associated with Prolonged Unconsciousness," *Archives of Neurology and Psychiatry*, 68: 727, 1952.

by Plum and Posner (1966) termed by them the "locked-in syndrome" (*cf.* Table IV-I).

From the observation that a certain amount of cerebral shock, somewhat similar to spinal shock is associated with acute brain lesions, the clinical evaluation of the effects of a given lesion should probably be made after an arbitrary period of ten days following the lesion. Sprague has suggested a similar period for evaluating animals after brain stem lesions. This also allows for the subsidence of brain swelling and edema. It does not mean, of course, that there may not be further recovery or long term changes, following this acute lesion.

In our discussion of this note on conscious man, it seems important to note that when using "knowing," it implies a thought process in man. From this viewpoint, we would state that there are products of brain activity called thoughts that perform a function, which is that of knowing. We would not deny that thoughts can also, to some extent, control brain function. It seems important to consider that although sleep-wakefulness cycles are valuable they should not confuse the issue of sleep equivalency with pathologic stupor. This is so, because in cases of patients with pathologic stupor, many of them continue to show sleep-wakefulness cycles, which can be recorded by associating responsiveness with changes in vital signs, or by continuously recording the EEG patterns which change during sleep and wakefulness. In patients with depressed consciousness of all types, and especially in patients who have undergone nondominant hemispherectomy, it is obvious that more careful quantitative studies of sleep-wakefulness cycles need to be done, and that continuous recording of the vital signs, and the electroencephalogram should be further correlated.

Kety (1963) has demonstrated that there are pronounced changes in oxygen utilization under conditions of deep stupor, and it is important that further studies of cerebral blood flow in gray and white matter, and oxygen utilization of the gray and white matter be correlated with distinct conditions of stupor.

In discussing the need for more sophisticated studies, it appears that quantitative and sophisticated tests of the type employed by Sperry (1968) in evaluating corpus collosum sectioned patients would be a valuable addition. Similarly more careful and sophisticated studies of attention, such as those carried out by Pribram (1968) are needed. The latter emphasizes again the importance of the frontal and parietal cortex in maintaining attention.

SUMMARY

A review of the problem of conscious man and hemispherectomy has not proven anything, but it has developed some critical points that require further careful evaluation. To a great extent, we have disproved the idea that the nondominant hemisphere is necessary for crude consciousness, in terms of appropriate response to environment. It also disproves the ideas of Lashley (1946) and others who have maintained that depression of all functional neural activity in terms of behavior was proportional to the amount of cortex removed. But most importantly, this study points out the great need for further careful studies on complete hemispherectomy patients and the need for more subtle and delicate testing methods. Such tests should emphasize attention focusing, ideational perception, and imagination, and adaptive processes. The role and abilities of the nondominant hemisphere in the storage and recall of memory engrams in parallel with the dominant hemisphere requires further investigation.

Sleep-wakefulness cycles need additional testing in a quantitative manner following nondominant hemispherectomy. Much additional and more precise EEG recording and activation are further needed in this condition, as well as in diencephalic decerebrate and midbrain decerebrate man. A further evaluation of these studies is also required in man following destruction of the dominant thalamus and following ventral pontine lesions with the so-called "locked-in syndrome."

Although we have summarized the classical stuporous syndromes (Table IV-I) it is apparent that a need exists for more quantitative documentation of serial or continuous clinical studies, with discrete brain stem lesions. Finally, the whole problem of oxygen utilization of gray and white matter requires further careful study following brain stem lesions, which produce deep stupor in man (Kety, 1967; Cushman *et al.*, 1972; Austin *et al.*, 1972; Kety *et al.*, 1948). In spite of our brief outline of brain stem stupor and the typical syndromes (*cf.* Table IV-I), there is still insufficient anatomic localization gained clinically from the presently recorded brain stem syndromes concerned with depressed conscious man. This can be improved by quantitative clinical studies correlative with more discrete lesions, verified anatomically.

It also can be benefitted by further correlative studies of the classical behavior syndromes in monkeys and apes, following discrete brain stem lesions, for most of the current lower animal studies have been done on the cat, dog, and rat. The lesions should include hemisection and transection of the diencephalon, (thalamus or hypothalamus); upper, mid, and lower mesencephalon; upper, lower, and ventral pons; and medulla. Correlative studies could be profitably divided into acute, subacute, and chronic, and include serial EEG, behavior, vital signs, reflexes, and eye movements. Also, valuable information would result from measurement of oxygen consumption of the rostral brain and preservation of the blood supply, irrespective of the level of the lesion. The latter feature can readily complicate and confuse any set of observations if not controlled. Ideally one would like to see angiographic control of the blood supply, if electrographic studies of the rostral remaining brain are to be of value.

REFERENCES

Amosov, N. M.: *Modeling of Thinking and the Mind.* New York, Spartan, 1967.

Arbib, Michael A.: *Brains, Machines and Mathematics.* New York, McGraw, 1964.

Austin, G. M., and Grant, F. C.: Physiologic observations following total hemispherectomy in man. *Surgery, 38:* 239–258, July, 1955.

Austin, G. M., Grant, F. C., and Lewey, F. H.: Studies on the occipital lobe. I. The significance of small areas of preserved central vision following occipital lobectomy. *Arch Neurol Psychiatry, 62:* 204–221, 1949.

Austin, G., and Hayward, W.: Time perception in patients with depressed consciousness and Parkinson's disease. *Confin Neurol, 31:* 22–36, 1969.

Austin, G., Rafiullah, M., and Hayward, W.: Physiologic aspect of sensory discrimination. *Surgery, 54:* 171–181, July, 1963.

Austin, G., Rouhe, S., Dayes, L., Laffin, D., and Hayward, W.: Effects of Vasospasm on Cerebral Blood Flow Measured by an Intravenous Isotope Technique. Presented at the American Association of Neurological Surgery, Boston, April 16–20, 1972.

Bakay, L., and Bendixen, H.: Central Nervous System Vulnerability in Hypoxaemic States. Isotope Uptake Studies. In Schade, J. P., and McMenemey, W. H. (Eds.): *Selective Vulnerability of the Brain in Hypoxaemia.* Philadelphia, Davis, 1963.

Barrett, R., Merritt, H., and Wolf, A.: Depression of consciousness as a result of cerebral lesions. In Kety, Seymour S. *et al.* (Eds.): *Sleep and Altered States of Consciousness.* Baltimore, Williams and Wilkins, 1967, pp. 241–276.

Bour, H., and Ledingham, I. McA.: *Carbon Monoxide Poisoning.* New York, Elsevier, 1967.

Cairns, H.: Disturbances of consciousness with lesions of the brain stem and diencephalon. *Brain, 75:* 109, 1952.

Carter, N. W., Rector, F. C., Jr., and Seldin, D. W.: Hyponatremia in cerebral disease resulting from the inappropriate secretion of antidiuretic hormone. *N Engl J Med, 264:* 67–72, January 12, 1961.

Chance, B.: Biochemical studies of transitions from rest to activity. In Kety, Seymour S. *et al.* (Eds.): *Sleep and Altered States of Consciousness.* New York, Williams and Wilkins, 1967, pp. 48–63.

Cherry, Colin: *On Human Communication.* The Massachusetts Institute of Technology, 1957.

Clemente, C., and Sterman, M.: Basal forebrain mechanisms for internal inhibition and sleep. In Kety, Semour S. (Eds.): *Sleep and Altered States of Consciousness.* New York, Williams and Wilkins, 1967, pp. 127–147.

Cushman, A., Rostan, H., Marvin, S., Laffin, D., Hayward, W., Ciesel, C., and Austin, G.: Cerebral Blood Flow in Gray and White Matter of Patients with Depressed Consciousness. Presented at the American College of Surgeons. September, 1972.

Davies, P., and Bronk, D.: Oxygen Tension in Mammalian Brain. Reprinted from Federation Proceedings, Vol. 16, No. 3, September, 1957.

Eccles, J. C.: The Neurophysiological Basis of Mind. Claredon Pr, 1953, p. 314.

Falconer, M.: Treatment of temporal lobe epilepsy by temporal lobectomy. A survey of findings and results. *Lancet, 1:* 827, 1955.

Freemon, Frank R.: Akinetic mutism and bilateral anterior cerebral artery occlusion. *J Neurol Neurosurg Psychiatry,* 1971, *34:* 693–698.

French, J.: Brain lesions associated with prolonged unconsciousness. *Arch Neurol Psychiatry, 68:* 727, 1952.

Gunther, Gotthard: Cognition and Volition. Dept. Cybernetics. U Ill Pr, 1971.

Hager, H.: Electron Microscopical Observations on the Early Changes in Neurons Caused by Hypoxidosis and on the Ultrastructural Aspects of Neuronal Necrosis in the Cerebral Cortex of Mammals. In Schade, J. P., and McMenemey, W. H. (Ed.): *Selective Vulnerability of the Brain in Hypoxaemia.* Philadelphia, Davis Co., 1963.

Hintz, H. W.: Whitehead's concept of organism and the mid-body problem. Dimensions of Mind. In Hook, Sidney (Ed.): *Dimensions of Mind,* New York, New York U Pr, 1960, pp. 97–105.

Hook, Sidney (Ed.): *Dimensions of Mind.* New York, New York U Pr, 1960.

Jefferson, M.: Altered consciousness associated with brain stem lesions. *Brain, 75:* 55, 1952.

Kahn, E., Corsby, E., Schneider, R., and Taren, J.: *Correlative Neurosurgery,* 2nd ed. Springfield, Thomas, 1969.

Kety, S.: Regional Circulation of the Brain under Physiological Conditions— Possible Relationship to Selective Vulnerability. In Schade, J. P. and McMenemey, W. H. (Ed.): *Selective Vulnerability of the Brain in Hypoxaemia.* Philadelphia, Davis Co., 1963.

Kety, S.: Relationship between energy metabolism of the brain and functional activity. Sleep and Altered States of Consciousness. Baltimore, Williams and Wilkins, 1967, pp. 39–47.

Kety, Seymour S., Evarts, Edward V., and Williams, Harold L. (Eds.): *Sleep and Altered States of Consciousness.* Baltimore, Williams and Wilkins, 1967.

Kety, S., Shenkin, H., and Schmidt, C.: The Effects of Increased Intracranial Pressure on Cerebral Circulatory Functions in Man. *J Clin Invest, 27:* 493–499, 1948.

Lansdell, H.: Evidence for a symmetrical hemispheric contribution to an intellectual function. 76th Annual Convention Proceedings, APA. 1968.

Lashley, K. S., and Clark, C.: The cytoarchitecture of the cerebral cortex of Ateles; critical examination of architectonic studies. *J Comp Neurol, 85:* 223–305, 1946.

Lindsley, D. B.: Attention, consciousness, sleep and wakefulness. In Field, J., Magoun, H. W., and Hall, V. E. (Eds.): *Handbook of Physiology.* American Physiology Society, Washington, 1960, Vol III, pp. 1553–1593.

Longmuir, I., and McCabe, M.: Tissue adaptation to Oxygen Lack. *J Theoret Biol, 8:* 124–129, 1965.

Masland, R. L., Austin, G. M., and Grant, F. C.: A study of the EEG following occipital lobectomy. Read at the Am EEG Sov Meeting, Atlantic City, 1947. *J EEG Clin Neurophysiol, 1:* 273–282, 1949.

McCouch, G. P., Austin, G. M., Liu, C. N., and Liu, C. Y.: Sprouting as a cause of spasticity. *J Neurophysiol, 21, 3:* 205–216, 1958.

Meyer, J., and Hunter, J.: Behavior deficits following diencephalic lesions. *Neurology* (Minn.), *2:* 112–130, 1952.

Ojemann, R. G.: Further experience with the Syndrome of "normal" pressure hydrocephalus. *J Neurosurg, 31:* 279–294, September, 1969.

Pask, Gordon: *An Approach to Cybernetics.* London, Hutchinson, 1961.

Penfield, W.: Functional localization in temporal and deep sylvian areas. *Res Publ Ass Nerv Ment Dis, 36:* 210, 1958.

Plum, Fred, and Posner, Jerome B.: *Diagnosis of Stupor and Coma.* Philadelphia, Davis Co., 1966.

Pribram, K.: Looking to see: Some experiments on the brain mechanism of attention in perception. Baltimore, Williams and Wilkins, 1968, pp. 150–162.

Raisman, G.: Neuronal plasticity in the septal nuclei of the adult rat. *Brain Res, 14:* 25–48, 1969.

Roberts, L.: Central brain mechanisms in speech. Brain Function. Volume III. Proc. of the Third Conf, Nov., 1963, Speech, Language and Communication. U of Cal Pr, 1966, pp. 17–36.

Rosen, Robert: Autonomous state classifications by dynamical systems. *Math Biosciences,* Vol. 14, No. 1 & 2, 151–167, June, 1972.

Russell, Bertrand: *Our Knowledge Of The External World.* New York, Mentor, 1960.

Russell, Bertrand: *My Philosophical Development.* Simon and Schuster, 1959.

Segarra, Jose M.: Cerebral vascular disease and behavior. *Arch Neurol, 22:* 408–418, May, 1970.

Shalit, M., Beller, A., and Feinsod, M.: Clinical equivalents of cerebral oxygen consumption in coma. *Neurology,* Vol. 22, February, 1972.

Shapiro, F. L., and Smith, H. T.: The treatment of barbiturate intoxication. *Modern Medicine,* 104–110, April 21, 1969.

Skultety, F.: Clinical and experimental aspects of akinetic mutism. *Arch Neurol* (Chic), *19:* 1–14, 1968.

Sperry, R.: Perception in the absence of the Neocortical Commissures. *Perception And Its Disorders.* Baltimore, Williams and Wilkins, 1968, pp. 123–138.

Sprague, J.: The effects of chronic brainstem lesions on wakefulness, sleep and behavior. In Kety, Seymour S. *et al.* (Eds.): *Sleep and Altered States of Consciousness.* Baltimore, Williams and Wilkins, 1967, pp. 148–194.

Stritch, S. J.: Shearing of nerve fibers as a cause of brain damage due to head injury. *Lancet,* 445–448, August 26, 1961.

Tart, C. T.: States of Consciousness and Stae Specific Sciences. Science, 176, No. 4040. 1972, pp. 1203–1210.

Thews, G.: Implications to Physiology and Pathology of Oxygen Diffusion at the Capillary Level. In Schade, J. P. and McMenemey, W. H. (Eds.): *Selective Vulnerability Of The Brain In Hypoxaemia.* Philadelphia, Davis Co., 1963.

Walker, A., Lichtenstein, R., and Marshall, C.: A critical analysis of electrocorticography in temporal lobe epilepsy. *Arch Neurol, 2:* 172, 1960.

Weinberg, Harry L.: *Levels Of Knowing And Existence.* New York, Harper and Brothers, 1959.

Whitehead, A. N.: The Concept of Nature. In Northrup and Gross (Eds.): *Whitehead Anthology.* New York, 1953, p. 219.

Whitty, C. M., and Zangwill, O. L.: *Amnesia.* New York, Appleton, 1966.

Zollinger, R. L.: Removal of Left Cerebral Hemisphere; Report of a Case. *Arch Neurol Psychiatry, 34:* 1055–1062, 1935.

[PART II]
CALLOSAL SECTION

[CHAPTER V]

THE CORPUS CALLOSUM: HISTORY OF THOUGHT REGARDING ITS FUNCTION

Robert J. Joynt

T HE CORPUS CALLOSUM IS perhaps no longer the *pons asinorum* of the early philosophers, but it is not yet clear that it is a "bridge to understanding" of brain function which is alway an ineluctable search. The physical prominence of the corpus callosum has made it an object of study and interest from the time when serious anatomical descriptions were first made. Its central location connecting the two hemispheres encouraged speculation about function particularly in a time prior to notions of cerebral lateralization and dominance. More recently, the clinicians correlated callosal lesions with neurological deficits—usually without success. Thus, the corpus callosum has a long heritage of anatomical description, functional speculations, and clinical correlations. A history of these will furnish the background to the greatly expanded knowledge of the role of the corpus callosum in brain function which has come about in the past two decades.

Galen in the second century A.D. described the corpus callosum using the Greek term, tule.* In dissecting the brain he notes, "Examine the region exposed (corpus callosum). It is like a callus, so that there appears to be a natural hollow there which receives from the overlying and surrounding tissues incompletely concocted nutriment" (Singer, 1956). However, he used the term in a less restricted sense including not only the midline commissure but also the white matter of the hemispheres. The more circumscribed usage did not appear until the nineteenth century. There are no references to anatomical descriptions of the corpus callosum prior to Galen although Aristotle, Herophilus, Erasistratus, and Rufus of Ephesus had already made good anatomical dissections with extensive descriptions of the nervous system in man and animals.

---

* The word, tule, occurs in Aristophanes play "The Acharnians," where it is used to denote the callus which develops on a porter's back from carrying loads. The philosopher, Protagoras, is credited with inventing a cushion to prevent this.

Vesalius in his *De humani corporis fabrica* published in 1543 gave the first extensive description of the corpus callosum, "When, as I said, the brain had been separated, it revealed a smooth and even upper surface of the corpus callosum, and also demonstrates this body to be continuous with the cerebrum, not to be arisen from the surface of the substance of the cerebrum which is softer and yellowish but from the deeper substance which is seen to be harder and white. . . . This portion of the cerebrum is not so large and thick that it requires special vessels, although it is, nevertheless, of great importance to the living. Indeed, it relates the right side of the cerebrum to the left; then it produces and supports the septum of the right and left ventricles: finally, through that septum it supports and props up the body formed like a tortoise (fornix) so that it may not collapse and, to the great detriment of all the functions of the cerebrum, crush the cavity common to the two (lateral) ventricles of the cerebrum."

Piccolomini, (1586) Professor of Anatomy at Rome, clearly made a distinction between the white and gray matter of the brain, but made no clear distinction between the white matter of the hemispheres and the corpus callosum. He refers to the white matter as the medulla. He states in one passage, "The cerebrum commences everywhere by convolutions and extends as far as the corpus callosum and that middle white part. The medulla commences at the corpus callosum and is, I say, that whole, internal, middle, and white body which is lengthened out and slips forth into the spine of the back. Not only are the cerebrum and its medulla distinguished and separated from one's dissection. For occasionally, working with slow deliberation and dexterity (with a fresh brain), I have separated the cerebrum from the corpus callosum and the whole middle, white part called the medulla." Malpighi in 1664 also made no division between the corpus callosum and the corona radiata by stating, "Regarding the marrow of the brain (white matter) or the corpus callosum, that rough substance appears to be more solid than the cortex and to be surrounded by veins and arteries; it seems to be for filling the intervening spaces."

Thomas Willis published his book, *Cerebri anatome*, in 1664. He was Professor of Natural Philosophy at Oxford and later practiced medicine in London. He was an excellent anatomist, and speculated widely on the function of various parts of the nervous system. He broke away from the ventricular theory of brain function which was still prominent at that time. The corpus callosum played a large role in his theory of brain mechanisms. He noted that the seat of imagination was placed there, as was memory in the cerebral cortex and the *sensus communis* in the corpus striatum. He also invoked the idea of reflex action by describing the sequential events following the entrance of a sensory impression on the nervous system. He described the event and the role of the corpus callosum as follows, "Regarding the former (common sense) we notice that as often as the external part of the soul has been affected, a sensory impression, like an optical appearance or like the undulations of water, is carried more inwardly, turning toward the corpora striata, and perception of the external impression occurs, the internal impression; if this impression is carried further and crosses through the corpus callosum, it is succeeded by imagination; then, if the same flowing of the spirits strikes against the cortex of the brain, as its farthest shore, it impresses on it the image or character of the sensible object; when thereafter the same image is reflected, it arouses the memory of the same thing."

In the next century, Felix Vicq d'Azyr, the French anatomist and physician to Marie Antoinette, discussed the commissures of the brain. He says, in 1784, "It seems to me that the commissures are intended to establish sympathetic communications between different parts of the brain, just as the nerves do between different organs and the brain itself, a consideration which can apply to all kinds of connections observed between the different parts of the brain. These two indications can in general be divided into two classes: the first run from one hemisphere to the other, the second between different regions of the same hemisphere. . . . I include in the first class the corpus callosum, appropriately named by some anatomists the great commissure of the brain. . . . As for these latter communications, it is worth remarking that they connect the right hemisphere with the left by means of the gray and soft substance (cortex) which also has, as one sees it, its connections, and which must play an important role in the unknown mechanism of its functions."

Gall, with the aid of Spurzheim, published his *Anatomie et physiologie du système nerveux* in 1810. Gall, unfortunately remembered for his role in phrenology, was an excellent anatomist. In the following passage he talks about the commissures of the brain and also differentiates between projection fibers and association fibers. He says on the mechanism of connection, "All parts of the cerebrum are connected with analogous parts of the other hemisphere by a similar mechanism and are thus united for mutually influencing and the attainment of a common end. Some of these parts being much larger and more distinct than in other systems, they have not escaped the attention of most ancient anatomists. Galen describes the corpus callosum. For a long time the name commissure has been given to this part, and it has been felt that it produced a communication and a reciprocal action. "The commissures," said Vicq d'Azyr, "seem to be destined to establish sympathetic communication between the different cerebral parts." It is certain that one can clearly demonstrate the existence of two systems in the brain and that the association system contains more numerous fibers and larger bundles than the projectional system."

The differentiation of white matter into different systems was taking place with the early work of Vicq d'Azyr and Gall, and was largely worked out by Theodore Meynert (1872) in the latter half of the nineteenth century. He noted the existence of arcuate fibers, commissural fibers, and projection fibers and commented, "The corpus callosum bundles unite identical parts of the cortex of the two halves of the cerebral hemispheres." Thus, much of the anatomical groundwork for speculations concerning function had been established. More advanced neuroanatomical staining methods developed at this time enabled many investigators to delineate more exactly the origin, course, and termination of fibers of the corpus callosum.

The last hundred years of speculation about function of the corpus callosum can be divided, like the history of man, into a dark age, renaissance, and a modern era. Also like the study of history, there are paradoxes so that if we call the work of the early 1940's the period of the renaissance, we ignore the many flashes of brilliant reasoning into callosal function which were made earlier by such people as Dejerine, Liepmann, and Bonhoeffer. Indeed, many would say that the dark ages followed the renaissance in this instance.

Dejerine in 1892 described his now famous instance of a callosal lesion in a patient with alexia and a right homonymous hemianopsia but with preserved ability to write. He reasoned that the intact visual cortex on the right side was disconnected from the speech area so that information could not be transferred across the posterior portion of the infarcted corpus callosum. Other investigators confirmed the lesion responsible for this clinical syndrome. Leipmann and Maas in 1907 described motor apraxia to verbal commands in the left hand due to a callosal lesion. In 1914 Bonhoeffer described a patient with a motor aphasia who had a preserved cortical speech area but had a capsular lesion on the left side and a callosal lesion. Thus, the speech area, he reasoned, was isolated and the alternative pathway across the callosum was no longer available for production of speech. Cajal (1960) paid heed to these observations and noted in his *Histologie du système nerveux de l'homme et des vertébrés:* "The bilateral disposition of the perceptual centers, and the unilaterality of memory justifies in our opinion the corpus callosum. It brings with it, in fact, the necessity of two kinds of association fibers, or at least of two kinds of collaterals; one direct, bringing the homolateral moiety of the image to the memory center, the other commissural or callosal which brings to the same center that part of the image which was projected to the perceptor center of the other hemisphere."

Unfortunately, the brilliant anatomical and behavioral correlations offered by these clinicians were largely ignored and rather vague clinical syndromes secondary to callosal lesions were cited by most investigators. Raymond in 1893 believed there was a definite "psychic syndrome" which was characterized by difficulty in association of ideas, loss of memory, changes in character and lability of emotions. However, there was a massive tumor of the frontal lobes in his case description. Gowers (1893) whose textbook was a compendium of the most recent knowledge noted in his second edition: "We do not yet know of any symptoms that are the result of damage to the callosal fibers; it is certain that the symptoms that have been present are indistinguishable from multiple tumors, and that their complete interruption (by softening from embolism) has caused no symptoms." Levy-Valensi in 1910 described a syndrome which lacked specific neurological signs such as involvement of the cranial nerves, or sensory loss, but characterized by rather nonspecific disturbances including drowsiness, coma, dementia, bilateral motor disability, and sphincter disorders. He did feel that there was some specific motor apraxia associated with callosal involvement. Ayala in 1915 added depression to this syndrome along with torpor, apathy, and inhibition. Alpers and Grant in 1931 described a syndrome which was "clear, without being absolutely characteristic." In this they included mental disturbances among which were inability to concentrate and to focus attention even for a short time; motor paralysis, usually of a minor nature and occasionally involving extremities on both sides but sparing the face; drowsiness; and motor apraxia. The latter they regarded an important sign of involvement of the corpus callosum but, unfortunately, not often present. Therefore, prior to the end of the 1930's and beginning of the 1940's, and with the exception of the clear analyses of a few cases already mentioned, most of the reports included large series with particular emphasis on changes in the mental state and very little emphasis on what we would now call aspects of the deconnection syndrome. Interestingly, Zinn noted in 1749 that the section of the callosum in a dog had no effect on motor or sensory function. However, Bykov and Speransky, (1941) working in Pavlov's laboratory, found that conditioned response to a tactile stimulus would eventually respond to a symmetrical area on the other side of the experimental animal but that sectioning of the corpus callosum would prevent this irradiation to the opposite side.

A fresh look was taken into callosal function in the later 1930's and 1940's with the work of Van Wagenen, Akelaitis, and their colleagues at Rochester, New York. Van Wagenen did partial or complete callosal sections in twenty-four patients. Two of these also had sections including the anterior commissure. These were almost all done on patients with epilepsy of long standing and acquired early in life. These were critical cases in the understanding of callosal function. The results were as follows. Akelaitis (1941a, 1941b, 1944, 1943) reported no change in the postoperative findings regarding stereognosis; personality changes; visual, auditory, or tactile gnosis; language function; and size, object, letter and color discriminative ability in the fields of vision. Bridgman and Smith (1945) on the same group of patients reported neither change in binocular depth perception nor in the ability to maintain and recover fusion in response to diplopia producing stimuli. Akelaitis, Risteen, Herren and Van Wagenen (1942) found that dyspraxia did not occur unless there was damage to one of the cerebral hemispheres preoperatively. There were some positive findings. However, these were reported as rather slight and transient. Smith and Akelaitis (1942) reported temporary shifts in laterality and a unilateral disturbance in motility. Bridgman and Smith (1945) found some loss in divergence and convergence necessary to maintain and recover single binocular vision, and felt that this deficit was minor and of questionable significance. Smith (1951) studied pre and postoperative ability in learning problems and found slight but inconsistent disturbances in finger maze learning and transfer of this learning to the opposite hand. Patients also reported some difficulties in coordinating the action of both hands, but this was not carefully worked out (Akelaitis, 1944–45). Parsons (1940) did psychological tests on these patients pre and postoperatively and the only significant change was slight impairment in the immediate memory as shown by the digit span test. Thus, their findings were largely negative even if there was some suggestions of difficulty. More recently, Goldstein and Joynt (1969; unpublished) showed that prominent defects in interhemispheric transfer did exist in two of these original patients reexamined almost three decades later. These early findings coupled with the negative reports of others, almost laid the corpus callosum to rest. For example, Dandy (1936) had partially sectioned the corpus callosum in approaching posterior third ventricle tumors and was unable to note mental changes. He concluded, "This simple experiment at once disposes of the extravagant claims to function of the corpus callosum." However, Trescher and Ford (1937) could find alexia in the left visual field of one of Dandy's patients with a posterior callosal section for removal of a ventricular colloid cyst. It was also in the early 1940's that McCulloch stated about the corpus callosum, ". . . the part it plays in ordinary activity and in normal behavior remains a mystery." Sweet (1941) in commenting on the cases studied at Rochester noted "If postmortem studies show that the corpus callosum was completely divided in their cases, strong evidence will be present that it is wrong to conclude that this intercerebral commissure is one of the essential links in the maintenance of eupraxia." The *coup de grace* was delivered by Lashley (1960) when he made a summary of his observations and others on association fibers including the corpus callosum and commented, "It is difficult to interpret such findings, but I think that they point to the conclusion that the associative connexions or memory traces of the conditioned reflex do not extend across the cortex as well-defined arcs or paths. Such arcs are either diffused through all parts of the cortex, pass by relay through lower centres, or do not exist."

Thus, we arrive at the modern era of study of callosal function which started with development of tests to measure behavior in the split brain animal. It is now obvious that the usual behavior observations did not reveal significant differences before and after callosal section and special tests had to be devised to bring these out. The animal studies initiated by Sperry and Myers have initiated a whole new field of research in this area. The group working at the California Institute of Technology has expanded these findings into study of callosal sectioned patients. Clinicians have now utilized these test methods in their analysis of callosal syndromes caused by disease.

The events of the past twenty years have even drawn the attention of science fiction writers. In *The Billion Dollar Brain* Len Deighton (1966) describes a mammoth computer and the most complex part is known as the "Corpus Callosum." Bremer (1956) characterized the new role of this exceptional part of the brain, "It is now obvious that the functioning of the corpus callosum is associated with the highest and most elaborative activities of the brain." It is the purpose of this symposium to relate the modern history of callosal function which is still developing.

REFERENCES

Akelaitis, A. J.: Psychobiological studies following section of the corpus callosum. A preliminary report. *Am J Psychiatry, 97:* 1147–57, 1941a.

Akelaitis, A. J.: Studies on the corpus callosum. II. The higher visual functions in each homonymous field following complete section of the corpus callosum. *Arch Neurol Psychiatry, 45:* 788–796, 1941b.

Akelaitis, A. J.: A study of gnosis, praxis and language following section of the corpus callosum and anterior commissure. *J Neurosurg, 1:* 94–102, 1944.

Akelaitis, A. J.: Studies on the corpus callosum. VII. Study of language functions (tactile and visual lexia and graphia) unilaterally following section of the corpus callosum. *J Neuropathol Exp Neurol, 2:* 226–262, 1943.

Akelaitis, A. J.: Studies on the corpus callosum. IV. Diagnostic dyspraxia in epileptics following partial and complete section of the corpus callosum. *Am J Psychiatry, 101:* 594–599, 1944–45.

Akelaitis, A. J., Risteen, W. A., Herren, R. Y., and Van Wagenen, W. P.: Studies on the corpus callosum. III. A contribution to the study of dyspraxia in epileptics following partial and complete section of the corpus callosum. *Arch Neurol Psychiatry, 47:* 971–1008, 1942.

Alpers, B. J., and Grant, F. C.: The clinical syndrome of the corpus callosum. *Arch Neurol Psychiatry, 25:* 67–86, 1931.

Ayala, G.: Contributo alo studio dei tumori del corpo calloso. *Riv di patol nerv ment, 20:* 449–492, 1915.

Bonhoeffer, K.: Klinischer und anatomischer Befund zur Lehre von der Apraxie und der 'motorischen Sprachbahn.' *Monatsschr Psychiatr Neurol, 35:* 113–128, 1914.

Bremer, F.: Physiology of the corpus callosum. *Res Publ Assoc Res Nerv Ment Dis 36:* 424–428, 1956.

Bridgman, C. S., and Smith, K. W.: Bilateral neural integration in visual perception after section of the corpus callosum. *J Comp Neurol, 83:* 57–68, 1945.

Bykov, K. M., and Speransky, A. D.: Observation upon dogs after section of the corpus callosum. Coll. Papers Physiol. Labs. I. P. Pavlov, *1:* 47–59, 1924.

Cajal, S.: *Histologie du système nerveux de l'homme et des vertébrés,* Paris, A. Maloine, 1909. From von Bonin, G.: *Some Papers on the Cerebral Cortex.* Springfield, Thomas, 1960.

Dandy, W. E.: Operative experience in cases of pineal tumors. *Arch Surg, 33:* 19–46, 1936.

Deighton, L.: *The Billion Dollar Brain.* New York, Putnam, 1966.

Dejerine, J.: Des différentes veriétés de cécité verbale. *C. R. Mem Soc Biol, 44:* 61–90, 1892. (March 19).

Gall, F. G.: *Anatomie et physiologie du système nerveux.* Translated in Clarke, E., and O'Malley, C. D.: *The Human Brain and Spinal Cord.* Berkeley and Los Angeles, U Cal Pr, 1968.

Goldstein, M. N., and Joynt, R. J.: Long term follow-up of a callosal sectioned patient. *Arch Neurol, 20:* 96–102, 1969.

Goldstein, M. N., and Joynt, R. J.: Unpublished observations.

Gowers, W. C.: *A Manual of Diseases of the Nervous System,* ed. 2. London, Churchill, 1893, p. 314.

Lashley, K. S.: In search of the engram. In *The Neuropsychology of Lashley,* New York, McGraw-Hill, 1969, Chapt. 29, p. 484.

Levy-Valensi, J.: Physiologie du corps calleux. *Presse Med, 19:* 72–74, 1911.

Liepmann, H., and Maas, O.: Fall von Linksseitiger Agraphie und Apraxie bei rechtsseitiger Lahmung. *J Psychol Neurol, 10:* 214–227, 1907.

Malpighi, M.: Tetras anatomicarum epistolarum, Translated in Clarke, E., and O'Malley, C. D.: *The Human Brain and Spinal Cord.* Berkeley and Los Angeles, U Cal Pr, 1968.

Meynert, T.: Von Gehirne der Säugethiere, Chap. XXXI in Stricker's *Handbuch der Lehre von dem Geweben des Menschen und der Thiere.* Translated in Clarke, E., and O'Malley, C. D.: *The Human Brain and Spinal Cord.* Berkeley and Los Angeles, U Cal Pr, 1968.

McCulloch, W. S.: Cortico-cortical Connections. In *Precentral Motor Cortex,* Bucy, P. (ed.): Urbana, U of Ill, 1944.

Parsons, F. H.: Psychological tests of eight patients one year after section of the corpus callosum. *Psychol Bull, 37:* 498, 1940.

Piccolomini, A.: *Anatomicae praelectiones explicantes mirificam corporis humani fabricam.* Translated in Clarke, E., and O'Malley, C. D.: *The Human Brain and Spinal Cord.* Berkeley and Los Angeles. U Cal Pr, 1968.

Raymond, F.: Contribution a l'étude des tumeurs de cerveau. *Arch de neurol,* 26: 273–300, 1893.

Singer, C.: *Galen on Anatomical Procedures,* London, Oxford U Pr, 1956, p. 231.

Smith, K. W., and Akelaitis, A. J.: Studies on the corpus callosum. I. Laterality in behavior and bilateral motor organization in man before and after section of the corpus callosum. *Arch Neurol Psychol, 47:* 519–543, 1942.

Smith, K. W.: Learning and the associative pathways of the human cerebral cortex. *Science, 114:* 117–120, 1951.

Sweet, W. H.: Seeping intracranial aneurysm simulating neoplasm. Syndrome of the corpus callosum. *Arch Neurol Psychol, 45:* 86–104, 1941.

Trescher, J. H., and Ford, F. R.: Colloid cyst of the third ventricle. Report of a case; operative removal with section of posterior half of corpus callosum. *Arch Neurol Psychiatry, 37:* 959-973, 1937.

Vesalius, A.: *De humani corporis fabrica.* Translated in Clarke, E., and O'Malley, C. D.: *The Human Brain and Spinal Cord.* Berkeley and Los Angeles, U Cal Pr, 1968.

Vicq d'Azyr, R.: *Historie de l' Academie royale des.* Translated in Clarke, E., and O'Malley, C. D.: *The Human Brain and Spinal Cord.* Berkeley and Los Angeles, U Cal Pr, 1968.

Willis, T.: *Cerebri anatome.* Translated in Clarke, E., and O'Malley, C. D.: *The Human Brain and Spinal Cord.* Berkeley and Los Angeles, U Cal Pr, 1968.

Zinn, J. G.: Dissertatio inauguralis. Gottingen, 1749. Cited in Elliot, F. A.: The corpus callosum, cingulate gyrus, septum pellucidum, septal area and fornix. In Vinken, P. J., and Bruyn, G. W. (Eds.): *Handbook of Neurology.* Amsterdam, North Holland Pub., 1969, Vol. 2.

[CHAPTER VI]

AUDITORY SPECIALIZATION OF THE RIGHT AND LEFT HEMISPHERES

Harold W. Gordon

AUDITORY FUNCTIONS HAVE asymmetrical representation in the cerebral hemispheres as have cognitive abilities for visual (Bogen, 1969a; DeRenzi and Spinnler, 1966; Kimura, 1963; Milner, 1965; Piercy *et al.*, 1960) and tactual modalities (DeRenzi *et al.*, 1968; DeRenzi and Scotti, 1969; Milner and Taylor, 1972; Nebes, 1971). These right-left differences are commonly investigated by comparisons of patient groups with unilateral cerebral lesions. For example, a standard auditory test is given to patients with right hemisphere damage and their scores are compared to those obtained by patients with left cerebral damage. Differences in scores imply differences in cerebral function. Asymmetries are also found in normal people when special techniques such as dichotic listening are employed. Competing inputs to the two ears tend to induce right-left perceptual differences that reflect asymmetrical cerebral performance. This chapter examines some of these differentially lateralized, auditory abilities and emphasizes important features of auditory cognition in the non-speech hemisphere.

Milner (1962) administered a standard musical abilities test (1960) to patients who were about to undergo surgical resection of either the right or left temporal lobe. The test battery consisted of six subtests of aspects of music such as tonal memory, timbre, and rhythm. The patients in the main group took each subtest twice—before surgery and again two weeks afterward.

The results showed a significantly inferior performance by patients with right temporal lobe excision as compared to patients with left lobe removal. The difference reflected a significant decrement in performance for right temporals after surgery, while performance of the left temporal group remained much the same. The subtests showing the largest differences were Tonal Memory and Timbre, followed by Loudness and Time. It can be concluded that excision of the right temporal lobe significantly impairs some musical abilities, but removal of the left temporal lobe does not. Or conversely, optimal performance on these

musical tests requires functional integrity of the right temporal lobe
more than of the left.

I recently studied the musical abilities of an adolescent male (age
15) who had undergone removal of the right hemisphere at age 7 because of acute encephalitis. The excision included all of the cortex
but spared the basal ganglia. Prior to the operation the patient was
left-handed; however, intracarotid injection of sodium amobarbital before
surgery localized speech to the left hemisphere. At present, the patient
is ambulatory, talks well, and goes to school. He cannot voluntarily
move his left arm but has adequate use of his left leg so that he can
walk rapidly and manage stairs with relative ease (For more details,
see Gott, 1973).

The Seashore Test of Musical Abilities was administered in one
session. The results revealed a severe deficit in most subtests—the patient not only scored below average (compared with standard norms of
young adolescent school children) but also failed to reach a level higher
than could have been attained by chance. Two exceptions were Timbre
and Loudness, where scores were subnormal but above chance level. In
contrast, Milner's temporal lobe patients, who also performed below
average, scored significantly above the chance level on all subtests.

The hemispherectomy patient returned for three additional sessions
in which only Pitch and Loudness subtests were repeated. The test
method was changed so that the stimuli could be channeled through
stereo headphones either to one ear alone or both ears together. The
third test session differed from the first two in that the test stimuli were
easier to discriminate. Results showed that performance on the Pitch
test still remained at chance level in each session including the one with
simplified discriminanda. In fact, further informal testing showed that
this patient could not consistently distinguish two tones that differed by
as much as one full musical step. Left ear scores were consistently higher
than either right ear or binaural scores, but none exceeded a level expected from chance guessing. In contrast, the scores in each session for
the Loudness test were above chance. The highest score was attained in
the third test session with the simplified stimuli. In contrast to what
happened on the Pitch test, the left ear usually performed the poorest,
sometimes falling below chance level, although ear differences were not
significant. Evidence from this subject supports the hypothesis that the
right hemisphere is important for pitch discrimination. However, one
cannot be sure that this patient could have performed better on these
tests had he retained his right hemisphere.

A brief mention should be made about this patient's singing. Ren-
ditions of melodies that he knew or with which he was familiar were

poor but, on the whole, recognizable. He did slightly better when he was allowed to sing a song of his own choosing. Musically, this patient is like any poor singing, normal person. In effect, he is "tone deaf," since his most severe errors occur when trying to sing correct pitch intervals.

A remarkable contrast exists between this patient and a young female (age 12) whose left hemisphere was removed at age 10 for a recurring tumour (For more details, see Gott 1973). She sang songs with virtually no pitch errors within weeks of her operation. At the same time, she had impaired comprehension and minimal speech. Two years after surgery she continues to sing any of her favorite songs without difficulty. However, if asked to repeat the lyrics instead of the melody, she often fails after the first few words and refuses to go on. In contrast, she can hum any melody excellently. To see if her humming ability was confined only to popular songs, the patient was asked to hum tone pairs from the Pitch test of the Seashore battery. By subjective measurement, she rendered each of the pairs with remarkable accuracy. Again, the hypothesis that pitch perception and production depend on an intact right hemisphere is supported.

Observations on these two patients are consistent with cases reported in the literature (For a review, see Bogen, 1969b). The best example is a 46 year old male whose left hemisphere was removed because of a recurrent tumour (Smith, 1966). Speech was minimal although the patient could repeat simple words and even name some objects. At first he had little propositional speech and was limited to expletives and one- or two-word phrases, "Uh, yes," "No," "Well, I . . .," etc. In contrast to his grossly impaired speech, he could sing with little hesitation. The patient sang not only with fairly good melody but also with the lyrics. In the absence of systematic testing, further evaluation of musical ability is difficult. Some contradictory evidence comes from a case of a nondominant hemispherectomy who retained his singing ability (Smith, 1969). But again, no systematic study was made.

Since few hemispherectomy cases are available (except of cases of birth injury), large-scale studies of musical abilities in these patients are nonexistent. However, a technique used for determining speech lateralization (Wada and Rasmussen, 1960) simulates many of the effects of a surgical hemispherectomy. The major difference, of course, is that the symptoms are reversible. Two hundred mg sodium amobarbital is injected into the common carotid artery and therefore into the blood supply of one hemisphere. The injected drug acts almost instantaneously to depress most, if not all, hemispheric functions on that side for a period of 3 to 5 minutes. During the period of paralysis, the non-injected hemisphere operates on its own, capable of seeing, hearing, feeling, and controlling the limbs on the contralateral side of the body. Since this "reversible hemispherectomy" is successful in determining speech lateralization for pre-surgical patients, it seemed worthwhile to pursue the question of singing in these patients at a time when information for medical purposes had been obtained (Gordon and Bogen, 1974).*

The subjects were seven epileptic patients who were candidates for major brain surgery and in whom it was necessary to determine the contribution of the hemispheres to speech. All patients were given right carotid artery injections with no apparent complications. Four were also injected on the left, though not within two days of the right-sided injection. Hemispheric dysfunction produced by sodium amobarbital was evidenced, in part, by flaccidity and lack of response in the contralateral limbs, eye deviation to the ipsilateral side, and general drowsiness. These symptoms appeared immediately after injection, and at this time speech samples were taken. The patient stated his name, days of the week, or made up sentences using key words introduced by the examiner. The patient also performed simple motor acts (e.g. clenching and unclenching his fist, extending a finger, etc.) in response to the examiner's commands and/or demonstrations.

The examiner asked the patient to sing songs familiar to him. In addition to, or instead of, suggesting the title of a song, the examiner would sing the first few bars to facilitate the patient's response. The patient was encouraged to sing the song without worrying about the quality of his performance.

A pre-examination session was begun just before the sodium amobarbital was introduced but after insertion of the needle into the carotid artery. During this period, the patient became acquainted with the test material. He was asked his name, the date, and to repeat several sentences. These were recorded on audio tape and used as baseline speech samples to which the test material could be compared. The patient then sang songs with which he was familiar, and these were also recorded for later comparison. Finally, when he seemed comfortable with the test situation and with singing, the patient was positioned on his back, knees drawn up, and arms raised straight above the body. Counting aloud slowly (1, 2, 3, etc.), the patient clenched and unclenched his fists as the sodium amobarbital was being injected. The injection lasted only 1 to 2 seconds at the end of which the contralateral arm and leg became flaccid while the ipsilateral side remained strong and responsive.

---

* The sodium amobarbital study was done in collaboration with Joseph E. Bogen, M.D., of Ross-Loos Medical Group, Los Angeles, and residents of the White Memorial Medical Center.

The examiner asked the patient to say his name, list the days of the week, and repeat some phrases and sentences. Then he requested limb movement by demonstration or by commands, such as "Make a fist," "Hold up your hand," or "Stick out your thumb." Finally the examiner stated the title or sang a few bars of the songs that were practiced during the pre-injection period until the patient started singing. The patient was usually encouraged to complete the song using only "La, la, la, . . ." instead of words, concentrating mainly on the melody.

Repeated checking of the responsiveness of the flaccid limbs provided an indication of the level of hemispheric depression, since the significance of the observed responses depended upon the unilaterality of the depression. Once the previously paralyzed contralateral limbs could be moved, either spontaneously or to command, the final examples of speaking and singing were recorded, and the time course of events during the session was transcribed and analyzed.

The most notable finding was that singing was severely deficient in six of seven cases when amobarbital was injected in the right carotid artery. Three of these patients ignored the examiner's repeated requests to sing, although one patient also could not speak until four minutes after onset of hemiparesis. The three remaining cases who sang upon request soon after amobarbital injection produced strikingly amelodic efforts compared to pre-injection samples. There was little tone variation except for unnatural pitch changes which were either much higher or much lower than necessary for the song. Rhythm, however, was much less affected.

In spite of poor singing ability, it was found that the patients could monitor and recognize the results of their own poor efforts. For example, one patient, when asked how his singing sounded, replied "Very groggy." Another patient who did not sing until two and one-half minutes after injection complained after her performance that her ". . . throat feels like a watermelon." Usually when the songs were sung, the patient was asked to avoid the words and sing "La, la, la, ..." However, one patient was requested to use the words along with the melody, resulting in characteristically amelodic singing but with every word pronounced correctly.

The one patient whose singing was not impaired after right-sided injection was strongly left-handed. In addition, the usual dosage of amobarbital failed to produce in this one patient complete depression of the right hemisphere as evidenced by persisting movements of the left limbs.

Important findings were also noted in four patients who were also injected with amobarbital in the left hemisphere on a different day. In three of these cases, speech was lost immediately after injection. Normal tonus and purposeful movements of the ipsilateral (left) limbs throughout the mute period indicated a low but conscious level of awareness. Verbal comprehension varied from patient to patient, but improvement was observed in each before speech was first regained.

No patient sang well until he had recovered some speech. However, the best case appeared to make several attempts to sing before any comparable effort to speak. In fact, she managed to sing along with the examiner, albeit poorly, at least one and one-half minutes before she could respond to any verbal commands (e.g., saying her name). Furthermore, her attempt at singing actually occurred sooner after left-sided amobarbital injection than it had after extensive coaxing following injection in the non-dominant (right) side.

The other two patients could not sing at all until they had regained some speech function. However, once singing was elicited, their performance showed little deficit and matched their pre-injection abilities. This was in contrast to residual defects in singing in these same patients, sampled at comparable time periods following right carotid injection.

The one patient who continued talking after left-sided injection was the only left-hander. His singing ability was hard to assess because his baseline performance was initially quite poor and therefore deficits were generally imperceptible after either left or right injection. The only evidence of asymmetry of musical performance was a lesser degree of confusion after right-sided injection. Typically, the patient would complete a song without hesitation, which contrasted to his performance after left-sided injection when he sometimes had to stop singing and ask for help in order to finish the song. Conclusions from the singing evidence hints at a reversed dominance in this patient, although amobarbital testing failed to localize speech. Later tests also indicated a reversal of hemispheric dominance (J. E. Bogen, Personal Communication; R. Saul, Personal Communication).

In summary, singing was severely impaired in right-handed patients after right hemisphere depression while at the same time speech was only mildly slurred. In contrast, both singing and speech were abolished by left hemisphere injection. However, singing recovered before speech in one patient and was restored to normal more quickly in the others.

The right hemisphere clearly has a major role in singing. Yet, the right hemisphere did not sing alone immediately after the left had been severely depressed. It is not clear whether this is due to the inability of the right hemisphere to function or to inhibition caused by the induced depression of the left hemisphere. It is known from hemispherectomy studies that the right hemisphere is quite capable of supporting singing on its own, yet there is no way of knowing how much time was needed for recovery of singing after the surgery. Also, it is uncertain whether effects of inhibition are the same with a transiently depressed hemisphere as compared to one that has been surgically removed. Whatever the state of mutual interaction of the two hemispheres, however, the general findings continue to support right hemispheric dominance in musical abilities.

To avoid some of the variability that comes from testing neurological patients, techniques have been devised to test cerebral asymmetry in normals. The most popular of these is "dichotic listening," which is a modification of early tests by Broadbent (1954). Two auditory messages are played to the left and right ear, respectively, through stereo headphones. It is accepted that contralateral ear-to-cortex pathways are the stronger and, as a result, ipsilateral pathways tend to be more blocked out during dichotic stimulation. Consequently, superior performance by one ear reflects superior performance by the contralateral hemisphere. For example, verbal test items are found to be superior in the right ear since it lies opposite the left speech hemisphere (Kimura, 1964). Conversely, when orchestral melodies are used as stimuli, the left ear proved to be dominant, indicating right hemisphere superiority (Kimura, 1961). However, it was unclear whether certain musical qualities rather than the melodies, *per se*, were responsible for hemispheric asymmetry. Accordingly, this hypothesis was tested with the method of dichotic listening (Gordon, 1970).

The subjects were 20 male undergraduates with estimated I.Q.s above 120. They were right-handed and all members of amateur musical performing groups. The testing session consisted of two nonverbal dichotic listening tests which were administered to the subjects on an individual basis. One of the dichotic tests consisted of two different melodies played on a soprano or alto recorder simultaneously, one to each ear (Kimura, 1961). The method of report was by multiple choice. Four melodies were played binaurally in succession, two of which were the original dichotic melodies. The subject was to select the original two from the four choices. The second test substituted chords for melodies and presented them in a similar manner. Two chords, recorded from an electric organ, were played simultaneously, one to each ear. As in the Melodies Test, the subject was to select these stimulus chords from a multiple choice of four.

The results were striking. Only the Chords Test demonstrated a significant ($p < .02$) left ear dominance. The implication is that chords were significantly better recognized by the right than by the left hemisphere. The conclusion follows from the argument that crossed auditory pathways are the stronger while ipsilateral pathways tend to be blocked by the method of simultaneous presentation of stimuli. Therefore, asymmetry of the ear scores reflects asymmetry of perception between the hemispheres.

In contrast to the Chords Test, there was no significant difference between the ears for the Melodies Test. It appears that perception of melodies in this test is equally distributed between the hemispheres. That is, cues that were used by the subjects to select the correct melodies can be used equally by either hemisphere. Or perhaps there were two distinct cues, one which was best recognized by the left hemisphere and one which was best recognized by the right hemisphere, so that asymmetry would be masked by the balance of dominance tendencies from each hemisphere.

The lack of asymmetry for melodies is in direct opposition to findings reported for previous tests where left ear dominance has been demonstrated (Kimura, 1961). It is likely that the discrepancy is due to the stimuli themselves rather than the test method or subject differences. The stimulus melodies in this test were played on an instrument that sounds much like a whistle. The subjective impression of such melodies is that rhythmic qualities are particularly accentuated in addition to the pitch-to-pitch variations. If the subjects were using the rhythm cues along with pitch variation, it is possible that these stimuli would not produce asymmetry of performance. Support for this view comes from Milner's original study where the Pitch and Rhythm subtests of the Seashore battery did not show significant changes after temporal lobectomy. Consequently, some other quality that was present in the chords must provide the kind of cue that is more likely to be asymmetrically represented between the hemispheres than the rhythm and pitch changes provided by these melodies. It is a matter for conjecture whether this cue also resembled the one that yielded significant asymmetries in the orchestral melodies tests previously reported.

The most obvious characteristic lacking in the chord stimuli was the dimension of time. Melodies have a temporal progression of notes and pitch changes, but chords are simply an assemblage of tones. Furthermore, the timbre-like quality of the chord tones is such that individual notes are nearly impossible to distinguish. Recognition therefore consists of a subjective impression rather than a tonal analysis or a positive identification of the chord names. For melodies, and particularly for melodies played on a whistle-like instrument, each of the tones is devoid of timbre quality; the distinguishing characteristic is the different temporal and sequential pattern of pitches. It is hypothesized that the right hemisphere superiority is concerned with successive pitch interval comparisons, or, said another way, the musical space between tones. Melody recognition becomes less of a right hemisphere task, however, as the time and rhythm factors become more salient for distinguishing the tone patterns.

A direct test in Carmon's laboratory (Halperin *et al.*, 1971) of temporal versus non-temporal qualities in a dichotic listening task has supported the hypothesis of non-temporal specialization of the right hemisphere. The subjects were undergraduate females. The test consisted of three-tone sequences which were arranged in pairs and presented in the usual dichotic paradigm. The important variable was the number of transitions in each three-tone sequence. Zero transitions implies a succession of three high or three low pitches. Two transitions is a sequence of high-low-ligh or low-high-low. The subject's task was to listen to dichotic presentation of the three-sequence pairs having either zero, one, or two transitions and then report as many of the six tones in the sequence as possible.

The results showed that more zero transitions were recalled correctly for the left ear, but for the two-transition sequences the right ear was dominant. The one-transition sequence revealed no ear differences. The dramatic shift from left ear to right ear superiority relative to the change from zero to two transitions, respectively, provided support for the hypothesis that the right hemisphere excels in non-temporal tasks. The left ear superiority for the zero order transition reflects a right hemisphere dominance when the major cue was based only on frequency determination. Conversely, the right ear superiority for the second order transition reflects left hemisphere dominance when tones were recognized by their temporal or sequential order.

The notion of non-temporality fits well with the data presented in this chapter. The major problem for the right hemispherectomy and sodium amobarbital patients was perception and production of pitch intervals. Also, the major deficits in Milner's right temporal lobe patients was in the Timbre and Tonal Memory subtests. For vision and touch, it is well-established that a special characteristic of the right hemisphere is spatial perception, but it is hard to see how a musical chord fits this description except in the abstract sense of a tonal distance between pitches. Instead, it might be better to consider "spatial" function as "non-temporal." On the other hand, there is mounting evidence that temporal and sequential order has been found to depend on the integrity of the *left* hemisphere not only for auditory (Efron, 1963) but also for visual (Carmon, 1975; Carmon and Nachshon, 1971) and tactual (D. Zaidel, Personal Communication) stimuli. Therefore, a more tenable dichotomy between cognitive abilities of the right and left hemispheres may involve the dimension of time or sequence—the left hemisphere is marked with its presence and the right hemisphere is characterized by its absence.

REFERENCES

Bogen, J. E.: The other side of the brain. I: dysgraphia and dyscopia following cerebral commissurotomy. *Bull Los Angeles Neurol Soc, 34:* 73–105, 1969a.

Bogen, J. E.: The other side of the brain. II: an appositional mind. *Bull Los Angeles Neurol Soc, 34:* 135–162, 1969b.

Bogen, J. E., and Gordon, H. W.: Musical tests for functional lateralization with intracarotid amobarbital. *Nature, 230:* 524–525, 1971.

Broadbent, D. B.: The role of auditory localisation in attention and memory. *J Exp Psychol, 47:* 191–196, 1954.

Carmon, A.: Spatial and temporal factors in visual perception of patients with unilateral hemispheric lesions. *In* Kinsbourne, M. (Ed.): *Hemispheric Asymmetry of Function.* Cambridge University Press. In press, 1975.

Carmon, A., and Nachshon, I.: Effect of unilateral brain damage on perception of temporal order. *Cortex, 7:* 410–418, 1971.

De Renzi, E., Faglioni, P., and Scotti, G.: Tactile spatial impairment and unilateral cerebral damage. *J Nerv Ment Dis, 146:* 468–475, 1968.

De Renzi, E., and Scotti, G.: The influence of spatial disorders in impairing tactual discrimination of shapes. *Cortex, 5:* 53–62, 1969.

De Renzi, E., and Spinnler, H.: Visual recognition in patients with unilateral cerebral disease. *J Nerv Ment Dis, 142:* 515–525, 1966.

Efron, R.: Temporal perception, aphasia and Déjà Vù. *Brain, 86:* 403–424, 1963.

Gordon, H. W.: Hemispheric asymmetries in the perception of musical chords. *Cortex, 6:* 387–398, 1970.

Gordon, H. W., and Bogen, J. E.: Hemispheric lateralization of singing after intracarotid sodium amobarbital. *J Neurol Neurosurg Psychiatry, 37:* 727–739, 1974.

Gott, P.: Language after dominant hemispherectomy. *J Neurol Neurosurg Psychiatry, 36:* 1082–1088, 1973.

Halperin, Y., Nachshon, I., and Carmon, A.: Shift of ear superiority in dichotic listening to temporally patterned nonverbal stimuli. *J Acoust Soc Am, 53:* 46–50, 1973.

Kimura, D.: Cerebral dominance and the perception of verbal stimuli. *Can J Psychol, 15:* 166–171, 1961.

Kimura, D.: Right temporal lobe damage: perception of unfamiliar stimuli after damage. *Arch Neurol, 8:* 264–271, 1963.

Kimura, D.: Left-right differences in the perception of melodies. *Q J Exp Psychol, 16:* 355–358, 1964.

Milner, B.: Laterality effects in audition. In Mountcastle, V. B. (Ed.): *Interhemispheric Relations and Cerebral Dominance.* Baltimore, Johns Hopkins, 1962.

Milner, B.: Visually-guided maze learning in man: effects of bilateral, hippocampal, frontal, and unilateral cerebral lesions. *Neuropsychologia, 3:* 317–338, 1965.

I would like to thank Dr. Ian Gill of San Marino for permission to test the right hemisperectomy boy and Drs. Philip J. Vogel and Joseph E. Bogen of Los Angeles for permission to test the left hemispherectomy girl. Also I want to thank Dr. J. Bogen for his helpful advice in preparation of this manuscript.

Milner, B., and Taylor, L.: Right-hemisphere superiority in tactile pattern-recognition after cerebral commissurotomy: evidence for nonverbal memory. *Neuropsychologia, 10:* 1–15, 1972.

Nebes, R. D.: Superiority of the minor hemisphere in commissurotomized man for the perception of part-whole relations. *Cortex, 7:* 333–349, 1971.

Piercy, M., Hécaen, H., and de Ajuriaguerra, J.: Constructional apraxia associated with unilateral cerebral lesions. *Brain, 83:* 225–242, 1960.

Seashore, C. E., Lewis, D., and Saetveit, J. G.: Seashore measures of musical talents. New York, The Psychological Corporation, 1960.

Smith, A.: Speech and other functions after left (dominant) hemispherectomy. *J Neurol Neurosurg Psychiat, 29:* 467–471, 1966.

Smith, A.: Nondominant hemispherectomy. *Neurology* (Minneapolis), *19:* 442–445, 1969.

Wada, J., and Rasmussen, T.: Intracarotid injection of sodium amytal for the lateralization of cerebral speech dominance. *J Neurosurg, 17:* 266–282, 1960.

[CHAPTER VII]

OLFACTION AND CEREBRAL SEPARATION

Harold W. Gordon

THIS CHAPTER IS concerned with the role of the corpus callosum in interhemispheric transmission. Judging by its physical prominence, it is not surprising that historically the callosum has attracted the attention of neurophysiologists and clinicians who have speculated, experimented, and theorized on its function and significance. Not only is it by far the largest of all cerebral fiber systems, but it is also one of the few structures in the brain that is not doubled into its right and left symmetrical parts. In fact, its unique singularity has inspired some to speculate that the corpus callosum may be the seat of the soul (Lancisi, 1929; La Peyonie, 1929). Scientific endeavors to attach functional significance to the great cerebral commissure rested on both histological (anatomical) mappings and clinical observations. The latter were made without the aid of modern diagnostic techniques or electronic equipment, relying on observational notations and in particular indications of abnormal or unusual activity. The behavioral records of all those patients found at post-mortem to be callosum-damaged were compared and a list of consistent behaviors was compiled. These were sometimes characterized as the "callosal syndrome" (Alpers and Grant, 1931; Bristowe, 1884). Symptoms such as lethargy, inattention, stupidity, apraxia, and hemiparesis were all generally described as the typical manifestations of this disorder (Bruce, 1890; Ironside and Guttmacher, 1929; Ransom, 1895; Van Valkenberg, 1913). Hindsight tells us these classifications were inadequate; but even at that time they were tenuous because of the involvement of other cerebral structures that invariably accompanied the callosal lesions. No one could unequivocally say which deficits were the specific result of callosal injury alone, although with more modern testing techniques, reports have described an updated hemispheric deconnection syndrome (Kaplan *et al.*, 1961; Geschwind, 1964; Geschwind and Kaplan, 1962). However, even today, one cannot consistently define typical behavior of patients with a damaged callosum without taking

Grant Support: N.I.M.H. Grant MH 03372; U.S.P.H.S. Trainee Grant GM 02031.
I would like to thank Professor Sperry for his helpful criticism in preparation of this manuscript.

into account the potentiating effects of extra-callosal damage (Gordon, *et al.*, 1970; 1971; Sperry *et al.*, 1969).

The first experimental indications of the callosum's significance in behavior came during the era of conditioned reflex experiments (Bykov, 1924). After section of the corpus callosum, a conditioned response was established in an animal by unilaterally pairing a cutaneous stimulus to food; subsequent presentation of the conditioned stimulus to the other half of the body did not elicit the reflex habit. This contrasted with retention of the reflex habit after subsequent stimulus presentation in a similar experiment but when the callosum remained intact. Although details of the surgery and experimental technique are unclear, a present-day interpretation would be that one hemisphere had controlled the behavior while the other, surgically dissociated, hemisphere was only an ineffectual, puzzled observer.

Evidence that supported this division of communication between the hemispheres after callosal section came from two independent studies on human patients with a transection of the splenium for removal of a cyst in the third ventricle (Maspes, 1948; Trescher and Ford, 1937). The important observation on these patients was that verbal material could be seen but not read in the left visual field. The implication was that information arriving in the right hemisphere did not transfer to the left speech area, presumably as a direct result of surgical interruption to the splenial fibers.

A number of studies in the late 1930's and early 1940's of patients who had undergone partial and complete forebrain commissurotomy for relief of intractable epilepsy (Van Wagenen and Herren, 1940) presented the opposing view which then prevailed over the evidence of callosal cross-communication (Akelaitis, 1941a; 1941b; 1941c; 1942a; 1942b; 1943; 1944; 1944–45; Akelaitis *et al.*, 1942; 1943; Bridgman and Smith, 1945; Goldstein and Joynt, 1969; Parsons, 1940; 1943; Smith, 1951; 1952; Smith and Akelaitis, 1942). Repeated testing showed that these callosum-sectioned patients could read from both visual fields and recognize objects or letters in either hand. It was claimed on the basis of these studies that information crossed between the hemispheres in commissural systems other than the callosum, either in the forebrain or subcortically. The conclusion was reached that no definite symptoms were attributable to the callosum itself. The major criticism of these studies, as well as those supporting functional significance of the callosum, is that human patients have extracallosal damage of unknown extent and that this complicates the observed symptoms and qualifies any conclusions derived from them.

A series of animal studies were started by Myers, a student in

Sperry's laboratory, in the early 1950's—about a decade after the initial human reports were being published. The experiments were on the visual system and the idea was to cut the corpus callosum in otherwise normal, brain-intact cats in order to see what effects division of this structure would have on the central visual pathways (Myers, 1955a; 1955b; 1956; 1961). Since visual stimuli can be channeled initially to one hemisphere in animals by also cutting the optic chisma and permitting vision through only one eye, it was Professor Sperry's plan to interrupt interhemispheric flow of visual information by cutting cross-connecting fibers as they emerged from the visual area in one hemisphere and passed through the callosum on their way to connect to the visual area of the opposite hemisphere. Accordingly, the corpus callosum and optic chiasma was divided and one eye was used to learn a visual discrimination task. The resultant failure to correctly perform the learned task by the previously occluded eye confirmed the hypothesis that cross-communication of information from visual stimuli was interrupted after callosal section. It might be said that the divided callosal pathways caused the memory engrams to be laid down in only one cerebral hemisphere and therefore be inaccessible to the opposite (untrained) eye. The result is that the brain-half connected to the trained eye can perform the discrimination task and the other cannot. In contrast, if the callosum had not been sectioned, a task learned through one eye can be performed through the other, even with chiasma section. Later experiments reinforced these findings (Bremer *et al.*, 1956; Bremer and Stoupel, 1956; Hamilton and Gazzaniga, 1964; Hamilton *et al.*, 1968; Sperry *et al.*, 1956; Trevarthen, 1962) and, except for the anterior commissure, localized the critical area for most visual cross-communication within the posterior-most portions of the corpus callosum (Black and Myers, 1964; Myers, 1959).

Another series of studies was begun in Sperry's and other laboratories on tactual discrimination tasks (Ebner and Myers, 1962; Glickstein and Sperry, 1960a; 1960b; Kohn and Myers, 1968, Lee-Teng and Sperry, 1966; Myers and Henson, 1960; Stamm and Sperry, 1957). It was expected from the previous results for vision that division of the corpus callosum would restrict transmission of tactual information between hemispheres. As with vision, tactile stimulation on the right projects primarily to the left hemisphere and stimulation on the left projects to the right. Again, cutting the callosum prevents cross-over between the hemispheres and therefore prevents comparison of information arriving through the separated right-left routes. As a result, a tactual discrimination task acquired with one hand or foot is remembered and performed only by the contralateral hemisphere while the ipsilateral hemisphere remains naive. In many of the tactual transfer studies, one or two animals (and in one report all (Ettlinger and Morton, 1966)) were exceptions to the general picture. These complications included partial or complete transfer of tactual training from one hand to the other. The discrepancies have not been fully resolved but can possibly be explained by incomplete commissural surgery or by extracallosal lesions causing learning in one hemisphere through ipsilateral tactual systems.

The important role of the transcallosal pathways for interhemispheric communication of vision and touch was repeatedly demonstrated. Forebrain commissurotomy produced a general pattern of behavioral deficits which were directly attributable to the surgical disconnection (Bianki, 1958; Gazzaniga and Young, 1967; Schrier and Sperry, 1959; Sperry, 1961; 1964a). Briefly stated, interruption of cross-communication permits the cerebral hemispheres to function separately and independently for a number of cognitive abilities. Complex stimulus processing, learning and memory, and ideation in one hemisphere often appear to be disassociated from similar activities occurring in the other hemisphere.

Sperry recognized this basic principle of functional independence to be a vital tool for wide-ranged study into relationships and interdependencies among brain structures within a single hemisphere, not to mention the obvious potentialities for cross-hemispheric experimentation (Sperry, 1961; 1964a). For example, he implied that after brain bisection, experimental lesions or ablations to one or more structures in one hemisphere could be studied without the complications produced by deficits or dysfunctions that followed bilateral lesions which were made when the callosum remained intact. The bonus from unilateral lesions is that the non-experimental hemisphere is available as a normal control. The arrangement is particularly ideal because up to the moment of surgical separation, each hemisphere had had the same experiences, been to the same places, and aged for the same period of time.

Another research advantage of complete forebrain commissurotomy is that unilateral lesions can be far more extensive than those in bilateral surgeries without interrupting the gross behavior of the animal. Massive cortical removals leaving intact only small islands of grey matter become feasible as long as the second hemisphere is available to provide a general background of lower level activity for vital functions. Sperry pointed out that the desirable goals for this technique would be to corner modality-specific memory engrams in an isolated cortical area of one hemisphere and then to add back an amount of intact cortex in other animals in order to make functional comparisons. Coupled with the interhemispheric studies, these techniques provide a general system by which functional centers and interconnecting pathways can be demarcated throughout the brain (Ettlinger, 1959; Glickstein *et al.*, 1963; Mishkin,

1958; Myers and Sperry, 1958; Sperry, 1959; Sperry *et al.*, 1960; Voneida, 1963; Webster and Voneida, 1964).

The expansion of research to human subjects came as a result of a reinstatement of commissurotomy surgery for alleviation of intractable epilepsy.* Dr. Philip J. Vogel of Los Angeles, assisted by Dr. Joseph Bogen of the Ross-Loos Medical Group, divided in a single operation the entire corpus callosum and anterior commissure at the midline, leaving two surgically intact, but separated, cerebral hemispheres (Bogen *et al.*, 1965; 1969; Bogen and Vogel, 1962). This procedure was attempted only as a last resort to reduce the interhemispheric spread of epileptic seizure activity which could not otherwise be controlled by conventional medication. The overwhelming majority of these patients enjoyed a significant reduction in amount and severity of abnormal activity contributing to their spells. In a few of the best cases, virtually no seizures have appeared since surgery; many have returned to lead fairly normal lives. However, the operation is not a cure, but merely a technique by which abnormal brain activity might be lessened so as to be brought under better control by medication.

Behavioral deficits are not observed in these patients except under special laboratory conditions, where tests are designed to contrast experiences of one hemisphere with those of the other. In this way, lack of transfer can be demonstrated directly for any number of sensory input-motor output tasks involving not only different sense modalities but also contrasting qualities within one modality. Initial studies were carried out for vision and touch (Gazzaniga *et al.*, 1962; 1963; 1965; 1967; Levy and Sperry, 1970; Nebes and Sperry, 1971; Sperry, 1964b), which will be summarized briefly; then other modalities were tested (Milner *et al.*, 1968; Sparks and Geschwind, 1968) including olfaction (Gordon and Sperry, 1968, 1969) which will be presented in detail.

Integration of visual inputs from left and right fields was found to depend upon mediation of cortical impulses through the corpus callosum. The optic chiasma was not divided in human surgery cases; yet information from left and right visual fields could be separated under brief visual exposure conditions and then cross-projected to areas in opposing occipital cortices. The consequences of complete forebrain commissurotomy is a striking left-right visual dissociation manifested by inability of comparison and a complete lack of connection between the two fields. This is not to say patients report a "gap" in their visual experience but, on the contrary, each hemisphere tends to extrapolate and fill-in as if nothing

---

* The first partial and complete commissurotomy operations on human subjects for control of epilepsy were performed in the late 1930's and early 1940's (Van Wagenen and Herren, 1940). See page 138.

were missing from the opposite half-field (Trevarthen and Kinsbourne, In preparation). The deficit of dissociation marks the inability of brain-bisection patients to compare stimuli seen in the right field to stimuli viewed in their left. Surgical intervention has eliminated avenues of hemispheric cross-communication and therefore has lateralized the divided inputs from each visual half-field into the separated cerebral halves.

Tactual sensations from the left and right extremities are also separate and project contralaterally to the cortex. Stimulation arising from an object felt by the right hand is processed by the left hemisphere and conversely, stimulation from the left hand is processed by the right hemisphere. Cerebral separation implies a disconnection of these lateralized inputs and therefore gives rise to a dissociation of stereognosis between the two hands. For example, an unseen object that is palpated by the left hand, and then added to a group of similar objects, cannot be retrieved a moment later by the right hand, and vice versa. The failure is not due to poor recognition since correct selection can be made by the hand originally feeling the object. Instead, the deficit is an instance of disrupted cross-communication between the cerebral hemispheres.

Speech lateralization dramatically illustrates the phenomenon of left-right functional separation (Gazzaniga and Sperry, 1967a; Sperry and Gazzaniga, 1966). While all patients readily name or describe objects felt in their right hand, they consistently fail to identify, and often disclaim similar objects in their left hand. Speech centers provide expression of cognitive functioning in the left hemisphere, but seem to have no direct access to right hemisphere activity. Instead, patients who lack connections to the left hemisphere must nonverbally disseminate information by pointing, gesturing, touching, or drawing. In other words, the right hemisphere is capable of reasoning, thinking, and solving problems, but must find some means, other than verbalization, to express itself.

The principle of "right hemisphere-silent, left hemisphere-articulate" is essential for studying laterality, separation, and sensory cognition in patients with separated cerebral hemispheres. When these patients can speak about test stimuli, their left hemispheres have been informed; when they cannot speak, but can demonstrate recognition by nonverbal methods, their right hemispheres have been informed. Using these phenomena as tools, cerebral organization for different stimuli and indifferent sense modalities can be investigated.

After vision and touch, it was of interest to know whether other modalities might be separately organized in these commissurotomy patients. Accordingly, olfaction was tested since it was expected that olfactognosis (odor recognition) would, in fact, be divided because decussating olfactory fibers were severed by forebrain commissurotomy and the remaining olfacto-cortical connections were not known to cross the midline. The following discussion is an illustration of the test program for the olfactory sense which generally describes typical experimental procedures that are followed in most behavioral testing for other sense modalities in these cerebrum-sectioned patients.

Olfactory receptor neurons are contained in the epithelial membrane lining the superior-most portion of each nasal cavity. These give rise to axons that pass dorsally without crossing through the cribiform plate to synapse with cells in the overlying olfactory bulb. Secondary neurons project via the olfactory tract to ipsilateral frontal and temporal lobes. Normally, midline crossing occurs at the level of the anterior commissure which had been severed, along with the corpus callosum, in cerebrum-sectioned patients. In keeping with visual and tactual experiments, it would be expected that odoriferous stimuli recognized through one nostril could not be compared or remembered when presented to the other nostril. More dramatically, the effect of speech lateralization should demonstrate correct naming of odors presented to one nostril, but only random guessing for those in the other. In short, olfaction is likely to be added to the list of senses divided by forebrain commissurotomy.

The main study was completed on five patients who underwent complete section of the corpus callosum and anterior commissure for alleviation of intractible epilepsy. At least two and as many as twelve experimental sessions were held for each subject. The apparatus and task requirements were kept simple to provide comfort and convenience for the patients and at the same time reduce complex interpretive confusion for the examiner. A series of five or six distinctive odors plus water were pre-arranged on a pseudo-random schedule and presented one at a time to either the left or right nostril. Familiar odors were selected from extracts, juices, lotions, and oils together with essences of tobacco, coffee, garlic, and fish. Each odoriferous substance was contained in a uniform glass vial—0.5 inch in diameter and 2.0 inches high—with a plastic screw cap. For each presentation, a finger or special plastic spatula was used to pinch shut one nostril, while the examiner uncapped the vial and held it just below the nostril to be stimulated. The patient sniffed once gently after which the vial was quickly removed and recapped, leaving the non-stimuated nostril closed until a response was made. Neither correct nor incorrect answers were reinforced, but the examiner said "Thank you" after each response and offered an occasional reassurance to the patient that he was doing well. Weak odors were commonly used throughout to avoid peripheral cross-over in the post-nasal cavity, and a fan eliminated lingering vapors. Half-minute pauses between each trial reduced receptor accommodation, and rest periods every 10 to 20 trials helped to prevent fatigue. Each session commenced with a pre-test where odors were presented one at a time with both nostrils open. The purpose was to assess the physical state (e.g. nasal congestion, attentiveness) of the patient, and determine which odors could be most easily recognized and named. Odors consistently misidentified in preliminary screening were eliminated from the test battery. The rest were included in the main test and were expected to be named or sufficiently described to qualify as a correct response.

The results were clear-cut. Odors presented to the left nostril were correctly and confidently named, indicating information had projected to the left hemisphere. This is consistent with the hypothesis based on anatomical grounds that major pathways were bisected in these patients and that the remaining nostril-cortex projections were ipsilateral. Contrarily, stimuli in the right nostril were identified at a rate indistinguishable from chance guessing. In fact, some patients denied smelling any right nostril odors at all and concluded the test vials must have contained water.

Some patients express (i.e. their left hemispheres express) concern when they expect aromatic stimulation through the right nostril and perceive nothing—or, for that matter, feel no objects in the left hand or see none in the left field. In general, however, they report no irregularities in their day-to-day activities, and, with the exception of some instances of conflict (Sperry, 1964b; 1964c), their behavior appears normal. The strange asymmetrical experiences created by behavioral testing in the laboratory are accepted by the patient and simply explained away. For example, the patient might say, "I have congestion in my right nostril, today, so I can't smell anything," or "That picture was flashed too fast (in my left field) for me to see," and so forth. Nonverbal tests prove these statements to be rationalizations with which the left hemisphere feels compelled to respond.

None of the experiments on the commissurotomy patients is without its pitfalls. The experimenter must constantly be on guard to halt patients who inadvertently circumvent central pathways by subtle cross-cueing schemes. For example, two patients were able to name odors in the right nostril at a low, but significant, level indicating possible leakage through posterior nasal cavity. In this case, the method of presentation was modified by closing both nostrils after sniffing; vapor turbulence was reduced and prevented from spreading into the interconnecting nasal passages. As a result, naming from the right, but not the left, nostril fell towards chance levels. Had this or other control tests failed, the only explanations remaining would have been that there still existed cross-connecting olfactory fibers, or else that these patients had bilateral control of speech.

Problems of this sort constantly plague testing in other modalities and deserve brief mention. In tactual tests, abnormal size differences, sharp edges, apparent temperature differences, and sounds accidentally made during manipulation can all provide cues which lead to the identification of an object. Visual tests must contain controls for eye movements, and for careful positioning of gaze to be sure stimuli project to the intended visual field. Other problems include subliminal verbalization—whereby the left hemisphere silently lists objects of the test series or otherwise communicates with the right hemisphere by small lip or tongue movements. One patient, for example, can articulate letters placed in his left hand, but suspiciously takes longer to name X, Y, or Z than A, B, or C. Other cross-cueing schemes have been discovered in the same clever patient where the stimulated hemisphere purposefully seeks out and fixates on objects in the room to cue the other. For example, if a picture of a box has been flashed to the right hemisphere, the patient's eyes rove about until he sees some square shape or cubic object. As he stares, the left hemisphere picks up the cue and guesses "box." At first impression the right hemisphere seems to have acquired speech or perhaps contained some cross-connecting visual fibers, but instead it was only the clever teamwork of two halves of the disconnected brain. Often two examiners are used to test these patients—not unwittingly to even out the odds.

Since odors to the left nostril but not those to the right can be named, it was concluded that olfactory connections to the left hemisphere followed ipsilateral routes. It seems logical to expect complementary ipsilateral pathways to exist for the right nostril but more data are needed to demonstrate this point. Accordingly, a simple nonverbal test was designed to permit right hemisphere expression and determine whether there can be olfactory recognition from the right nostril.

A series of objects that might be easily associated with the test odors were lined up in free view of the patient. Pretrials assessed ability to recognize and reliably match these objects with appropriate odor stimuli. If there were confusions with odor-object pairing in these free association trials, the stimuli were excluded from the test series. Typical associations were lemon juice—plastic lemon, perfume—small perfume bottle, fish oil—carved fish, and so on. The series of odors, excluding water, was presented in vials just as in the previous naming test, but this time the patient was instructed to look at the associated objects in front of him, and then select his answer by pointing out the one that best represented the olfactory stimulus. While it is true that both hemispheres can see the response objects, only the right should have sufficient information to make correct selections.

The results clearly confirmed that aromatic stimuli could be recognized by pointing after presentation to the right nostril. This performance was shown by four of five patients indicating that failure of identification of odors in the right nostril was limited to trials that required verbal responses. Evidence was also seen that the left hemisphere was incognizant of the odors presented and therefore, the accuracy of the pointing responses was determined by correct identifications from the right hemisphere. For instance, on one occasion a patient was commended for pointing to a high percentage of correct odor-object combinations. The left hemisphere was not aware of this good performance and verbally expressed surprise since it had assumed the left-hand choices to have been random guesses and most likely incorrect. Undoubtedly, the right hemisphere silently thanked the examiner for his compliment.

In another instance, a stimulus vial containing fresh coffee grounds was presented to the patient's right nostril for which the correct association was a plastic coffee cup. Instead of simply pointing, however, the patient made two responses simultaneously. The left hemisphere momentarily "forgot" that the task had been changed to nonverbal pointing, and identified "water" as it had been accustomed in the previous naming test. Concurrently, the left hand (controlled by the right hemisphere) reached out and correctly picked up the coffee cup. The patient apologized for speaking but offered the excuse that previous instructions were to say "water" if a stimulus had no smell. When questioned further about picking up the coffee cup, the reply was that the left hand had been allowed to go where it wanted and that it sometimes "has a mind of its own."

One patient had failed to consistently pair objects with right nostril stimuli even though appropriate associations were made in pretrials. Severe right hemisphere damage was suspected from evidence of presurgical seizure history and post-operative motor deficits. Constant verbal complaints about a cold in the right nostril provided an excuse for refusal to conscientiously select associated objects. "How can I choose," the patient protested, "if my nose is so stuffed I can't smell anything?" However, there was no evidence of nasal congestion. It seems likely in this case that the left hemisphere exerted considerable influence in the selection of objects despite possible right hemisphere recognition. In one session, however, the patient appeared to be more cooperative and correctly selected a significant number of odor-object associations possibly indicating a relaxation of left hemisphere control. But in later trials on the same day, protestations increased as they had in other sessions and the usual random choice pattern was resumed. The brief indication that the right hemisphere recognized right nostril odors was encouraging but deficient olfactognostic abilities of the right hemisphere of this patient could not be ruled out.

If lateralization of olfactory input has been adequately established then it should be possible to corroborate the results by combining olfactory tasks with those in other lateralized sense modalities. In part, the bimodal nature of the pointing test has already implied success for such a study: an odor was presented in the right nostril for olfactory identification but had to be matched to an associated object perceived by vision. Information from the two modalities must have been pooled in the right hemisphere in order to have correctly coordinated an appropriate motor response.

The present study was administered using the same paradigm of bimodal association. Instead of vision, however, objects paired with olfactory stimuli were to be selected on the basis of tactual cues alone. Hypothetically, when stereognostic and olfactognostic information projected to the same hemisphere, right or left, the patient would be able to select the correct answer. Conversely, when sensory information from the two modalities projected separately to opposite hemispheres, the responses would not be expected to rise above a level attained by random guessing. For example, an odor presented to the right nostril is recognized by the right hemisphere, while an object found by the right hand is recognized in the left hemisphere; the two cannot be compared because of the divided commissures. But if the object was felt by the left hand instead, then both tactual and olfactory stimuli would have been projected to the right hemisphere and a successful comparison could have been made.

Odors were presented in vials held under one nostril as in previous tests where identification had been demonstrated by naming or pointing. After sniffing, patients were instructed to remain silent and select by touch alone one from a group of associated objects that best corresponded to the given odor. One hand was used for the first series of 10 to 20 trials followed by the other hand in a second series, thereby completing a session that included data from each of the four nostril-hand combinations.

The general results were consistent with previous predictions. Each of the two patients available for study significantly matched odors with associated objects as long as tacual and olfactory stimuli were both available to the same hemisphere (i.e. in the two contralateral nostril-hand combinations). In contrast, odor-object matches could not generally be made when each modality was projected to opposite hemispheres (i.e. in the two ipsilateral combinations). Convincingly, it was shown that either hemisphere, right or left, could successfully pool information by combining both sensory cues, supporting the general notion that cross-modal tasks can be performed within either hemisphere and without the need for expressive language ability.

Further scrutiny of olfactory-tactual data however, showed that the left hemisphere performance was about 25 percent superior to that of the right. That is, odor-object pairings were more often correct for the left nostril-right hand combination than for the right nostril-left hand. A superiority, though much less striking, was also seen for the left nostril naming versus right nostril pointing tasks. The source of these differences is unclear. One possibility is that the left hemisphere is more efficient at making cross-modal connections. In other words, the left hemisphere would be expected to compare stimuli from two or more modalities and therefore obtain a higher matching score than the right hemisphere. Data from the olfacto-tactual study seem to support this prediction but it would be of interest to compare with other studies on cross-modal matching for corroboration.

Another likely explanation for the left-right asymmetry is that receptors in the right nostril, or pathways in the right brain, are inefficient when compared to corresponding receptors or pathways of the left. A possible source for such asymmetrical deficiency in perception is brain damage sustained during surgical manipulation or from pathological causes. It must be noted, however, that the right hemisphere in these patients excels in performance of most perceptual tasks when the response is nonverbal in spite of possible extra-callosal damage. Therefore, if olfactory deficits observed in these studies are to be attributed to non-callosal pathology, they must be considered modality-specific.

A final possibility that cannot be ruled out is the predisposition of the left hemisphere to interfere with responses from the right. The reason for this stems largely from the left hemisphere's strong tendency for bi-lateral motor control, plus special advantages provided by its speech functions. In previous studies performance deficits generated similar conclusions that ipsilateral influence from the left hemisphere affected contralateral control from the right; interference in the reverse situation was minimal (Levy *et al.*, 1970; Sperry, 1965–69). Furthermore, it is not unreasonable to expect verbal capacity to provide significant advantages for the left hemisphere. For example, most laterality tasks are explained to the patients verbally, and although answers may not be vocalized, they are solicited by verbal requests, thus favoring responses from the speech hemisphere. In other words, when an examiner talks to a patient, he is mainly speaking to the left hemisphere even when he may be specifically testing for an answer from the right! It is only when a particular task caters to special abilities of the right hemisphere and when verbal elements are notably lacking that "dominant" interference can be decoupled (Bogen, 1969; Levy *et al.*, 1972; Levy-Agresti, 1968; Nebes, 1971; see also Chapters IX, X, XIII).

Another study was conducted on a patient who underwent partial cerebral separation for intractible epilepsy (Gordon *et al.*, 1970; 1971). Only the anterior two thirds of the corpus callosum plus the anterior commissure were divided leaving the splenium intact. The results provide a surprising modification to the conclusions regarding olfactory projections and right-left asymmetry reported in this chapter. The same tests of naming, pointing, and cross-modal matching were used but results were strikingly different than expected. In contrast to previous cases with complete surgical section, this patient retained the ability to name odors presented to his right nostril at a level significantly above chance guessing even though left hemisphere lateralization of speech was confirmed by pre-surgical administration of intracarotid amobarbital.* Furthermore, he could cross-match olfacto-tactual stimuli by successfully pairing odors with their associated objects for any of the nostril-hand combinations. This remarkable lack of disconnection symptomology for olfaction extended to other modalities as well. However, cross-transfer of visual and tactual information between the hemispheres can be attributed to fiber cross-projections from the occipito-parietal areas coursing through the intact splenium. On the contrary, olfactory fibers are known to cross the midline only in the anterior commissure which, according to the surgeons, is completely divided in this patient. One is forced to conclude that the nature of information that passes through the posterior one third of the corpus callosum either includes olfactory fibers *per se* or carries some abstracted version of additionally processed olfactory stimuli.

Notwithstanding the apparent paucity of disconnection symptoms in the partially commissurotomized patient, the same left-right asymmetry was seen in olfactory recognition as in patients with complete commissure section. As before, over 25 percent more odors were recognized in the left nostril. Scores were consistently better than those obtained from the right nostril in all tests of naming, pointing, and odor-subject pairing.

It is difficult to apply the same arguments to explain the olfactory

---

* This procedure acts like a "reversible hemispherectomy" whereby sodium amobarbital is injected directly into the carotid artery which anaesthetizes one hemisphere evidenced by flaccidity and non-responsiveness of the limbs on the contralateral side of the body. If speech is present in the injected hemisphere the patient stops talking for several minutes until the drug becomes dilute allowing the contralateral limbs to be moved purposefully; otherwise the patient continues talking throughout the test period and is able to repeat words and phrases or answer questions.

asymmetry in this patient as had been used for the complete commissurotomies because of the intact splenium. Brain damage may be a factor, but so may deficits in transcallosal communication. Deficient perceptions may be a factor, but so may interhemispheric interference. In the end, the presence of only a partial corpus callosum may have a detrimental influence rather than an accentuating one as indicated for audition (Gordon, 1971) or motor coordination (Preilowski, 1972).

The "correct" explanation is elusive and not forthcoming from the present data. Problems such as these are not uncommon in split-brain work. They are handled by constant re-evaluation of how the left hemisphere is working, how the right hemisphere is working, and how they both "talk" to each other across the midline.

REFERENCES

Akelaitis, A. J.: Psychobiological studies following section of the corpus callosum. A preliminary report. *Am J Psychiatry, 97:* 1147–57, 1941a.

Akelaitis, A. J.: Studies on the corpus callosum. VIII. The effects of partial and complete section of the corpus callosum on psychopathic epileptics. *Am J Psychiatry, 98:* 409–414, 1941b.

Akelaitis, A. J.: Studies on the corpus callosum. II. The higher visual functions in each homonymous field following complete section of the corpus callosum. *Arch Neurol Psychiatry, 45:* 788–796, 1941c.

Akelaitis, A. J.: Studies on the corpus callosum. V. Homonymous defects for color, object and letter recognition (homonymous hemiamblyopia) before and after section of the corpus callosum. *Arch Neurol Psychiatry, 48:* 108–118, 1942a.

Akelaitis, A. J.: Studies on the corpus callosum. VI. Orientation (temporal-spatial gnosis) following section of the corpus callosum. *Arch Neurol Psychiatry, 48:* 914–937, 1942b.

Akelaitis, A. J.: Studies on the corpus callosum. VII. Study of language functions (tactile and visual lexia and graphia) unilaterally following section of the corpus callosum. *J Neuropathol Exp Neurol, 2:* 226–262, 1943.

Akelaitis, A. J.: A study of gnosis, praxis and language following section of the corpus callosum and anterior commissure. *J Neurosurg, 1:* 94–102, 1944.

Akelaitis, A. J.: Studies on the corpus callosum. IV. Diagnostic dyspraxia in epileptics following partial and complete section of the corpus callosum. *Am J Psychiatry, 101:* 594–599, 1944–45.

Akelaitis, A. J., Risteen, W. A., Herren, R. Y., and Van Wagenen, W. P.: Studies on the corpus callosum. III. A contribution to the study of dyspraxia in epileptics following partial and complete section of the corpus callosum. *Arch Neurol Psychiatry, 47:* 971–1008, 1942.

Akelaitis, A. J., Risteen, W. A., and Van Wagenen, W. P.: Studies on the corpus callosum. IX. Relationship of the grasp reflex to section of the corpus callosum. *Arch Neurol Psychiatry, 49:* 820–825, 1943.

Alpers, B. J., and Grant, F. C.: The clinical syndromes of the corpus callosum. *Arch Neurol Psychiatry, 25:* 67–86, 1931.

Bianki, V. L.: Effect of partial section of the corpus callosum in dogs on the differentiation of visual, auditory, and cutaneous stimuli. *Sech Physiol J USSR, 44:* 660–666, 1958.

Black, P., and Myers, R. E.: Visual function of the forebrain commissures in the chimpanzee. *Science, 146:* 799–800, 1964.

Bogen, J. E.: The other side of the brain. I: Dysgraphia and dyscopia following cerebral commissurotomy. *Bull Los Angeles Neurol Soc, 34:* 73–105, 1969.

Bogen, J. E., Fisher, E. D., and Vogel, P. J.: Cerebral commissurotomy: A second case report. *JAMA, 194:* 1328–1329, 1965.

Bogen, J. E., Sperry, R. W., and Vogel, P. J.: Commissural sections and the propagation of seizures. In Jasper, H. H., Ward, A. A., and Pope, A. (Eds.): *Basic Mechanisms of the Epilepsies,* Boston, Little, Brown & Co., 1969.

Bogen, J. E., and Vogel, P. J.: Cerebral commissurotomy in man: Preliminary case report. *Bull Los Angeles Neurol Soc, 27:* 169–172, 1962.

Bremer, F., Buhane, J., and André-Balisaux, G.: Physiologie et pathologie du corps calleaux. *Schweiz Arch Neurol Neurochir Psychiat, 78:* 31–47, 1956.

Bremer, F., and Stoupel, N.: Transmission interhémisphérique des influx visuels par le corps calleux. *J Physiol, 48:* 411–444, 1956.

Bridgman, C. S., and Smith, K. U.: Bilateral neural integration in visual perception after section of the corpus callosum. *J Comp Neurol, 83:* 57–68, 1945.

Bristowe, J. S.: Cases of tumour of the corpus callosum. *Brain, 7:* 315–333, 1884.

Bruce, A.: On the absence of the corpus callosum in the human brain, with the description of a new case. *Brain, 12:* 171–190, 1890.

Bykov, K.: Versuche an Hunden mit Durchschneiden des Corpus Callosum. *Zbl ges Neurol Psychiat, 39:* 199, 1924.

Ebner, F. F., and Myers, R. E.: Corpus callosum and the interhemispheric transmission of tactual learning. *J Neurophysiol, 25:* 380–391, 1962.

Ettlinger, G.: Visual discrimination follows successive temporal ablation in monkeys. *Brain, 82:* 232–250, 1959.

Ettlinger, G., and Morton, H. B.: Tactile discrimination performance in the monkey: transfer of training between the hands after commissural section. *Cortex, 2:* 30–49, 1966.

Gazzaniga, M. S., Bogen, J. E., and Sperry, R. W.: Some functional effects of sectioning the cerebral commissures in man. *Proc Natl Acad Sci, 48:* 1765–1766, 1962.

Gazzaniga, M. S., Bogen, J. E., and Sperry, R. W.: Laterality effects in somesthesis following cerebral commissurotomy in man. *Neuropsychologia, 1:* 209–215, 1963.

Gazzaniga, M. S., Bogen, J. E., and Sperry, R. W.: Observations on visual perception after disconnection of the cerebral hemispheres in man. *Brain, 88:* 221–236, 1965.

Gazzaniga, M. S., Bogen, J. E., and Sperry, R. W.: Dyspraxia following division of the cerebral commissures. *Arch Neurol, 16:* 606–612, 1967.

Gazzaniga, M. S., and Sperry, R. W.: Language after section of the cerebral commissures. *Brain, 90:* 131–148, 1967.

Gazzaniga, M. S., and Young, E. D.: Effects of commissurotomy on the processing of increasing visual information. *Exp Brain Res, 3:* 368–371, 1967.

Geschwind, N.: Disconnexion syndromes in animals and man. *Brain, 88:* 237–294, and *88:* 585–644, 1965.

Geschwind, N., and Kaplan, E.: A human cerebral disconnection syndrome. A preliminary report. *Neurology, 12:* 675–685, 1962.

Glickstein, M., Arora, H. A., and Sperry, R. W.: Delayed response performance following optic tract section, unilateral frontal lesion and commissurotomy. *J Comp Physiol Psychol, 56:* 11–18, 1963.

Glickstein, M., and Sperry, R. W.: Intermanual transfer in split-brain monkeys after somatic cortical ablation. Paper at APA, 1960a.

Glickstein, M., and Sperry, R. W.: Intermanual somesthetic transfer in split-brain rhesus monkeys. *J Comp Physiol Psychol, 53:* 322–327, 1960b.

Goldstein, M. N., and Joynt, R. J.: Long-term follow-up of a callosal-sectioned patient. *Arch Neurol, 20:* 96–102, 1969.

Gordon, H. W.: Functional deficits following partial surgical section of the forebrain commissures in man as determined by an auditory test. *Proc 79th Annual Convention of the Am Psychol Assoc* (Div. 6) *6*(2): 793, 1971.

Gordon, H. W., Bogen, J. E., and Sperry, R. W.: Tests for hemispheric deconnection symptoms following partial section of the corpus callosum in man. *Anat Rec, 166*(2): 308, 1970.

Gordon, H. W., Bogen, J. E., and Sperry, R. W.: Absence of deconnexion syndrome in two patients with partial section of the neocommissures. *Brain, 94:* 327–336, 1971.

Gordon, H. W., and Sperry, R. W.: Olfaction following surgical disconnection of hemispheres in man. Paper presented at 9th Annual Psychonomic Society Meeting, St. Louis, 1968.

Gordon, H. W., and Sperry, R. W.: Lateralization of olfactory perception in the surgically separated hemispheres of man. *Neuropsychologia, 7:* 111–120, 1969.

Hamilton, C. R., and Gazzaniga, M. S.: Lateralization of learning of color brightness discriminations following brain bisection. *Nature, 201:* 220, 1964.

Hamilton, C. R., Hillyard, S. A., and Sperry, R. W.: Interhemispheric comparison of color in split-brain monkeys. *Exp Neurol, 21:* 486–494, 1968.

Ironside, R., and Guttmacher, M.: The corpus callosum and its tumours. *Brain, 52:* 442–483, 1929.

Kaplan, E., Geschwind, N., and Goodglass, H.: A human split-brain syndrome. *Proc Ann V A Med Res Conf, 12:* 38, 1961.

Kohn, B., and Myers, R. E.: Visual information and intermanual transfer of latch-box problem solving in monkeys with commissures sectioned. *Exp Neurol, 23:* 303–309, 1968.

Lancisi, cited by Ironside and Guttmacher: De Sede Cogitantis Animae. The corpus callosum and its tumours. *Brain, 52:* 442–483, 1929.

La Peyronie, cited by Ironside and Guttmacher: The corpus callosum and its tumours. *Brain, 52:* 442–483, 1929.

Lee-Teng, E., and Sperry, R. W.: Intermanual stereognostic size discrimination in split-brain monkeys. *J Comp Physiol Psychol, 62:* 84–89, 1966.

Levy, J., Nebes, R. D., and Sperry, R. W.: Expressive language in the surgically separated minor hemisphere. *Cortex, 7:* 49–58, 1970.

Levy, J., and Sperry, R. W.: Crossed temperature discrimination following section of forebrain neocortical commissures. *Cortex, 6:* 349–361, 1970.

Levy, J., Trevarthen, C., and Sperry, R. W.: Perception of bilateral chimeric figures following hemispheric deconnexion. *Brain, 95:* 61–78, 1972.

Levy-Agresti, J.: Ipsilateral projection systems and minor hemisphere function in man after neocommissurotomy. *Anat Rec, 160:* 384, 1968.

Maspes, P. E.: Le syndrome expérimental chez l'homme le la section du splénium du corps calleux. Alexie visuelle pure hémianopique, *Revue neurol, 80:* 100–113, 1948.

Milner, B., Taylor, L., and Sperry, R. W.: Lateralized suppression of dichotically presented digits after commissural section in man. *Science, 161:* 184–186, 1968.

Mishkin, M.: Visual discrimination impairment after cutting cortical connections between the inferotemporal and striate areas in monkey. *Am Psychol, 13:* 414, 1958.

Myers, R. E.: *Anatomical, physiological, and psychological aspects of interocular transfer of pattern discrimination in cats after elimination of the crossed optic fibers.* Ph.D. Thesis, U. of Chicago, 1955a.

Myers, R. E.: Neural basis of bilateral perceptual integration. *Science, 122:* 877, 1955b.

Myers, R. E.: Function of corpus callosum in interocular transfer. *Brain, 79:* 358–363, 1956.

Myers, R. E.: Localization of function in the corpus callosum. *Arch Neurol, 1:* 88, 1959.

Myers, R. E.: Corpus callosum and visual gnosis. In Delafresnaye, J. F. (Ed.): *Brain Mechanisms and Learning.* Springfield, Thomas, 1961, pp. 481–505.

Myers, R. E., and Henson, C. O.: Role of corpus callosum in transfer of tactuo-kinesthetic learning in chimpanzee. *Arch Neurol (Chicago), 3:* 404–409, 1960.

Myers, R. E., and Sperry, R. W.: Interhemispheric communication through the corpus callosum. *Arch Neurol Psychiatry, 80:* 298–303, 1958.

Nebes, R. D.: Superiority of the minor hemisphere in commissurotomized man for the perception of part-whole relations. *Cortex, 7:* 333–349, 1971.

Nebes, R. D., and Sperry, R. W.: Hemispheric deconnection syndrome with cerebral birth injury in the dominant arm area. *Neuropsychologia, 9:* 247–259, 1971.

Parsons, F. H.: Psychological tests of patients one year after section of corpus callosum. *Psychol Bull, 37:* 498, 1940.

Parsons, F. H.: Eight cases of section of corpus callosum in individuals with a history of epileptic seizures: Psychological tests. *J Gen Psychol, 29:* 227–241, 1943.

Preilowski, B. F. B.: Possible contribution of the anterior forebrain commissures to bilateral motor coordination. *Neuropsychologia, 10:* 267–277, 1972.

Ransom, W. B.: On tumours of the corpus callosum. *Brain, 18:* 531–550, 1895.

Schrier, A. M., and Sperry, R. W.: Visual-motor integration in split-brain cats. *Science, 129:* 1275–1276, 1959.

Smith, K. U.: Learning and the associative pathways of the human cerebral cortex. *Science, 114:* 117–120, 1951.

Smith, K. U.: Experimental analysis of the associative mechanism of the human brain in learning functions. *J Comp Physiol Psychol, 45:* 66–72, 1952.

Smith, K. U., and Akelaitis, A. J.: Studies on the corpus callosum. I. Laterality in behavior and bilateral motor organization in man before and after section of the corpus callosum. *Arch Neurol Psychiatry, 47:* 519–543, 1942.

Sparks, R., and Geschwind, N.: Dichotic listening in man after section of neo-cortical commissures. *Cortex, 4:* 3–16, 1968.

Sperry, R. W.: Preservation of high order function in isolated somatic cortex in callosum-sectioned cats. *J Neurophysiol, 22:* 78–87, 1959.

Sperry, R. W.: Cerebral organization and behavior. *Science, 133:* 1749–1757, 1961.

Sperry, R. W.: The great cerebral commissure. *Sci Am, 210*(1): 42–52, 1964a.

Sperry, R. W.: Brain bisection and mechanisms of consciousness. In Eccles, J. C. (Ed.): *Brain and Conscious Experience.* New York, Springer-Verlag, 1964b.

Sperry, R. W.: Problems outstanding in the evolution of brain function. *James Arthur Lecture on the Evolution of the Human Brain,* New York, The American Museum of Natural History, 1964c.

Sperry, R. W.: Mental unity following surgical disconnection of cerebral hemispheres. *The Harvey Lectures, Series 62.* New York, 1965–1969.

Sperry, R. W., and Gazzaniga, M. S.: Language following surgical disconnection of the hemispheres. In Darley, F. L. (Ed): *Brain Mechanisms Underlying Speech and Language.* New York, Grune and Stratton, 1966.

Sperry, R. W., Gazzaniga, M. S., and Bogen, J. E.: Role of the neocortical commissures. In Vinken, P. J., and Bruyn, G. W. (Eds.): *Handbook of Clinical Neurology, Vol. IV.* Amsterdam, North Holland Publ., 1969.

Sperry, R. W., Myers, R. E., and Schrier, A. M.: Perceptual capacity of the isolated visual cortex in the cat. *Q J Exp Psychol, 12:* 65–71, 1960.

Sperry, R. W., Stamm, J. S., and Miner, N.: Relearning tests for interocular transfer following division of optic chiasm and corpus callosum in cats. *J Comp Physiol Psychol, 49:* 529–533, 1956.

Stamm, J. S., and Sperry, R. W.: Function of corpus callosum in contralateral transfer of somesthetic discrimination in cats. *J Comp Physiol Psychol, 50:* 138–143, 1957.

Trescher, J. H., and Ford, F. R.: Colloid cyst of the third ventricle. *Arch Neurol Psychiatry, Chicago, 37:* 959–973, 1937.

Trevarthen, C. B.: Double visual learning in split-brain monkeys. *Science, 136:* 258–259, 1962.

Trevarthen, C. B., and Kinsbourne, M.: Perceptual completion of words and figures by commissurotomy patients. In preparation, 1974.

Van Valkenberg, G. T.: Experimental and pathologico-anatomical researches on the corpus callosum. *Brain, 36:* 119–165, 1913.

Van Wagenen, W. P., and Herren, R. Y.: Surgical division of commissural pathways in the corpus callosum. Relation to spread of an epileptic attack. *Arch Neurol Psychiatry, 44:* 740–759, 1940.

Voneida, T. J.: Performance of a visual conditioned response in split-brain cats. *Exp Neurol, 8:* 493–504, 1963.

Webster, D. B., and Voneida, T. J.: Learning deficits following hippocampal lesions in split-brain cats. *Exp Neurol, 10:* 170–182, 1964.

[CHAPTER VIII]

DOMINANCE OF THE MINOR HEMISPHERE IN COMMISSUROTOMIZED MAN FOR THE PERCEPTION OF PART-WHOLE RELATIONSHIPS

Robert D. Nebes

THE ASYMMETRIC REPRESENTATION in man's right and left hemispheres of certain higher cognitive functions has been known for one hundred years. During this time the dominance of the left hemisphere for verbal skills has been decisively demonstrated, both for the expression of language and for the perception of language related stimuli, such as meaningful sounds (Faglioni, Spinnler, and Vignolo, 1970), letters (Faglioni, Scotti and Spinnler, 1969), familiar objects (Kinsbourne and Warrington, 1962) and colors (Kinsbourne and Warrington, 1964). The functional specialization of the right hemisphere, however, has only recently begun to be investigated. Minor hemisphere damage has been associated with deficits on tasks involving: visual-spatial relations (Newcombe and Russell, 1969), nonsense shapes (Kimura, 1966), faces (deRenzi, Faglioni, and Spinnler, 1968) and melodies (Milner, 1962).

Several attempts have been made to classify the psychological properties common to stimulus materials, the perception of which is more affected by damage to one hemisphere than by damage to the other. The left hemisphere has been postulated to best handle those stimuli which are verbal, verbalizable (Lansdell, 1968) or familiar (Kimura, 1963), while the right is more concerned with stimuli which, due to their novelty or visual complexity, cannot be easily given verbal labels (Kimura, 1966; deRenzi, 1968).

Other investigators have proposed that, underlying the differing cognitive deficits found after unilateral brain damage, there is a basic dichotomy in the two hemispheres' methods of processing sensory information. They have used varying terms to describe the different perceptual organizations in the left and right hemispheres, such as: symbolic vs. visual-spatial (Zangwill, 1961), analytic vs. gestalt (Levy-Agresti and Sperry, 1968), associational vs. apperceptive (deRenzi, Scotti, and Spinnler, 1969) and propositional vs. appositional (Bogen, 1969). The concepts of hemispheric action implied by these terms, however, are very similar, in that they all assign to the major hemisphere the tasks of sequentially analyzing sensory input, abstracting out the relevant details, and attaching verbal labels, while the right hemisphere attends to the overall configuration of the stimulus situation, synthesizing the fragmentary chunks of perceptual data received from sampling of the sensory surround into a meaningful percept of the environment. The right hemisphere is thus viewed as giving spatial context to the detailed analysis carried out by the major hemisphere.

In order to test this theory of minor hemispheric function, three experiments were carried out on human commissurotomy patients, comparing the abilities of the right and left hemispheres to perceive the relationship between the part or parts of a stimulus and the whole. The subjects were seven right-handed epileptics who, in order to relieve intractable seizures, had undergone a complete surgical division of the corpus callosum, anterior and hippocampal commissures (Bogen and Vogel, 1962; Bogen, Fisher and Vogel, 1965). Previous studies on these patients had demonstrated that, postoperatively, higher-level functions in each hemisphere proceeded fairly independently of activity in the other hemisphere (Sperry, Gazzaniga, and Bogen, 1969). The right hemisphere thus recognized visual stimuli only if they fell in the left visual half-field (Gazzaniga, Bogen and Sperry, 1965) and somesthetic stimuli only if they contacted the left side of the body (Gazzaniga, Bogen and Sperry, 1963). This separation of the subjects' peripheral sensory world allowed independent testing of the two hemispheres, either by restricting tactile input to one hand, or by restricting visual input to one half-field. Thus, by comparing the subject's accuracy on somesthetic tasks with his right and left hands, or on visual tasks in the right and left visual fields, it was possible to determine directly the relative abilities of the left and right hemispheres in a single individual on exactly the same test.

The first experiment (Nebes, 1971) attempted to reduce the part-whole operation to its most basic level by asking the subjects to judge from visual or somesthetic examination of an arc, the size of complete circle from which it had come. Since the stimuli were all arcs or circles, complicating variables such as stimulus novelty, complexity and verbalizability were reduced to a minimum. The stimuli were made from three sizes of Plexiglas® ring: 1½, 1¼ and 1 inch in inner diameter. For each size there was a set consisting of a complete ring and four arcs: 280°, 180°, 120° and 80°.

Three different procedures were used to administer these stimuli. In the first, Somesthetic-Visual (Figure VIII-1a), the subject placed either his right or left hand beneath a screen and haptically examined one of

b.

c.

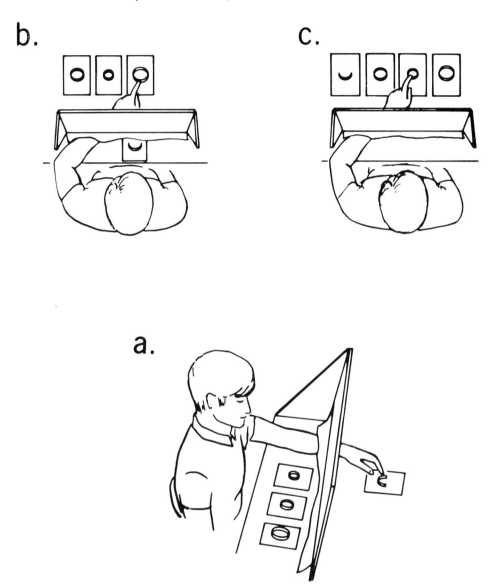

a.

Figure VIII-1. Experimental test procedures: a) Somesthetic-visual; b) Visual-somesthetic; c) Somesthetic-somesthetic.

the arcs with his index finger, while simultaneously viewing three sizes of complete circle. When he had decided from which of these circles the segment he was feeling had come, he withdrew his hand and pointed to it. In the second procedure, Visual-Somesthetic (Figure VIII-1b), the arc was presented visually while the subject tactually explored the three circles behind the screen, tapping his choice. In the third procedure, Somesthetic-Somesthetic (Figure VIII-1c), both the arc and the circles were hidden from view, making it an intramodal matching task.

Two control tests were also run to determine each patient's ability to match under these same three conditions, circles of different size and arcs of different curvature. In the Circle Matching control, for example, using the first procedure the subject would feel a complete circle behind the screen and then have to pick it out visually from among the three complete circles before him. The arcs in the Arc Matching control were all of the same length, but since they had been cut from three different sized circles, they differed in their rate of curvature. These two control tests thus measured the patient's ability to match wholes to wholes or parts to parts, as contrasted to the experimental task of matching a part to a whole.

The results (Figure VIII-2) show that four of the five patients performed significantly better with their left hand than with their right on all three forms of the test. Very few trials, 36 or less, were necessary to establish this left hand superiority. In the first and third procedures the right hand scores of the four subjects were all at the chance level. On the control tasks, where circles were matched to circles or arcs to arcs, the two hands were equally proficient.

Only L. B. differed from this general picture of left hand superiority. However, he was also the only patient capable of blindly cross matching the test stimuli between his two hands. It thus appears that in L. B. somesthetic information from each hand was not restricted to the contralateral hemisphere, and thus the scores attained by his right and left hands do not represent a truly independent expression of each hemisphere's capacity for the task. In the other patients the demonstrated left hand advantage can be safely attributed to a superiority on the part of the right hemisphere for this problem. The part-whole nature of the task is obviously the vital factor differentiating the performances of the two hemispheres, as the left hemisphere was not inferior to the right on the control tasks, which except for the fact that like stimuli were being matched, was identical to the experimental test. Thus the right hemisphere excels the left in choosing a complete stimulus from examination of a piece.

The stimuli used in the second experiment (Nebes, 1972) were more complex than those in the first, for, instead of consisting of only a piece of the contour, the whole structure was present, but in a fragmented condition. Here, the subject had to perceive the relationship of the pieces of the stimulus to the overall configuration. The visual stimuli were twenty line drawings, each depicting a geometric shape

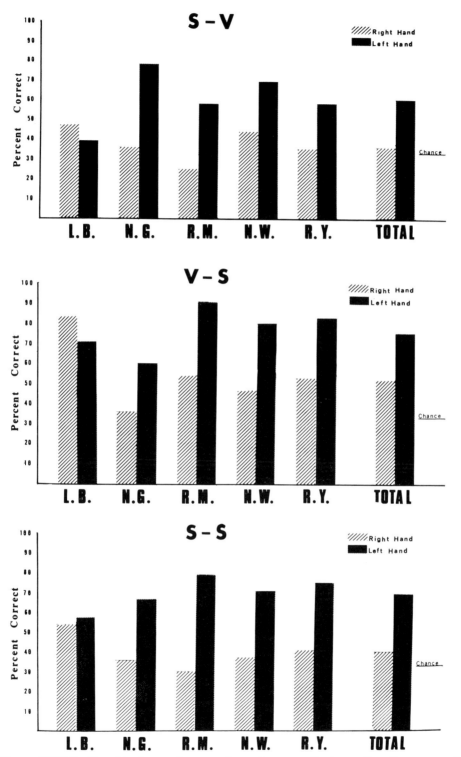

Figure VIII-2. Results for each commissurotomy patient on the three experimental forms of the arc-circle matching test.

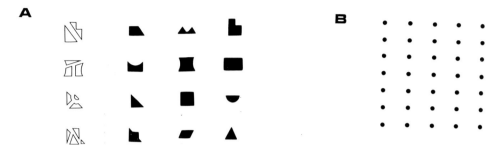

Figure VIII-3. Examples of items in the figural unification test; b) Example of stimulus in the dot pattern test.

that had been cut up and the pieces drawn apart, maintaining, however, their original orientations and relative positions (Figure VIII-3a). The subject was presented with one of these figures in free view while he simultaneously explored with his right or left hand three solid shapes hidden behind a screen. When he had decided which of the somesthetic shapes the fragmented figure would form if the pieces were reunited, he tapped it. The subject was also given a control test using the same procedures and somesthetic stimuli as the experimental task, but having for visual cues complete geometric shapes. Here all that was required was a straight visual-tactual match of stimulus contours.

The results of the experimental test (Figure VIII-4) show six of the seven patients to be far more accurate with their left hand than with their right. The average score for the left hand was 16.9 of 20 correct, while for the right it was only 9. None of the subjects except L. B. scored above chance with their right hand. Just how poorly the right hands performed can be seen by comparing them to five laboratory technicians, all of whom had perfect scores with both hands. The task was thus fairly simple for normals and for the left hands of commissurotomy patients, but was exceedingly difficult for their right hands. On the control test using nonfragmented visual stimuli, the commissurotomy patients did equally well with either hand, the left hand averaging 19.1 of 20 correct, the right 18.6. This demonstrated that it was not the tactile discrimination or the intermodal nature of the task which caused the right hand-left hemisphere system to fail on the experimental task, but rather the necessity for perceiving the total configuration constituted by the spatially separated pieces.

The third study (Nebes, 1973) involved a part-whole phenomenon investigated by the Gestalt psychologists in the early part of this century (Wertheimer, 1958). They showed that, although the elements of an array can be grouped in many different ways, certain arrangements tend to dominate our perception due to several factors which act to organize

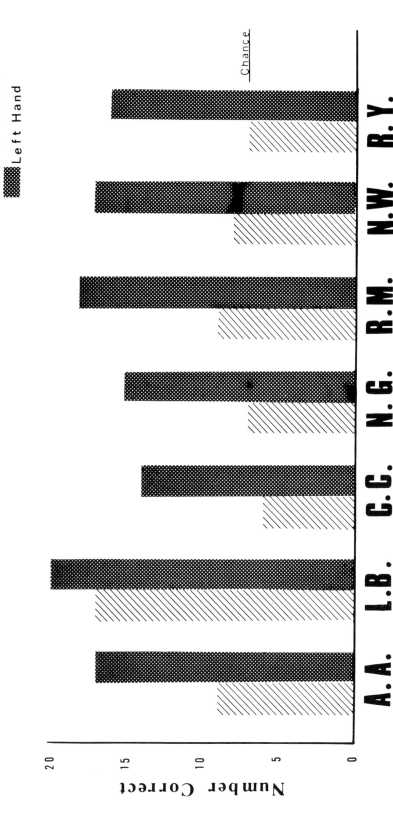

Figure VIII-4. Results for the right and left hands of the commissurotomy patients on the figural unification test.

the field. One of the strongest of these factors is proximity; the closer the spacing between items, the more likely it is that they will be seen as belonging together, forming an aggregate. This is illustrated in Figure VIII-3b, which shows a square array of dots arranged such that the points along one dimension are more closely spaced than along the other. People tend to see such an array as being composed of lines of dots running parallel to the axis with greater concentration of points. They thus impose an organization upon the field, perceiving a pattern due to the relationship of the elements.

In order to test the competence of the right and left hemispheres on this type of part-whole perception, a series of dot arrays were constructed. In half of these, the proximity relationships were such that the dots lines appeared to run horizontally, while in the others they appeared to run vertically. The patient was told to signal the slope of the lines by raising his index finger if it was vertical and not moving if it was horizontal. The subject sat before a translucent projection screen upon which the stimuli were rear projected. Before each trial he fixated a central dot; the stimulus was then flashed for 1/50th of a second either to the right or to the left of the fixation point. The orientation of the lines in the array and the alternation between the two half-fields were varied in a predetermined random order. Each subject was given 320 trials, with the two hands taking turns signalling for blocks of 40 trials. The test was given originally to five commissurotomy patients. Two of these, however, failed to score above the chance level in either field, and thus only the three patients who had had a great deal of previous tachistoscopic experience were used in this study.

The results (Table VIII-I) show that, regardless of which hand was used to signal, all three patients made significantly fewer errors on those arrays presented in the left visual field (LVF) than on those presented in the right (RVF); thus, it was the stimuli projecting to the minor hemisphere which were most accurately perceived. It is especially interesting that on this task, L. B. showed a definite right hemisphere dominance, although on the previous two experiments there was apparently no difference in ability between his right and left hemispheres. This strongly suggests that L. B. differs from the other patients, not in

TABLE VIII-I
DOT PATTERN RESULTS

	LVF *Rt. Hand*	*LVF* *Left Hand*	*RVF* *Rt. Hand*	*RVF* *Left Hand*
Vertical Array	107/120	106/120	94/120	90/120
Horizontal Array	106/120	107/120	82/120	63/120
Total	213/240	213/240	176/240	153/240
		426/480		329/480

possessing hemispheres which are equipotential for the performance of part-whole tasks, but in possessing a bilateral tactual system which permits his right hemisphere to work through either hand. The use of visual stimuli in the present task thus allows this inherent superiority of his minor hemisphere to be exposed.

The three experiments reported here demonstrate that the minor hemisphere in man excels the major in the performance of at least one cognitive operation—generating from partial or fragmented information a percept of the whole stimulus. The ease with which the left hemisphere solved perceptual problems as long as they did not involve this part-whole aspect shows that it was not the type of stimulus material nor the mode of response which caused the differential performances on the part of the two hemispheres but rather, the mental manipulation required to see the whole in the part. This cognitive operation in many ways resembles the "speed of closure" factor identified by Thurston (1944) in his factor analysis of human perceptual abilities. He described it as the capacity to perceive an apparently disorganized and unrelated group of parts as a meaningful whole, to construct a total picture from incomplete or limited material. Thurstone believed this factor to be closely related to synthetic reasoning. Tests having a high loading on "closure speed" usually require the subject to identify line drawings of objects, most of the contours of which are missing. Performance on closure tests such as the Street Completion Test (deRenzi and Spinnler, 1966), the Gollin Figures (Warrington and James, 1967) and the Mooney Faces (Lansdell, 1968; Newcombe and Russell, 1969) have been shown to be severely affected by right hemispheric damage.

In man, therefore, it appears that the principal locus for this part-whole or closure type of process is the right hemisphere, a fact which is consistent with the previously stated models of hemispheric operation. The usefulness of such a perceptual ability is obvious, as it permits the formation of a concept of the structure and organization of the environment without the necessity of subjecting the entire sensory input to a detailed analysis; instead, predictions can be made from the partial data available, according to some innate or learned perceptual rules and transformations.

REFERENCES

Bogen, J. E.: The other side of the brain. *Bull Los Angeles Neurol Soc, 34:* 73–105, 1969.

Bogen, J. E., and Vogel, P. J.: Cerebral commissurotomy: a preliminary case report. *Bull Los Angeles Neurol Soc, 27:* 169–172, 1962.

Bogen, J. E., Fisher, E. D., and Vogel, P. J.: Cerebral commissurotomy a second case report. *JAMA, 194:* 1328–1329, 1965.

deRenzi, E.: Nonverbal memory and hemispheric side of lesion. *Neuropsychologia, 6:* 181–189, 1968.

deRenzi, E., and Spinnler, H.: Visual recognition in patients with unilateral cerebral disease. *J Nerv Ment Dis, 142:* 515–525, 1966.

deRenzi, E., Scotti, G., and Spinnler, H.: Perceptual and associative disorders of visual recognition. *Neurology, 19:* 634–642, 1969.

deRenzi, E., Faglioni, P., and Spinnler, H.: The performance of patients with unilateral brain damage on face recognition tasks. *Cortex, 4:* 17–34, 1968.

Faglioni, P., Scotti, G., and Spinnler, H.: Impaired recognition of written letters following unilateral hemisphere damage. *Cortex, 5:* 120–133, 1969.

Faglioni, P., Spinnler, H., and Vignolo, L. A.: Contrasting behavior of right and left hemisphere damaged patients on a discrimination and semantic task of auditory recognition. *Cortex, 5:* 366–398, 1970.

Gazzaniga, M. S., Bogen, J. E., and Sperry, R. W.: Laterality effects on somesthesis following cerebral commissurotomy in man. *Neuropsychologia, 1:* 209–215, 1963.

Gazzaniga, M. S., Bogen, J. E., and Sperry, R. W.: Observations on visual perception after disconnection of the cerebral hemispheres in man. *Brain, 88:* 221–236, 1965.

Kimura, D.: Right temporal lobe damage. *Arch Neurol, 8:* 264–271, 1963.

Kimura, D.: Dual functional asymmetry of the brain in visual perception. *Neuropsychologia, 4:* 275–285, 1966.

Kinsbourne, M. and Warrington, E. K.: A disorder of simultaneous form perception. *Brain, 85:* 461–486, 1962.

Kinsbourne, M. and Warrington, E. K.: Observations on colour agnosia. *J Neurol Neurosurg Psychiat, 27:* 296–299, 1964.

Lansdell, H.: Effect of extent of temporal lobe ablations on two lateralized deficits. *Physiol Behav, 3:* 271–273, 1968.

Levy, J.: Possible basis for the evolution of lateral specialization of the human brain. *Nature, 224:* 614–615, 1969.

Levy-Agresti, J., and Sperry, R. W.: Differential perceptual capacities in major and minor hemispheres. *Proc Nat Acad Sci, 61:* 1151, 1968.

Milner, B.: Laterality effects in audition. In Mountcastle, V. B. (Ed.): *Interhemispheric Relations and Cerebral Dominance.* Baltimore, Johns Hopkins Press, 1962.

Nebes, R. D.: Superiority of the minor hemisphere in commissurotomized man for the perception of part-whole relations. *Cortex, 7:* 333–349, 1971.

Nebes, R. D.: Dominance of the minor hemisphere in commissurotomized man on a test of figural unification. *Brain, 95:* 633–638, 1972.

Nebes, R. D.: Perception of spatial relationships by the right and left hemispheres of commissurotomized man. *Neuropsychologia, 11:* 285–289, 1973.

Newcombe, F., and Russell, W. R.: Dissociated visual perception and spatial deficits in focal lesions of the right hemisphere. *J Neurol Neurosurg Psychiatry, 32:* 73–81, 1969.

Sperry, R. W., Gazzaniga, M. S., and Bogen, J. E.: Interhemispheric relationships: the neocortical commissures; syndromes of their disconnection. In Vinken, P. J., and Bruyn, G. W. (Eds.). Amsterdam, North Holland Pub. Co., 1969, Vol. 4, pp. 273–290.

Thurstone, T. T.: A factorial study of perception. Chicago, U of Chicago Pr, 1944.

Warrington, E. K., and James, M.: Disorders of visual perception in patients with localized cerebral lesions. *Neuropsychologia, 5:* 253–266, 1967.

Wertheimer, M.: Principles of perceptual organization. In Beardslee, and Wertheimer, M. (Eds.): *Readings in Perception.* Princeton, Van-Rein, 1958.

Zangwill, O. L.: Asymmetry of Cerebral Function. In Garland, H. (Ed.): *Scientific Aspects of Neurology.* London, E. & S. Livingstone, 1961.

[CHAPTER IX]

CEREBRAL ASYMMETRIES AS MANIFESTED IN SPLIT-BRAIN MAN

Jerre Levy

B OGEN AND GAZZANIGA (1965) and Sperry and Gazzaniga (1966) have provided a picture of hemispheric function in the commissurotomy patient showing the left hemisphere to be verbally competent, but suffering from constructional dyspraxia, while the right hemisphere manifests the reverse.

Starting from this base of knowledge, one can ask, "Is the left hemisphere dyspraxic for construction tasks because of some lack in visuomotor control, or because such tasks require a cognitive ability that the left hemisphere lacks? If the latter, what is the lacking ability?" Of the right hemisphere we can ask, "Does the minor hemisphere suffer from expressive aphasia because it cannot wrest control of the linguistic expressive mechanisms from the left hemisphere, or is the right hemisphere simply incapable of thinking of words? If so, why?"

In trying to understand the reasons for the verbal deficit of the right hemisphere in the brain-divided patient, a number of tasks were devised, each requiring varying amounts of precision skills, each permitting varying amounts of possible interference from the left hemisphere (Levy, Nebes, and Sperry, 1971). Figure IX-1 shows the results of a letter arranging task. Here the hidden left hand was presented with plastic letters and the patient was told to arrange the letters so that they spelled a sensible word. In this case the patient spelled "kid," but then wrote "cat." At a level far beyond chance the left hand could perform such tasks although the patient could not name the spelled word, and often made wild guesses. Thus, in a task requiring little motor skill, the right hemisphere could not only independently think of a word, but one which corresponded to a given set of letters, a quite abstract task.

However, on a much less abstract task, merely writing the name of an object felt by the left hand, the right hemisphere did poorly. Figure IX-2 shows a patient's efforts after feeling a tobacco pipe with the left hand. Presumably under control of the contralateral hemisphere, the left hand, hidden from view, wrote "PI," but the correct word was not

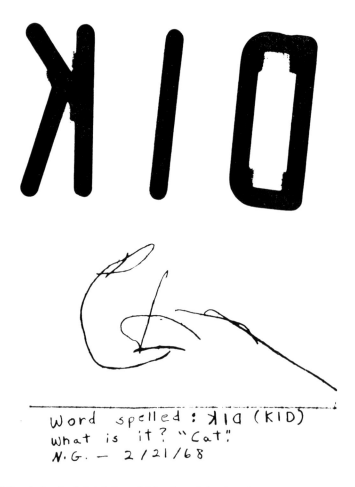

Figure IX-1. A typical trial in which the right hemisphere "spells" a word, but cannot then write it.

completed. On a less abstract task than the letter arrangement, but one requiring more motor skill and permitting the possibility of left hemisphere interference, the right hemisphere shows poor performance.

At first these results seem to suggest that the linguistic expressive difficulty of the right hemisphere is mainly due to lack of sufficient motor control, that the right hemisphere can think of words, but can't express them. Yet, note the drawing at the bottom of Figure IX-2. After changing "PI" into "pencil" and spontaneously scratching out the last four letters, the patient said, "I don't know what it was I felt." With his left hand still hidden, he was told to draw a picture of what he had felt. He rapidly and with no difficulty drew the sketch of a pipe.

Figure IX-2. A patient's attempt to communicate by writing and drawing the name and form of an object held in the left hand (a tobacco pipe) (Reprinted from *Cortex, 7:* 49–58, 1971).

Why should there be motor difficulty in printing the word "pipe," but none in drawing a picture of one? Nebes found with another commissurotomy patient that he could write nouns which had been projected to his right hemisphere, but not verbs (Levy, Nebes, and Sperry, 1971). Obviously motor control can neither account for the picture-word difference in the first patient, nor the noun-verb difference in the second, and it is not unreasonable to guess that the motor interference by the left hemisphere occurs as a secondary consequence of an intrinsic language disability of the right hemisphere. Thus, we can draw the tentative conclusion that the right hemisphere's expressive aphasia results, not from an incapacity to gain control of motor pathways, but rather from a lack of internal language. Studies examining this conclusion and a discussion of why such linguistic disability exists, if, in fact, it does, will be delayed for the moment while the left hemisphere's constructional dyspraxia is considered.

Once again the aim in studying hemisphere deficiencies was to separate lack of praxic skills from a possible underlying incapacity in cognitive processing mechanisms. A test was therefore devised which required a rather high-level ability to manipulate spatial relationships, but which only involved a rather simple motor response, namely pointing (Levy-Agresti and Sperry, 1968).

The test was a modified, cross-modal (tactual-visual) version of the Spatial Relations subtest of the Differential Aptitude Test Battery (Bennett, Seashore, and Wesman, 1947). Figure IX-3 shows two of thirteen items in the test. For each item 3 wooden blocks were constructed which differed slightly in shape or in relationship of parts. Correspondingly, the 3 blocks were drawn in opened-up form on a card. It was

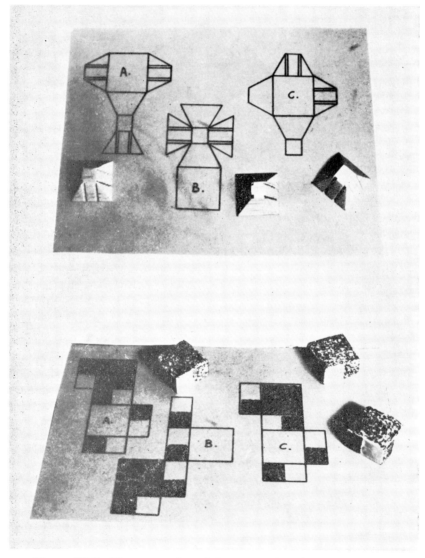

Figure IX-3. Two examples of items on the visualization test.

the subject's task to feel one of the 3 blocks with either his right or left hand hidden from sight and then to inspect the card with free vision and to choose the drawing which matched the block he was feeling. It was necessary to mentally fold the drawings and to choose the one which matched the tactually perceived block. At no time did subjects see the block, nor were they told whether their choices were correct or not. In this way each item could be presented many times with no learning taking place.

In all, six patients were tested on a preliminary, simplified version of the cross-modal test. Of these, three, all having right hemisphere damage, were totally unable to even grasp the idea of building a three-dimensional conception from two-dimensional drawings. The other three patients passed the preliminary test and were given the cross-modal test. The results were consistent for these three patients: their left hands were superior to their right hands. However, one patient, A.A., suffered a sensory deficit in his right hand, so that his results do not necessarily imply visuo-spatial superiority of the minor hemisphere. A second patient, N.W., although having right hemisphere damage, was still above the 1 out of 3 chance level with her left hand, but not so with her right, even though her right hand is far superior to her left on most tasks. L.B., having no known brain damage, was above chance with both hands, but vastly superior with his left hand and minor hemisphere.

In addition to the quantitative superiority of the left-hand, right-hemisphere, evidence was obtained which indicated a qualitative difference in the two hemispheres with respect to the strategies that were used to solve the problems. L.B.'s left and right hand scores on the 13 items were compared with each other and with N.W.'s left hand scores, as well as with scores of a nonoperated epileptic control. The rank correlation between the two hands was .60, showing only a minimally significant similarity. However, L.B.'s left hand scores and N.W.'s left hand scores correlated .75, and L.B.'s right hand scores and those of the control correlated .83. It thus appears that L.B.'s and N.W.'s minor hemispheres found the same items to be more similar in difficulty than did L.B.'s minor and major hemispheres. Again L.B.'s major hemisphere was more similar to the control subject than it was to its twin minor hemisphere.

These correlations imply that the right and left half-brains used different strategies in performing the test. On inspecting those items whose rank scores differentiated most clearly between the hemispheres, we found that the major hemisphere did best on items most susceptible to easy language description, that is, items whose properties could be easily analyzed, and that the minor hemisphere did best on items which yielded themselves to perceptual-spatial differentiation. Figure IX-4 shows the two items for which the performance of the two hemispheres showed the greatest divergence. In terms of perceptual visualization, the drawings on item 2 are much easier to differentiate than those on item 7. The drawings on item 2 represent three quite distinct objects, while those on item 7 represent three cubes which differ only in the number

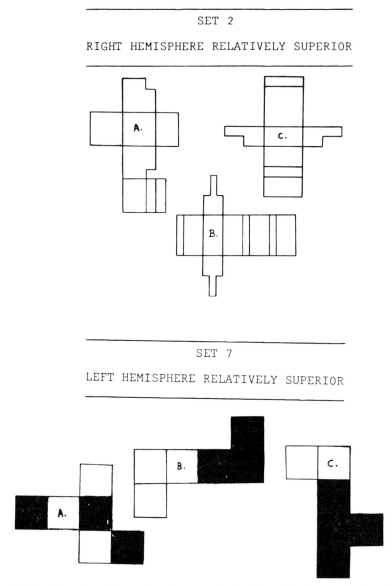

SET 2

RIGHT HEMISPHERE RELATIVELY SUPERIOR

SET 7

LEFT HEMISPHERE RELATIVELY SUPERIOR

Figure IX-4. The two items showing greatest disparity in rank for left and right hands.

or in relationship of rough surfaces. In terms of verbal description, on the other hand, it is much easier to differentiate the three blocks represented in item 7 than those in item 2.

These results support the notion that the major hemisphere's deficiencies on perceptual-motor tasks result from cognitive incapacities. Further, there is a strong suggestion in these observations that the major hemisphere's performance is not only quantitatively inferior to that of the minor hemisphere, but is also qualitatively different.

Confronted with two hemispheres, each possessing its own set of special properties and lacking just those properties possessed by the other, one gets the suspicion that to ask why the minor hemisphere is mute or why the major hemisphere suffers certain disabilities in visualization, may be similar to asking why a girl isn't a boy and vice-versa. It may simply be that the abilities and deficiencies of a given hemisphere, *of necessity*, stand in reciprocal relation. Whatever provides the possibility for one function excludes the possibility of another. If true, then the adaptive advantage of lateral specialization in an animal with language is immediately obivous.

There are two avenues of investigation open to examine the above ideas. A functional reciprocity between the skills and shortcomings of a hemisphere will be confirmed if, given a sufficiently refined description of a hemispheric capacities, it can be shown that the existence of a given set of properties logically implies the absence of another set of properties. Alternatively, if people with incompletely lateralized hemispheres are found to have a significantly greater difference in their abilities to perform the two kinds of tasks normally associated with the functions of the two half-brains than do typical, fully lateralized individuals, then it can, not unreasonably, be supposed that bilaterality of left- or right-hemisphere properties interferes with behavior depending on reciprocal properties.

In collaborative studies, Colwyn Trevarthen, Roger Sperry, and I (Levy, Trevarthen, and Sperry, 1972; Levy and Trevarthen, 1972) have attempted to increase the resolving power of our investigative tools in looking at hemispheric functions. It was hoped that, by doing so, data might emerge which would lead us to a deeper comprehension of the functional relationships obtaining within and between the hemispheres.

In previous research with commissurotomy patients, one of the main difficulties has been that if we utilized man's most important sensory modality, vision, then we failed to utilize his highest level of consciousness. In order to confine visual input to one or the other hemisphere it was necessary to have the patient fixate in midline while the visual stimulus or stimuli were presented in one or both half-fields of vision. Attention was therefore directed toward midline when we presented our cues in the periphery. As Trevarthen (1968) has pointed out, there are two visual systems, one concerned with fully conscious, detailed information processing of the central behavioral field, the other operating at a lower level of consciousness, responding to cues in the periphery, and guiding the organism through space. To fully utilize the specifically cortical visual system necessitates fixation on the stimulus itself. It is probable that many of the difficulties encountered in extracting any information at all from the minor hemisphere were a consequence of this off-center stimulus presentation.

To overcome these problems we utilized the fact that each hemisphere of the commissurotomy patient, when presented with a stimulus which extends across the central fixation point, does not merely perceive that part of the stimulus which projects to the hemisphere, but instead effects an hallucinated completion (Trevarthen and Kinsbourne, 1972). A square, for example, presented in midline to these patients, is perceived as a complete square by each hemisphere, in spite of the fact that only the left half of the square stimulates the right hemisphere and the right half, the left hemisphere. Neither hemisphere appears to be aware that only a half-stimulus is responsible for its perception.

It is thus possible to join the left half of one stimulus to the right half of another stimulus at midline, and each hemisphere of the commissurotomy patient, in looking at such a chimera, will perceive a different, but complete, stimulus. With this technique different information can be sent to the two hemispheres simultaneously while the patient's attention is directly "on center."

A two-channel tachistoscope, described previously (Levy, Trevarthen, and Sperry, 1972), was used to provide a fixation field and for stimulus presentation. Subjects were instructed to fixate on a small red dot just prior to stimulation, and a continuing record of electro-oculograms provided confirmation of an appropriately centered gaze. Stimuli were exposed for no more than 150 msec., too brief a time for reflexive eye movements to shift the stimulus into the wrong half-field of vision.

Stimulus input was thus accomplished through the central behavioral space, was simultaneous for the two halves of the brain, and involved no intrinsic biasing in favor of one or the other hemisphere. Two forms of output were used, one deliberately biased, the other not. The unbiased output involved pointing with the left and right hands alternately at a choice from among an array which corresponded, in some designated fashion, with what had been seen in the tachistoscope. Depending on the subject's choice we could know whether he was responding to the left-field stimulus (with his right hemisphere) or to the right-field stimulus (with his left hemisphere). A variant of this procedure, once we determined which hemisphere was dominant for a function, was to have the subject point only with the hand which that hemisphere disfavored, i.e. the ipsilateral hand. Any bias operating under these conditions would work against the dominant hemisphere, and therefore if the hemisphere still appeared dominant, we could be certain of a cognitive effect, independent of hand usage. The biased output was a verbal description of the perceived stimulus, thus forcing the readout through the language hemisphere (in our patients, the left). The purpose of this biased output was to confirm or not that the language hemisphere had access only to stimuli in the contralateral visual field as well as to compare hemispheric dominance for a task under free and forced response conditions.

The first question we investigated was whether there was any hemispheric asymmetry in the perception of form and, if so, whether such asymmetry was specific for particular stimuli, e.g. faces (see Hécaen and Angelergues, 1962), or for certain classes of stimuli, e.g. nameable vs. nonnameable (nonsense) forms, (Milner, 1967) or holistic vs. analyzable forms. Figures IX-5 to IX-8 show the chimeric and choice stimuli used.

The results were clear. Irrespective of the particular stimulus and irrespective of the pointing hand, in the unbiased response situation, the nonlanguage hemisphere was overwhelmingly dominant, controlling the

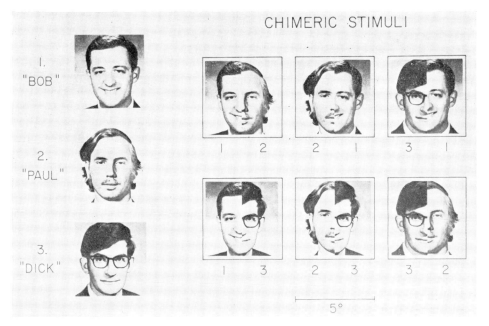

Figure IX-5. Stimuli and choices for face test (Reprinted from *Brain, 95:* 61–78, 1972).

CHIMERIC STIMULI

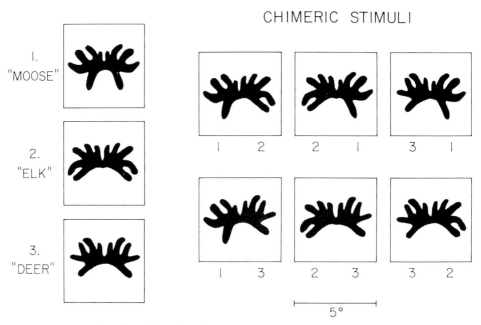

Figure IX-6. Stimuli and choices for antler test (Reprinted from *Brain*, *95*: 61–78, 1972).

CHIMERIC STIMULI

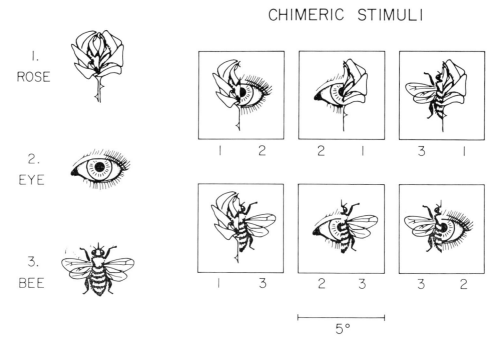

Figure IX-7. Stimuli and choices for object test (Reprinted from *Brain*, *95*: 61–78, 1972).

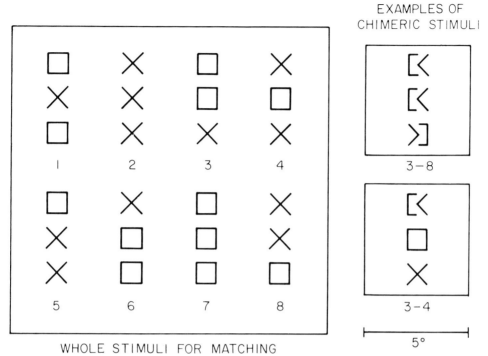

WHOLE STIMULI FOR MATCHING

Figure IX-8. Stimuli and choices for pattern test (Reprinted from *Brain, 95:* 61–78, 1972).

correct choice an average of 87 percent of the time. The distinction between faces and other kinds of stimuli had no functional significance. However, although the nameable and non-nameable classification had no effect in the free response situation, in the forced verbal response situation, the language hemisphere was much superior in the tests with well-known objects than in those with stimuli whose names had only recently been taught by the experimenters. Figure IX-9 summarizes the results.

Possibly the most interesting conclusion from these findings is that the nonlanguge hemisphere is not only dominant for recognition tasks which the language hemisphere does poorly (faces, antlers), but also for those which it does extremely well (objects, patterns), as measured on the verbal read-out tests. It is as if the language hemisphere only comes into play when its particular abilities are specifically called for. The so-called "minor" hemisphere, thus, not only does those things which are difficult, but also those things which are easy, for the "major" hemisphere. Further, it is not that the mute hemisphere recognizes nonsense forms better than nameable forms, but rather that the language hemisphere can respond accurately only to the latter.

I shall now return to the question whether the right hemisphere

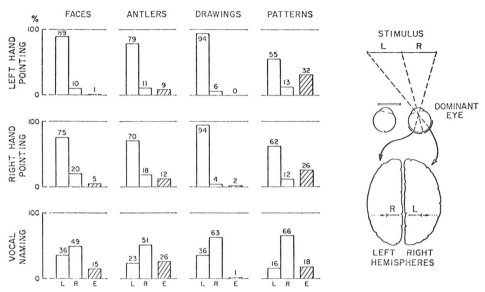

Figure IX-9. Results of form recognition tests (Reprinted from *Brain, 95:* 61–78, 1972).

really lacks internal language, and, if so, why. Trevarthen and I (Levy and Trevarthen, 1972), utilizing the same paradigm as in the previously discussed study with chimeric stimuli, presented the same object chimeras (Figure IX-7), but required a response based on a different set of rules.

As stated, we had seen on the object-chimera test a strong dominance of the mute hemsiphere for visual matching. In order to look at internal language, we substituted for the original choice pictures of a bee, an eye, and a rose, pictures of a key, a pie, and toes (Figure IX-10), and instructed the patients to point to the picture which rhymed with what they saw. The substitution of rhyming pictures for identical pictures and the change in instruction to the patients, produced a complete switch in dominance from the right to the left hemisphere. When we presented whole, nonchimeric pictures entirely in the left visual field, and therefore solely to the right hemisphere, the patients were unable to perform the rhyming pictures test. We therefore concluded that even though the right hemisphere had an advantage over the left in visuo-visual mapping, visuo-phonic mapping was totally beyond the capacities of the right hemisphere, and that internal language was, for the most part, absent.

We also found the right hemisphere to be dominated by the left in tests of verbal meaning (matching a word to its pictorial representation) and conceptual categorization (matching a picture of a sewing box to one of a pair of scissors, for example).

It is important here to note an additional conclusion, namely, that a

1.
TOES

2.
PIE

3.
KEY

Figure IX-10. Choice objects for
Rhyming Objects test.

hemisphere apparently assumes control of the motor output when it is superior for a given task.

On the basis of the foregoing observations the failures of the right and left hemispheres seem to be consequences of insufficiencies, not only in complex cognitive processes, but in the most basic prerequisites for language and perception, respectively. What are these prerequisites that the right and left hemispheres lack?

Language develops in the infant first as an attempt to communicate his desires, and secondly as an attempt to communicate his ideas. In both cases the baby must differentiate some specific from a global whole. If he is hungry, he must be able to analyze his general feeling of discomfort to a sufficient degree that he recognizes it is food he wants and not a dry diaper. In spite of many mothers' contention to the contrary, there is no evidence that an infant's wail is differentiated beyond conveying either rage or misery, but even his earliest speech reflects a quite specific object. Only when his analytic powers reach a certain level of proficiency can language develop.

Is it this power of differentiation of a part from a whole which the right hemisphere possesses insufficiently? That the left hemisphere is almost obsessed with parts is supported by the observations of Paterson and Zangwill in 1944, McFie and Zangwill in 1960, and of Warrington, James, and Kinsbourne in 1966 that patients with intact left hemispheres, but lesions in the right, always drew pictures piece-meal, item-by-item and detail-by-detail without any grasp of the object as a whole. Patients with intact *right* hemispheres, but lesions in the left, showed the reverse: oversimplified pictures with good Gestalt, but lacking detail.

The very peculiar defect in simultaneous perception called "simultanagnosia" by Wolpert in 1924 has been described in recent years by Kinsbourne and Warrington (1962) and may have bearing on the question of part-whole differentiation. Patients with this defect are unable to simultaneously perceive all the various details of a picture. They can see only one object at a time, irrespective of the visual angle subtended by the object. Luria and co-workers (1963) found that a patient with simultanagnosia had normal eye movements in tracking a single object, but abnormal movements in looking at pictures.

Of the five patients observed by Kinsbourne and Warrington (1962), four had left hemisphere lesions, and the one patient with a right hemisphere lesion performed poorly on the vocabulary and similarities subtests on the WAIS, but competently on the Performance Scale, suggesting a reversal in language dominance. The authors stated that the syndrome is entirely different from the piece-meal perception seen in patients with right hemisphere damage. We are therefore faced with the problem of explaining a left-hemisphere syndrome defined primarily as an inability to see more than one thing at a time.

If the left hemisphere lesions in these patients disrupted the neural circuitry responsible for searching out detail, for analyzing complexity into its component parts, then the resulting perceptions might have been a meaningless jumble of light and form if the right hemisphere had been absent. But, in the presence of an intact right hemisphere, whose special task it is to apprehend a meaningful Gestalt and which, in addition, is incapable of analysis, such left hemisphere lesions might easily produce a perceiver whose world is a reification of the Embedded Figures Test, and who, therefore, is confined to detecting a single embedded figure.

The biological utility of an analytic deficiency in the right hemisphere is easy to understand if an analytic mode of information processing specifically interferes with Gestalt apprehension, if, in other words, it produces a creature who "can't see the forest for the trees." It was this idea of a basic incompatibility between the kinds of cognitive processing needed for language and perception that led to the hypothesis that if both hemispheres in the adult retain the capacity to develop language, as is the case with the typical left-hander, then such a person would have a perceptual deficit. It was guessed that the neural organization underlying expressive verbal ability precluded Gestalt appreciation and necessitated looking at the world of sensation in such a way that it *could* be described in language. Perhaps it was the seeking after describable or nameable features by the left hemispheres of people with right cerebral damage, that caused the facial agnosias seen by Hécaen (Hécaen and Angelergues, 1962). Faces, after all, are strongly resistant to analytic description. We do not recognize people by noting that, "This person has dark hair, blue eyes, freckles, and glasses and that therefore it must be Mary." We do so by an almost instantaneous perception of the essential Gestalt. Possibly the language competent left hemisphere must rely on the inductive method and is in large part lacking any ability to visualize stimuli which are resistant to verbal description.

The minor hemisphere's inability to recall verbal labels of objects, events, or sensations may be a necessary outcome of its superior ability to recall an image of the object, event, or sensation itself. Likewise, the neural organization underlying the left hemisphere's verbal fluency and symbolic reasoning is inadequate for the concrete, holistic, spatially synthesized visualizations so proficiently performed by the mute half of the brain.

Cerebral asymmetry of function in an animal with language may be the only design for a brain which optimizes both linguistic and Gestalt perceptual functions.

To assess this possibility comparisons were made for the verbal and performance scores on the Wechsler Adult Intelligence Scale in groups of left- and right-handed graduate students at Caltech (Levy, 1969). Studies by Reitan in 1955 and Arrigoni and De Renzi in 1964, have shown that the verbal and performance scales of the WAIS measure what are normally left and right hemisphere functions, respectively. Earlier studies of brain-damaged sinistrals indicate that left-handed people tend to possess more bilateralized representation of language than do dextrals (Goodglass & Quadfasal, 1954).

Consistent with the idea that language interferes with spatial perception, the results showed that while the mean verbal I.Q.'s of the two groups did not differ, the sinistrals had significantly inferior performance I.Q.'s. The verbal and performance I.Q.'s of dextrals were 138 and

130 respectively, while those of sinistrals were 142 and 117. The discrepancy between verbal and performance I.Q.'s was much greater among the sinistrals, being 25 I.Q. points as opposed to only 8 I.Q. points for the dextrals. The lateralization of perception into the mute hemisphere can be explained in terms of an interference with perception by language, an interference which was clearly seen in a group of people who are likely to have at least some bilateral language ability. Additional confirmation for the proposed antagonism comes from several other studies. In a variety of tests of visuo-spatial ability, sinistrals have been found to be impaired (Silverman, Adevai, and McGough, 1966; James, Mefferd, and Wieland, 1967; Miller, 1971; Nebes, 1971a, b) as compared with dextrals. In his "circle segment test" Nebes has found the left hemispheres of commissurotomy patients to be poorer than the right, and left-handers to be poorer than dextrals, thus cleanly demonstrating a sinistral deficiency on a right-hemisphere task.

Thus, our observations reveal a left hemisphere dominance when a verbal response is required, when a nonverbal response depends on recall of auditory images (visuo-phonic mapping), when linguistic processing (visuo-semantic mapping) is called for, or when abstract conceptualizing is needed—all functions which the right hemisphere performs poorly, if at all. On the other hand, the right hemisphere is dominant for all visual matching tasks, irrespective of the nature of the material—nameable or non-nameable, holistic or analyzable—and irrespective of the ease with which the left hemisphere can perform the task as measured by verbal read-out. The left hemisphere can therefore be described as an abstract, temporal analyzer which maps stimulus input into semantic and phonemic realms, while the right hemisphere is a concrete, spatial synthesizer which maps into a visuostructural realm. If these descriptions are valid, then, as previously suggested, the functions of the two hemispheres seem to be logically incompatible.

The evidence would, accordingly, strongly suggest that the abrupt evolutionary change from the functionally symmetric hemispheres of the ape to the profoundly asymmetric hemispheres of man is correlated with the discontinuity from mute to speaking animals. Those ancient ape-men who possessed both brain bisymmetry and language, but did not possess the ability to see a hungry lion embedded like a hidden figure in the tall savannah grass, paid for their speech with their lives. Their cousins, also possessing language, and, in addition, a mute, Gestalt-synthesizing, figure-ground-separating, hemisphere, saw the lions, escaped, and, for good or ill, fathered the race of Man. Why are the left-handers still with us? Evolutionary law demands that any genotype which survives, if it is inferior in some way to others, must, by virtue of

Figure IX-11. Artistic production of a young commissurotomy patient when instructed to draw a man.

its survival, be superior in another way. In the California Institute of Technology study (Levy, 1969), 8 of the 10 sinistral graduate students, but only 4 of the 15 dextral graduate students had W.A.I.S. Verbal I.Q.'s as high as 140 [χ^2 (with Yates' correction) $= 4.87$, df $= 1$, p $< .05$]. Does the typical left-hander have superior abstract conceptualization ability? Is the survival of the species optimized when a certain fraction of its members, though being neither hunters nor food gatherers, are specialized for pure reasoning?

Possibly in the simplest, but most accurate fashion, one of the young commissurotomy patients expressed the functions of his two half-brains in a drawing. He was asked only to draw a man. His production, shown in Figure IX-11, has the right side visualizing a girl and the left conceptualizing her meaning.

REFERENCES

Arrigoni, G., and DeRenzi, E.: Constructional apraxia and hemispheric locus of lesion. *Cortex, 1:* 170–197, 1964.

Bennett, G. K., Seashore, H. G., and Wesman, A. G.: *Differential Aptitude Tests* (Space Relations, Form A). New York, The Psychological Corporation, 1947.

Bogen, J. E., and Gazzaniga, M. S.: Cerebral commissurotomy in man: Minor hemisphere dominance for certain visuo-spatial functions. *J Neurosurg, 23:* 394–399, 1965.

Goodglass, H., and Quadfasal, F. A.: Language laterality in left-handed aphasics. *Brain, 77:* 521–548, 1954.

Hécaen, H., and Angelergues, R.: Agnosia for faces (prosopagnosia). *Arch Neurol* (Chicago), *7:* 92–100, 1962.

James, W. E., Mefferd, R. B., Jr., and Wieland, B.: Repetitive psychometric measures: Handedness and performance. *Percept Mot Skills, 25:* 209–212, 1967.

Kinsbourne, M., and Warrington, E. K.: A disorder of simultaneous form perception. *Brain, 85:* 461–486, 1962.

Levy, Jerre: Possible basis for the evolution of lateral specialization of the human brain. *Nature, 224:* 614–615, 1969.

Levy, Jerre, Nebes, R. D., and Sperry, R. W.: Expressive language in the surgically separated minor hemisphere. *Cortex, 7:* 49–58, 1971.

Levy, Jerre, Trevarthen, Colwyn, and Sperry, R. W.: Perception of bilateral chimeric figures following hemispheric deconnexion. *Brain, 95:* 61–78, 1972.

Levy, Jerre, and Trevarthen, Colwyn: Hemispheric specialization tested by simultaneous rivalry for mental associations. (In preparation.)

Levy-Agresti, Jerre, and Sperry, R. W.: Differential perceptual capacities in major and minor hemispheres. *Proc Natl Acad Sci, 61:* 1151, 1968.

Luria, A. R., Pravdina-Vinarskaya, E. N., and Yarbuss, A. L.: Disorders of ocular movement in a case of simultanagnosia. *Brain, 86:* 219–228, 1963.

McFie, J., and Zangwill, O. L.: Visual-constructive disabilities associated with lesions of the left cerebral hemisphere. *Brain, 83:* 243–260, 1960.

Miller, Edgar: Handedness and the pattern of human ability. *Br J Psychol, 62:* 111–112, 1971.

Milner, Brenda: Brain mechanisms suggested by studies of temporal lobes. In Darley, F. L. (Ed.): *Brain Mechanisms Underlying Speech and Language.* New York, Grune and Stratton, 1967.

Nebes, R. D.: Superiority of the minor hemisphere in commissurotomized man for the perception of part-whole relations. *Cortex, 7:* 333–349, 1971a.

Nebes, R. D.: Handedness and the perception of part-whole relationship. *Cortex, 7:* 350–356, 1971b.

Paterson, A., and Zangwill, O. L.: Disorders of visual space perception associated with lesions of the right cerebral hemisphere. *Brain, 67:* 331–358, 1944.

Reitan, R. M.: Certain differential effects of left and right cerebral lesions in human adults. *J Comp Physiol, 48:* 474–477, 1955.

Silverman, A. J., Adevai, G., and McGough, W. E.: Some relationships between handedness and perception. *J Psychosom Res, 10:* 151–158, 1966.

Sperry, R. W., and Gazzaniga, M. S.: Language following surgical disconnection of the hemispheres. In Darley, W. L. (Ed): *Brain Mechanisms Underlying Speech and Language.* New York, Grune and Stratton, 1966.

Trevarthen, Colwyn B.: Two mechanisms of vision in primates. *Psychologische Forchung, 31:* 299–337, 1968.

Trevarthen, Colwyn B., and Kinsbourne, Marcel: Manuscript in preparation, 1972.

Warrington, E. K., James, M., and Kinsbourne, M.: Drawing disability in relation to laterality of cerebral lesion. *Brain, 89:* 53–82, 1966.

Wolpert, K. I.: Die Simultanagnosie; Störungen der Gesamtauffassung. *Z ges Neurol Psychiat, 93:* 397–415, 1924.

[PART III]

FUNCTIONAL RELATIONS

[CHAPTER X]

FUNCTIONAL RELATIONS OF DISCONNECTED HEMISPHERES WITH THE BRAIN STEM, AND WITH EACH OTHER: MONKEY AND MAN

Colwyn Trevarthen

IN THIS PAPER I wish to develop concepts of cerebral organization of function which were outlined originally to explain findings on the visual processes and visuomotor coordination of split-brain monkeys. In applying them to man, I shall summarise experiments with human commissurotomy patients performed expressly to test more recent formulations of primate visual mechanisms, and their special features in man.

A—MONKEY

Different Levels of Visual Process

In experiments on double learning with split-brain rhesus monkeys, I found that, while a pronounced separation of two hemispheric systems for perception and learning of visual signs could definitely be confirmed, the disconnected hemispheres were not wholly independent in their activities (Trevarthen, 1962; 1965). As Myers (1956) had found for the cat, and Sperry (1958) and Downer (1958) had shown for the monkey, each of the disconnected hemispheres could learn a visual discrimination task independently of the other. A split-brain monkey could attend separately to one or both of two contradictory discriminations presented simultaneously to both hemispheres (Trevarthen, 1962). Nevertheless, internal cerebral adjustments, that were coupled with intentions to use one or the other arm and hand, could result in perception and learning being confined to one hemisphere, even though the other hemisphere, or at least the receptor field connected with it, was equally stimulated at the same time. A central factor, not due to any external circumstances, and not attributable in any direct way to the act of response and feedback from it, determined which hemisphere would see and learn.

Two chiasma-callosum sectioned subjects showed similar differences in the degree of hemispheric interaction for particular forms of visual stimuli, and these differences were not associated with the order of presentation of the tasks. It was therefore proposed that certain visual processes, related to the psychological assimilation or processing of the shapes to be discriminated, were subserved by a brain mechanism that was not divided in two by commissurotomy and chiasma section (Trevarthen, 1965; 1968).

Direct tests for interhemispheric comparison of stimuli confirmed that a monkey with optic chiasma and all interhemispheric commissures sectioned could perceive a relationship of size, orientation or number, between two visual stimuli that were made visible separately to the two eyes by means of polaroid filters (Trevarthen, 1963; 1968). This result did not accord with known anatomy of the retino-geniculo-striate pathway and it was therefore inferred that midbrain circuits are involved in certain basic visual perception processes (Trevarthen, 1965).

Although no definite hypothesis presented itself at this stage, it was proposed that while stimuli perceived as objects of quite different kind of identity were seen and remembered by two separate cortical visual mechanisms in split-brain subjects, stimuli perceived relationally or linked in a perceptual synthesis, and therefore different quantitatively or in strength along a perceived dimension (e.g. size or dividedness), could in some cases be seen with visual, presumably midbrain circuits that were not divided by midline surgery that split the forebrain.

Other evidence for unification of visuo-motor functions below the hemispheres, or in duplicate bilateral representations of body-centred space in each of the disconnected hemispheres, also came from studies of the ability of split-brain monkeys with the optic chiasma divided, or those with complimentary visual and motor ablations in the two hemispheres to orient to and reach and grasp objects anywhere in the visual field with all eye-hand combinations (Myers, Sperry and McCurdy, 1962). The behaviour of the split-brain monkeys in these tasks strongly suggested that they retained a near normal unified field for coordinated ocular and manual orientation. Experiments by Bossom and Hamilton (1963) on adaptation to prismatic displacement of visual targets showed that the brain mechanisms controlling hand-aiming to an object fixated with the eyes were indivisible by midline surgery, even if this was carried back to include bisection of the cerebellum. The inputs of the two eyes, split by chiasma section, were still coupled in binocular orienting functions, and the guidance mechanism of each arm and hand could acquire an adjusted control of aiming with one eye which would be immediately effective for the other eye.

Two Vision Theory

In 1966, my thinking on these results was stimulated by Schneider's findings with rodents (Schneider, 1967, 1969). He made a beautifully clear demonstration of a two step hierarchical organization of both visuo-motor and visual-perceptual processes in the brain of the golden hamster. His surgical and behavioural experiments showed that while the midbrain tectum was essential to visual orienting and localization and had particular control over motor displacements of the head and body, the visual striate cortex was essential to visual discrimination of patterns and the control of acts instrumental in obtaining food in a two choice task. He also showed how midbrain-governed orientation might be involved in a test designed to investigate differential perception of patterns projected on two response screens in a Y-maze.

Previous signs that visual perception in monkeys might include sub-hemispheric (midbrain) processes had been recorded at least as far back as Klüver's experiments (Klüver, 1941; 1942), and amplified, for example, by Denny-Brown and Chambers (1955; Denny-Brown, 1962) and recently by Weiskrantz and Humphrey (Weiskrantz, 1963; Humphrey and Weiskrantz, 1967; Humphrey, 1970), and Pasik, Pasik and Schilder (1969).

The visual abilities of monkeys lacking the visual cortex have proved difficult to ascertain. A small part of vision remains after the operation, but that little is not simple. In particular, it resists analysis in terms of units for detection of small, geometrically simple, peripheral features. Effects changing the balance of stimulation in the whole field, or its overall configuration, seem to be the most likely to engage the behaviour of a destriate monkey, but objects are not identified or distinguished by their specific visual details. Denny-Brown's clinical tests of the reaction-of destriate and decollicular monkeys to moving objects show relationship to Schneider's findings with the hamster and support his emphasis on the link between processes of visual perception and the motor functions which are in direct control of information pick-up from the visual world. Humphrey's observations on the recovery of visual locating and change-detecting in a monkey after striate cortex ablation also reinforce the idea that subhemispheric or nonstriate visual integrations provide a context for visual discrimination, and a basis for orientation of the eyes and selective visual attention.

On the basis of the effects of lesions in different parts of the central visual mechanism, and the visual processes of split-brain monkeys, I have outlined a teleological theory of primate visual psychology and brain mechanisms that relates the findings with split-brain monkeys to Schneider's two vision theory for the hamster (Trevarthen, 1968). The distinguishing characteristics of *ambient* and *focal* vision are discussed. Ambient vision is defined as motion-dependent vision of three-dimensional space round the body by which postural and attention-orienting movements of the body and its parts are regulated. Focal vision is the function by which information on the details of form, hue and refined three-dimensional arrangement is obtained for full perception of the identity and usefulness of each individual object (Fig. X-1, a).

Object Perception by Touch vs. Proprioceptive Control of Posture (Fig. X-1b)

Apparent contradictions in the results obtained in tests of intermanual transfer of touch learning by split-brain monkeys indicates that, as in vision, perception of objects in space by reaching and grasping is subserved by structures which cannot be split by cerebral commissurotomy, in addition to the strictly cortical and splitable mechanisms of touch stereognosis for perceiving objects in more detail with the fingers

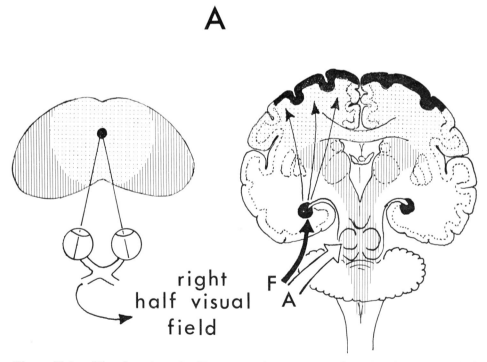

Figure X-1a. Visual system, in diagrammatic representation, showing anatomical relations of pathways for focal (F) and ambient (A) vision. Focal-ambient synthesis in the "association" cortex (stippled) is divided by commissurotomy.

B

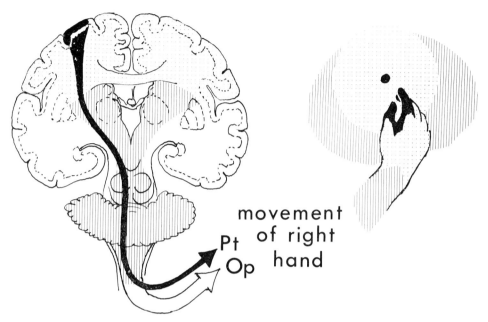

movement
of right
hand

Pt
Op

Figure X-1b. Comparable diagram for hand functions. Orientation and transport of the hand to the target under proprioceptive control (Op) is not divided by commissurotomy. Cortical control of precision manipulation and object stereognosis by touch, etc. (Pt) is divided.

(Glickstein and Sperry, 1960; Ebner and Myers, 1962; Ettlinger and Morton, 1966). Bilateral projection of information about skin deformations and mechanical changes in joints and muscles of the arms and shoulders, i.e. projection from the ipsilateral as well as the contralateral limb to each hemisphere, provides for bimanual communication of some of the experiences associated with the tests used, so that objects contacted by the two hands separately are perceived as located in one place and as single rigid shapes (Ettlinger and Morton, 1963; Black and Myers, 1965; Mark and Sperry, 1968). Glickstein and Sperry (1960), distinguished the movements for locating the task and orienting the hands to it ("testing" the stimuli), which did show evidence of intermanual transfer of experience, from perceptual recognition of the forms or textures to be discriminated, which did not transfer.

The unity of postural adjustment and orientation under proprioceptive control following commissurotomy is also shown in the way spontaneous changes of posture and locomotion are regulated after the operation. Split-brain animals behave as whole individuals, essentially the same as before surgery. Their movements are smoothly and automatically well-formed and well coordinated, except for occasional episodes of double volitional activity observed most frequently in the first weeks after surgery (Ettlinger, 1965, pp 103–106; Trevarthen, 1968). While reflex feedback from both sides of the body to each hemisphere is undoubtedly functional in maintaining integrated patterns of movement with deconnected hemispheres, reflexly (Gazzaniga, 1966; Mark and Sperry, 1968), the smooth and unhesitant voluntary locomotion and change of posture must also depend on unified programmes integrated at subhemispheric levels (Paillard, 1960).

One-Sided Attention Shows Brain-Stem Involvement in Cerebral Lateralisation of Function

When split-brain monkeys with chiasm transected are forced to use ipsilateral eye-hand combinations for the first time after the operation, their orientation with the hand to grab a rapidly moving object remains intact, but their discriminatory attention to visual stimuli is impaired and on occasion they even act as if the stimulus received by the eye could not be seen (Downer, 1959; Trevarthen, 1965). For example, in reaction time tests with a 1 cm diameter neon light as signal and target, a highly trained but recently operated split-brain monkey, using an ipsilateral eye and hand combination, may stare in the direction of the lighted cue and fail to move (Ettlinger, 1965, p. 106). In double learning tests, one line of visual input is frequently not assimilated at all, and such perceptual neglect by one half-brain always corresponds with spontaneous lateralisation or response to the arm and hand which has more complete neural control in the other hemisphere (Trevarthen, 1962; 1965).

The movements which chiasma-callosum sectioned monkeys make when they are reaching with an arm to a visual discrimination test stimulus received by the ipsilateral eye are often impulsive, perseverative and poorly directed, and the hand and fingers are crudely aimed. Films reveal that much of the anticipatory shaping of the hand for precise contact control is lost; like the defect of hand use which follows transection of the corresponding pyramidal tract (Lawrence and Kuypers, 1965; Brinkman and Kuypers, 1972). Yet, the same limb acts with normal precision and smooth coordination as soon as it is permitted to operate with the preferred contralateral eye, and both forelimbs are employed normally as soon as the operated animal is permitted to climb, walk, jump or run freely.

These observations, described in detail in earlier reports, brings out the distinction between discriminatory use of a hand under cortical visual control, and larger-scale coordinations of postural change and locomotion in which subhemispheric and bilateralised hemispheric systems are brought into play.

Cerebral Asymmetry of Function in Monkeys

Integration of cerebral with sub-hemispheric mechanisms is involved in any asymmetry of cortical control in behaviour, for both the flow of information to the hemispheres and the postural foundations underlying any asymmetry of motor activity in praxis are determined by orientations and central attention changes under brain stem control.

There is no evidence, yet, that monkeys of any species have a genetically regulated handedness such that one hand is more frequently dominant in the population as a whole, or in a family line, than the other. Nevertheless, cerebral asymmetry of psychological functions does occur in monkeys. A study with baboons of cerebral lateralisation of the psychological schema for a complex bilateral manipulative skill required to open a problem box demonstrated that, in the normal subject, internal patterning of the use of the two hands on the complex object of manipulation had been located asymmetrically in the brain (Trevarthen, 1975). A baboon that had achieved a high degree of skill in this task with right hand leading or dominant, was subjected to chiasm section and forebrain commissurotomy. Post-operative tests showed that cortical control had been consolidated, for both hands, more within the left hemisphere than the right. This lateralization of psychological function corresponded with the functional asymmetry visible in the acts performed by the two hands which had assumed complimentary roles, one being dominant, the other subordinated to it.

Monkeys which have learned a two-choice visual pattern discrimination before split-brain surgery, with chiasma section, have been reported to show better retention with one eye after surgery (Gazzaniga, 1963). It has been claimed that this shows hemispheric dominance for the visual learning, but a post-surgical adjustment favouring one hemianopic eye at the expense of the other, might have led to the same result. Further work is needed to test the possibility that visual perception processes may be lateralised asymmetrically in the brain of a normal monkey.

B—MAN

Two Consciousnesses of Which One Can Speak

Human commissurotomy patients have two cerebral mechanisms which perceive objects, and hand signals, words, numbers or other signs, separately (Sperry, 1968; 1969). They show little intermanual transfer of experience for objects felt, and with pictures or signs exposed tachisto-scopically a few degrees off-centre, either to left or to right of a monitored fixation point, they demonstrate completely independent perceptual awarenesses for the two fields, being unable to compare, contrast, identify or relate in any way the visual experiences on the two sides.

Each of the disconnected hemispheres is capable of perceiving the identity of a familiar object or a representative of a familiar class of objects either by its appearance, or by the shape it feels in the hand, and these two alternative modes of getting information about such an object are immediately associated. But only the left hemisphere can generate speech or writing to report its experiences of objects (Sperry, Gazzaniga and Bogen, 1969). Very rarely, a fragmentary spoken or written response may be initiated by the right hemisphere after hemispheric deconnection, but such responses are rapidly overridden by the left hemisphere, possibly in reaction to the commencement of verbal report.

In tasks demanding perception of the stereoconfiguration of unfamiliar (unnamed) shapes, either by feeling them in the hand or by seeing them, the right of two disconnected hemispheres is generally superior. This hemisphere appears to have a better sense of spatial coordination in perceiving shapes, patterns, diagrams, pictures, etc. (Bogen, 1969; Levy-Agresti and Sperry, 1969; Sperry, 1970).

Unity of Ambient Visual Perception

In contrast to the above hemispherically isolated functions, normally dependent on traffic of commissural information for the attainment of mental unity, tests of the unity of ambient vision reveal that splitting of vision is not complete. If appropriately stimulated, patients with hemispheres divided may relate left and right visual half fields and may speak accurately about events confined to the left of the vertical meridian (Trevarthen, 1970; Trevarthen and Sperry, 1973). Demonstration of this perceptual unity of function requires application of long-lasting and large stimuli undergoing change in place, size, shape, intensity or colour, and extending well into the peripheral field. Any attempt on the part of the subject to specify details, or to give highly elaborate identification of objects seen in the field, or of effects relating the two halves of the field, results in automatic re-orientation of the eyes to obtain fixation of the identifying parts, in confabulation, or in loss of the percept and a report that the thing has partly or completely disappeared. The most accurate reports of bilateral percepts seen as a whole, or verbal description of left field effects have been obtained for the spatial and motion features of stimuli. The reported percepts always structure space round the subject rather than signifying a fully identified, particular object.

Veridical left-field percepts of the direction of rotation of an object, that depended on the integration of quite complex perspectival transformations, were described by the subject, who also gave simple verbal responses accurately to the occurrence of appearances, disappearances or displacements in the left peripheral field at about the threshold of sensitivity of normal subjects. The rhythmic pattern and speed of motion stimuli also appeared to be perceived by a visual process representing both halves of the visual field in the left hemisphere, in all subjects tested.

Preliminary tests indicate that the general psychological time field also remains essentially undivided, although more elaborate or refined temporal perceptions may be subdivided by forebrain commissurotomy. If two small lights are caused to appear briefly (10 msec.) each side of the fixation point, a commissurotomy subject may, if he is perceiving both of them, say if they are simultaneous or which occurs before the other. Times as short as 10 msec. have been correctly discriminated in this way.

In summary: Under favourable circumstances, visual events were noticed by commissurotomy patients in an undivided bilateral and temporally unified space around the body and their strength, quality or motion, and general spatial configuration were related to this space much as they would be by normal subjects, in spite of the surgical deconnection of the hemispheres.

Performance as good as this with seated split-brain subjects keeping still to maintain central fixation, was highly dependent upon a particular condition of mental orientation with attention distributed peripherally This state was easily disrupted, and the subjects themselves could describe break-up of the bilateral field of view, generally with disappearances of stimuli on one side while those on the other side remained clearly perceived.

Subhemispheric Control of Cortical Processes

As with chiasma-callosum sectioned monkeys, which showed spontaneous lateralization of vision in left or right half of the forebrain depending on which hand was being used, lateralization of seeing of human commissurotomy patients to one half of the visual field was influenced by requiring response with one or the other hand, and the side of perception could be switched by interchanging hands. In the case of human subjects, the lateralization of perception was, on most occasions, further and more profoundly effected by asking the subject to speak about his experiences, causing him to use the left hemisphere and to shift his vision to favour the right field.

It was, however, remarkable to observe that on many occasions, while a subject was freely talking about his visual experiences in the two fields (as, for example, when attempting to relate or integrate two stimuli, one on the left and one on the right, in a single configuration), he would spontaneously report, verbally, the disappearance of the right stimulus while the left remained visible. This is contrary to the rule that the left speaking hemisphere can only see things to the right of a point fixated. The subjects reported perceiving some kind of rivalry between the simple left and right percepts in the periphery, and though usually it was the left stimulus which could not be seen, or which was seen to disappear when they were talking, sometimes the percept of the right stimulus was lost.

Further information about the effects on visual perception of preparation to respond with left or right hand was obtained in an experiment with commissurotomy subject N.G. which was intended to explore phenomena of perceptual completion and neglect about the vertical meridian of the visual field. Polygon forms cut out of white card were placed on a black table-top while the subject kept fixation on a small white spot on the table. She was asked to put a mark with a felt-top pen in the geographic middle of each shape (elongated rectangle, triangular, or bilobed, etc.), using either the left or the right hand to do so. The shapes were put entirely to the left of the vertical meridian, entirely to the right, or straddling it to various extents in an unpredictable series. Responses were absent, abortive or highly inaccurate to stimuli placed in the field contralateral to the responding hand. On several occasions, while N.G. was using her left hand, she made a very small and brief intention movement of her left arm when a stimulus was placed in the right field, and then said, "It's disappeared!" She insisted that the large white stimulus shape, which subtended to 10 to 20° had been visible, but that it vanished when she wanted to mark it with the pen in her left hand. She kept her eyes on the designated central fixation spot and continued to report that the stimulus in the right field was not visible, even while it was moved slowly about by the experimenter. However, the instant a small piece of the stimulus crossed the vertical meridian, her left hand made a very rapid, apparently involuntary movement to "catch" it, as if the target for a pounce held in a high state of readiness had suddenly popped into view (Fig. X-2).

This phenomenon can only be explained in terms of interlateral, probably interhemispheric, communication of an inhibitory nature, leading first to erasure or occlusion of the right field percept from consciousness, and then report of loss emanating from the left hemisphere. The inhibition evidently occurred when the left hand was intended to hit the object initially perceived, or as an immediate consequence of the small intention movement emitted by the left arm.

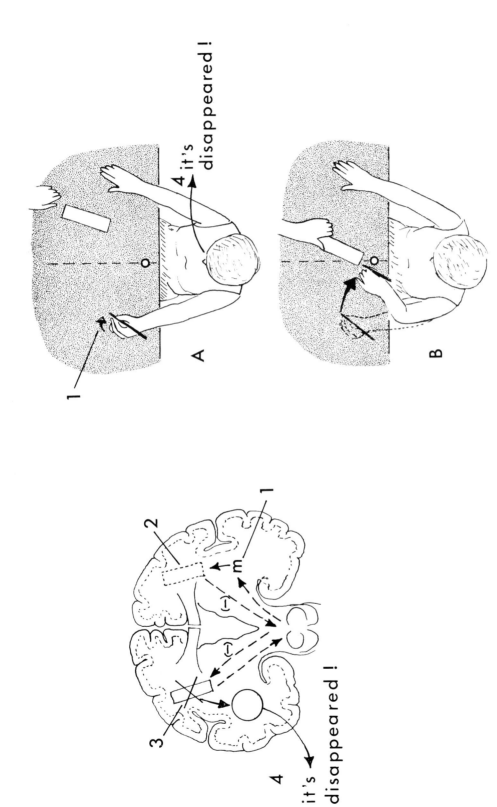

Figure X-2. Interhemispheric specific inhibition, linked to motor intention, which suppresses the visual percept of a goal object. A. Subject loses sight of object in the right visual field. B. Response triggered only when the object crosses the vertical meridian and appears in the left visual field. Fixation point marked by white dot circled with black.

The Split Brain Is not Really a Two-Channel Processor

This remarkable selective disregard by the process of visual consciousness of physically strong sensory "information" brings us to consider the brain functions of active uptake or disregard of sensory information in perception building, and to ask what are the effects of commissurotomy on these assimilatory functions. Ideas of the cortex as a sensory information processer, capable of perceptual synthesis and association between different modalities of sensation all on its own, lead to a theory of the split cortex as a "two channel information processer" and the commissurotomy patient as having "double processing capacity." However, appropriate tests reveal that this theory will not do, that it is too simple-minded.

Visual search experiments carried out at the California Institute of Technology and discussed by my colleague Marcel Kinsbourne in this volume, show that even the simplest act of perception by a commissurotomy patient brings cortical processes of visual information pickup under control of a unified subhemispheric orienting system (Kinsbourne, Trevarthen and Sperry, 1974). Reciprocal interactions between cortex and subcortex maintain a degree of unity in the act of visual consciousness even when the two cortices are disconnected, and since the process of visual recognition requires this integration of cerebral activity, the commissurotomy patient lacking all direct neural links between cortical circuits is, in any sense, far from normal in perceptual processing capacity. The results we have obtained are not too strongly stated by saying that commissurotomy results in a marked deficit in readiness to perceive throughout the visual field, and a sluggishness or drop in attentional lability for orienting perception selectively.

Finger-tapping tests show that bilateral motor control is somewhat impaired by commissurotomy and that concentration on a concurrent verbal thinking and speech activity may lead to greater interference, even in regulation of such an automatic act as rhythmic tapping of the index finger, than any normal subject will show (Kreuter, Kinsbourne and Trevarthen, 1972). With tachistoscopically exposed letters distributed to left and right of the fixation point, selective recognition of a target letter mixed with a number of other letters is so affected by unstable perceptual neglect of one or other field that, with even the simplest finger movement for a response signal, it is not possible to examine processes of visual search as one does with normal subjects.

These experiments show that the corpus callosum is normally part of the mechanism by which perceptual capacity is distributed or aimed in the whole visual perceptual field to sustain selective visual consciousness. They also show that there is no single thing as perceptual capacity, thought of as the diameter of a tubular channel for conduction of bits of information, but rather that the making up of a percept depends upon integrative processes of different kind, occupying the circuits in the brain stem as well as those in the cortex and subcortex of the disconnected hemispheres, in an hierarchical system.

It is especially important to distinguish aiming of perceptual synthetic operations within the body-centred orientational field, as a basis for actual orientation of body parts, like the eyes or hands, or of the body as a whole, in selective information pickup, from specification inside the brain of the identifying features and configuration of an object to be perceived. All the evidence points to retention of unity for the basic process of perceptual orientation in commissurotomy patients, at the brain stem level. The evident separation by the operation of detailed or focal analysis of stimulation patterns to identify objects in two hemispheric domains has been studied by other methods.

Perceptual Completion with Deconnected Hemispheres

It is one of the best substantiated facts of perception psychology that the detailed world we are conscious of seeing differs considerably from what in fact is presented to us in patterns of stimulation on the retina. The brain processes of perception take significant parts of the stimulus information, defined either in physical terms as the light pattern picked up from the optical array and its transformations, or physiologically as discharges in a population of nerve axons in a section of the visual input pathway (e.g. the optic nerve). In making this selection, the brain discards a large part of the stimulus or input and adds to the remainder to create a phenomenal representation which is of immediate relevance to determination of ongoing voluntary activity or thought. Formal studies of percepts usually employ very brief or very simplified stimuli to bring out this synthetic aspect of the process, but selective and constructive acts of perception are surely far more significant in complex natural fields of stimulation actively and freely employed. That only a part of an object may be detected in receptor processes while the whole is perceived perfectly well, is shown by perceptual filling in of the blind spot, or across scotomata resulting from loss of a piece of cortex in the occipital lobe (Teuber, 1966).

We have found that the total absence of striate cortex for one half of the visual field in each hemisphere of a commissurotomy patient does not prevent that hemisphere from completing percepts into the unsignalled or hemianopic field (Trevarthen and Kinsbourne, 1974). Incomplete geometric figures, pictures or words projected on the vertical meridian of the field are perceived as complete and reported as complete either verbally (in speech), for the left hemisphere, or in drawings, for the right hemisphere. It is interesting that the right hemisphere is likely to perform this act of perception, with completion of that part of the perceived object lying to the right of the vertical meridian, even when the right hand is used to draw with. For left hand drawings, perceptual control is invariably from the right hemisphere.

The process of perceptual completion to the left by the left hemisphere in control of speech, and to the right by the right hemisphere in control of drawing, is a very strong process in commissurotomy patients. As is shown, partial commissurotomy leaving the splenium intact, results in sufficient interhemispheric communication of visual stimulus information to stop completion occurring (Fig. X-3). In the subject with right-occipital lesion, resulting in this case in severe prosopagnosia, completion is evident but not as strong as in the patients with total commissurotomy. The case with right hemispherectomy showed some visual completion to the left. The agenesis case, however, was indistinguishable from normal subjects who invariably perceived these simple stimuli veridically (i.e. they did not show completion at all).

Tests were continued with the two total commissurotomy subjects N.G. and L.B. to obtain more data on completion and neglect by both hemispheres with verbal report and drawing, and they were also tested for the effect of a strong simultaneously presented stimulus in the apparently hemianopic field on the responses made. Both subjects could incorporate some information from both fields into their verbally reported or drawn perceptions, if the different stimuli on the two sides were sufficiently simple and appropriately weighted. In fact, L.B. occasionally produced a synthesis exhibiting double mirror-symmetric completion which indicates bihemispheric control of the response. This was particularly well brought out when we made up "chimeric" stimuli by combining two different half-stimuli joined down the vertical meridian. In some instances he doubly completed and drew a combination, each percept being reproduced as intact on both sides, and the two imbedded in each other.

Hemispheric Differences in Seeing, Studied with Stimulus Chimeras

Chimeric stimuli, and the phenomenon of perceptual completion provide us with excellent technique for weighing the perception processes of the two hemispheres of a commissurotomy patient against each other. Jerre Levy, Roger Sperry and I have used such stimuli to find out what kinds of visual perceptual tasks each hemisphere is best equipped to perform, and the competitive outcome where two hemispheres are vieing for control of a response which may be varied (Levy, Trevarthen and Sperry, 1972).

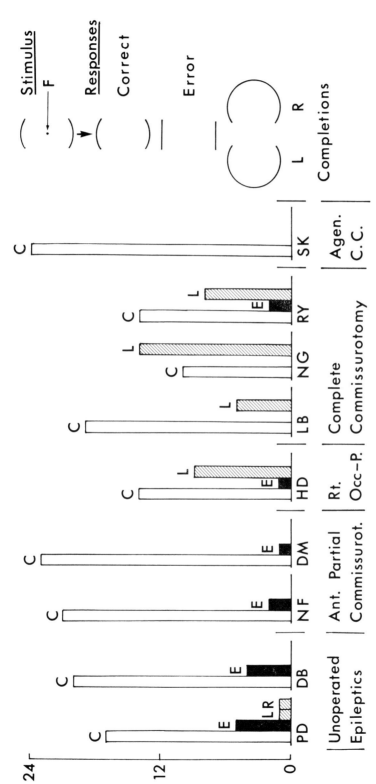

Figure X-3. Visual perception test with nine subjects with different brain conditions. Twenty-four centrally-placed line figures, based on circle, star, square and triangle, were used. The percepts were reported by speech and scored as correct (C), erroneous on both sides (E), or correct on one side of the fixation point (F), but with features perceptually completed (or neglected) on the left (L) or right (R) (Trevarthen and Kinsbourne, 1974).

In brief, we have found that verbal mediation, in the formulation of either an overt spoken response, or internally to make an association between separate percepts by rhyming "in the head," is always performed preferentially by the left hemisphere, and only the right half of the chimera is responded to. When the subject is asked to make a direct visual match of what he saw in the tachistoscope with one of a group of alternative whole stimuli, this is done much more strongly and accurately with the right hemisphere, no matter if the left or the right hand is used for pointing. Any instruction favouring wordless/visual matching of appearances, and therefore requiring retention of an image of the stimulus object sufficient to identify it a few seconds later, brings out the perception of the right hemisphere; any requirement to say what the object was, to think in words without speaking, or to reason about the meaning of the object in a context of objects of different appearance causes the left hemisphere to assume command of response, even if this entails pointing with the left hand to an appropriately matching object.

It should be noted that, in performing the visual matching, the subject looked down from the tachistoscope after the chimeric stimulus had been exposed on centre in his visual field, scanned the array of whole stimuli to make a match, fixed his gaze on his choice, then directed his left or right index finger to it. This is essentially an oculomotor scanning to locate a target for pointing. We know from studies with split-brain monkeys that either hand can reach to a visually fixated point no matter which hemisphere is seeing there, and that the two hands may be aimed together at such a point even if one hand is invisible beneath a screen (Mark and Sperry, 1968). Aiming of either hand to the located matching stimulus is performed within a unified mechanism of control for orienting the body and its parts. Nevertheless, with the human commissurotomy patients readying the right hand did have an effect, somewhat reducing the accuracy of responses, and occasionally a match was made by the left hemisphere when the right hand was pointing. Probably this kind of match was done with some participation of a verbal analysis and labeling of distinctive features of the stimulus object sought.

We employed appropriate double instructions, to respond in two ways or to replace preparation to respond verbally by an actual response according to visual matching and *vice versa*, and showed that in most cases there is a percept stored in each hemisphere when chimeric stimuli are used. Apparently the act of response tends to cast a vote in favour of one of the two stored percepts and, in most cases, the other percept is thereby left aside, for there was remarkably little evidence of conflict in most of these tests. Always somewhat exceptional in his degree of double awareness, L.B. did sometimes talk about blends of two objects, or did point to both component matches in a few trials towards the end of the extensive series of tests. Nevertheless, he never did become clearly aware that the stimuli had been built up as chimeras of two different pictures. Normal subjects invariably perceived the double composition of the stimuli and the midline join, at least within a dozen or so trials with different chimeras, each exposed for 150 msec. These tests confirm the conclusion from earlier experiments of Gazzaniga, Bogen and Sperry (1965) that there may be double visual consciousness in the brain of a commissurotomy patient, with the added information about the clear superiority of the right hemisphere for visual perception of Gestalts and matching of appearances, as has also been found by Bogen (1969).

DISCUSSION

The experiments reviewed here demonstrate that visual awareness depends, first, upon appropriate orientation of attention under the control of brain stem mechanisms which are in close reciprocal communication with the hemispheres, and, second, upon analytic and synthetic operations located beyond the striate cortex which can build up the detailed percept of an identified object, the structure and composition of which has been accurately modelled by the brain. The former processes can by themselves lead to abolition of a percept, and hemispheric perception processes are kept under regulation with respect to brain stem functions orienting visual attention.

The studies of both monkey and human subjects show that a parallel distinction may be made for the mechanism of perception by touch with the hands, though the precise cerebral mechanisms certainly differ from those underlying visual perception with the foveae. The implication is that a principle of cerebral design, related to the way sensory information is taken up by acts of selective attention, regardless of the particular modality of sense, determines what functions are confined to the cerebral cortex and therefore subject to deconnection by commissurotomy.

Demonstration that a neural schema governing an acquired bimanual skill in the baboon may be lateralized to one half of the cerebrum indicated that in subhuman primates the corpus callosum is involved in the process of skill learning and in asymmetric differentiation of the neural trace.

In man, the cerebral mechanism of intelligence grows progressively more asymmetric as the cortex and the commissures mature, as has been most clearly shown for language. In most of the commissurotomy patients studied at the California Institute of Technology this process is already well-advanced, though differences observed between those operated as teenagers and those operated later in life suggest that both visual and language processes are still far from fully developed in the former.

The chimera tests show that perception of the shape, organization and whole structure is best served in the *right* hemisphere which can store a comprehensive image adapted to direct matching against a like object from a very numerous potential array of objects of differing appearance. The tests indicate that, in visual perception, the *left* hemisphere is better at seizing on well-recognized, familiar, component features in the object, identifying this way by one or two known and distinctive or key parts. It is well-established to be superior at employing verbal symbols to communicate the nature of objects seen, and it has the benefit of language to make numerous associations which are not based only on the immediate appearances of things.

Objects in foci of attention separately perceived in the hemispheres are in rivalry for control of brain stem functions or orientation by which foci are first selected. Under certain circumstances, a sub-hemispheric set favouring employment of one hemisphere may lead to loss of percepts within the domain of the other hemisphere. Because the two hemispheres differ in their modes of operation in synthesis of visual awareness of objects and situations, their deconnection must produce a loss of all perception processes requiring their joint action, except where communication through the undivided ambient visual system is sufficient. Ambient vision is, however, capable of sustaining only the semiconscious or unconscious registration of a space for initial orientation of acts or intentions or for the immediate control of locomotion and posture.

In consequence, commissurotomy patients show losses of cognitive function directly attributable to hemispheric deconnection (Geschwind, 1965; Sperry, 1969). Examples well documented in our tests under conditions of free vision include the inability to learn names given to unfamiliar faces, and colour anomia. I have also recorded, but not systematically studied, manifestations of very poor verbal recall for actions observed visually, as in comic strips or the cinema. In all of these cases we appear to have a functional deficit due to the special visual abilities of the right hemisphere being cut off from the speech skills of the left hemisphere.

Normally, therefore, the cerebral hemispheres function in close integration with subhemispheric systems, and they also operate together in sustaining full cognitive process through mediation of the commissures.

REFERENCES

Black, P., and Myers, R. E.: A neurological investigation of eye-hand control in the chimpanzee. In Ettlinger, E. G. (Ed.): *Functions of the Corpus Callosum.* London, Churchill, 1965.

Bogen, J.: The other side of the brain. I: Dysgraphia and dyscopia following cerebral commissurotomy. *Bull Los Angeles Neurol Soc, 34:* 73–105, 1969.

Bossom, J., and Hamilton, C. R.: Interocular transfer of prism-altered coordinations in split-brain monkeys. *J Comp Physiol Psychol, 56:* 769–774, 1963.

Brinkman, J. and Kuypers, H. G. J. M.: Split-brain monkeys: cerebral control of ipsilateral and contralateral arm, hand and finger movements. *Science, 176:* 536–539, 1972.

Denny-Brown, D.: The midbrain and motor integration. *Proc R Soc Med, 55:* 527–538, 1962.

Denny-Brown, D., and Chambers, R. A.: Visuo-motor function in the cerebral cortex. *J Nerv Ment Dis, 121:* 288–289, 1955.

Downer, J. L. de C.: Role of corpus callosum in transfer of training in *Macaca mulatta. Fed Proc, 17:* 37, 1958.

Downer, J. L. de C.: Changes in visually guided behaviour following midsagittal division of optic chiasm and corpus callosum in monkey *(Macaca mulatta). Brain, 82:* 251–259, 1959.

Ebner, F. F., and Myers, R. E.: Corpus callosum and the interhemispheric transmission of tactual learning. *J Neurophysiol, 25:* 380–391, 1962.

Ettlinger, G. (Ed.): *Functions of the Corpus Callosum.* London, Churchill, 1965.

Ettlinger, G., and Morton, H. B.: Callosal section: its effects on performance of a bimanual skill. *Science, 139:* 485–486, 1963.

Ettlinger, G., and Morton, H. B.: Tactile discrimination performance in the monkey: Transfer of training between the hands after commissural section. *Cortex, 2:* 30–49, 1966.

Gazzaniga, M. S.: Effects of commissurotomy on a preoperatively learned visual discrimination. *Exp Neurol, 8:* 14–19, 1963.

Gazzaniga, M. S.: Visuo-motor integration in split-brain monkeys with other cerebral lesions. *Exp Neurol, 16:* 289–298, 1966.

Gazzaniga, M. S., Bogen, J. E., and Sperry, R. W.: Observations on visual perception after disconnection of the cerebral hemispheres in man. *Brain, 88:* 221–236, 1965.

Geschwind, N.: Disconnection syndromes in animals and man. *Brain, 88:* Part I, 237–294; Part II, 585–644, 1965.

Glickstein, M., and Sperry, R. W.: Intermanual somesthetic transfer in split-brain rhesus monkeys. *J Comp Physiol Psychol, 53:* 322–327, 1960.

Humphrey, N.: What the frog's eye tells the monkey's brain. *Brain Behav Evol, 3:* 324–337, 1970.

Humphrey, N., and Weiskrantz, L.: Vision in monkeys after removal of the striate cortex. *Nature, 215:* 595–597, 1967.

Kinsbourne, M., Trevarthen, C., and Sperry, R. W.: Bilateral visual search with deconnected cerebral hemispheres. (In preparation.) 1974.

Klüver, H.: Visual functions after removal of the occipital lobes. *J Psychol, 11:* 23–45, 1941.

Klüver, H.: Functional significance of the geniculo-striate system. *Biol Symp, 7:* 253–299, 1942.

Kreuter, C., Kinsbourne, M., and Trevarthen, C.: Are deconnected cerebral hemispheres independent channels?: Effect of unilateral loading on bilateral finger tapping. *Neuropsychologia, 10:* 453–461, 1972.

Lawrence, D. G., and Kuypers, H. G. J. M.: Pyramidal and nonpyramidal pathways in monkeys. Anatomical and functional correlation. *Science, 148:* 973–975, 1965.

Levy-Agresti, J., and Sperry, R. W.: Differential perceptual capacities of major and minor hemispheres. *Proc Natl Acad Sci, 61:* 1151, 1969.

Levy, J., Trevarthen, C., and Sperry, R. W.: Perception of bilateral chimeric figures following hemispheric deconnexion. *Brain, 95:* 61–78, 1972.

Mark, R. F., and Sperry, R. W.: Bimanual coordination in monkeys. *Exp Neurol, 21:* 92–104, 1968.

Myers, R. E.: Function of corpus callosum in interocular transfer. *Brain, 79:* 358–363, 1956.

Myers, R. E., Sperry, R. W., and McCurdy, N. M.: Neural mechanisms in visual guidance of limb movement. *Arch Neurol, 7:* 195–202, 1962.

Paillard, J.: The patterning of skilled movements. In Field, J. (Ed.): *Handbook of Physiology—Neurophysiology, Vol. III.* Washington, American Physiological Society, 1960, pp. 1679–1708.

Pasik, P., Pasik, T., and Schilder, P.: Extrageniculostriate vision in the monkey: Discrimination of luminous flux-equated figures. *Exp Neurol, 24:* 421–437, 1969.

Schneider, G. E.: Contrasting visuomotor functions of tectum and cortex in the golden hamster. *Psychol Forsch, 31:* 52–62, 1967.

Schneider, G. E.: Two visual systems. *Science, 163:* 895–902, 1969.

Sperry, R. W.: Corpus callosum and interhemispheric transfer in the monkey, *Macaca mulatta* (abstract). *Anat Rec, 131:* 297, 1958.

Sperry, R. W.: Mental unity following surgical disconnection of the cerebral hemispheres. *Harvey Lectures, Ser. 62.,* 293–323, 1968.

Sperry, R. W.: Perception in absence of the neocortical commissures. *Res Publ Assoc Nerv Ment Dis, 48:* 123–138, 1969.

Sperry, R. W.: Cerebral dominance in perception. In Young, F. A., and Lindsley, D. B. (Eds.): *Early Experience and Visual Information Processing in Perceptual and Reading Disorders.* Washington, Natl Acad Sci, 1970, pp. 167–178.

Sperry, R. W., Gazzaniga, M. S., and Bogen, J. E.: The neocortical commissures: Syndrome of hemisphere deconnection. In: Vinken, P. J., and Bruyn, G. W. (Eds.): *Handbook of Clinical Neurology.* Amsterdam, North Holland Pub Co, 1969.

Teuber, H.-L.: Alterations of perception after brain injury. In: Eccles, J. C. (Ed.): *Brain and Conscious Experience.* New York, Springer, 1966, pp. 182–216.

Trevarthen, C. B.: Double visual learning in split-brain monkeys. *Science, 136:* 258–259, 1962.

Trevarthen, C. B.: Processus visuels interhémisphériques localisés dans le tronc cérébral. Leur mise en évidence sur des singes à cerveau dédoublé. *C R Soc Biol (Paris), 157:* 2019–2022, 1963.

Trevarthen, C.: Functional interactions between the cerebral hemispheres of the split-brain monkey. In: Ettlinger, E. G. (Ed.): *Functions of the Corpus callosum.* London, Churchill, 1965.

Trevarthen, C. B.: Two mechanisms of vision in primates. *Psychol Forsch, 31:* 299–337, 1968.

Trevarthen, C.: Experimental evidence for a brain-stem contribution to visual perception in man. *Brain Behav Evol, 3:* 338–352, 1970.

Trevarthen, C.: Manipulative strategies of baboons, and the origins of cerebral asymmetry. In: Kinsbourne, M. (Ed.): *Hemispheric Asymmetry of Function.* Cambridge University Press (in press), 1975.

Trevarthen, C., and Kinsbourne, M.: Perceptual completion of words and figures by commissurotomy patients. (In preparation.) 1974.

Trevarthen, C., and Sperry, R. W.: Perceptual unity of the ambient visual field in human commissurotomy patients. *Brain, 96:* 547–570, 1973.

Weiskrantz, L.: Contour discrimination in a young monkey with striate cortex ablation. *Neuropsychologia, 1:* 145–164, 1963.

[CHAPTER XI]

CEREBRAL EMBRYOLOGY
AND THE SPLIT BRAIN

Colwyn Trevarthen

S INCE SPERRY'S REVIEW IN 1961, split-brain studies have led to a conception of brain organization like that shown in Figure XI-1, b. Also
shown as a diagram is a previous conception, A, which accords with the
early work of what may be called the classical period of the split-brain
experiments of Myers and Sperry. This figure is designed to contrast
two historical positions in the course of the development of an understanding of the effects of commissurotomy on brain function.

The evidence for the more elaborate scheme, which brings out the
columnar and hierarchical design of brain systems, comes both from work
with animals and from human commissurotomy subjects (Trevarthen,
1969). Briefly, the most important features are as follows:

Each hemisphere contains primary receptive cortical areas which are
essential to the fine discrimination by touch, or vision, i.e. by one perceptual system at a time. These communicate with the secondary "association" areas and downwards to brain-stem sensory and motor fields in
which all sensory modalities are associated. In each hemisphere the primary fields are concerned with uptake of information from distal parts
(hands and feet) on the other side of the body, or from the opposite
half of visual space. Motor control of distal extremities is also organized
so that each hemisphere regulates refined praxis of the opposite limbs
only, and a component of oculomotor exploration, concerned with filling
in perceptual details with information from the contralateral half of the
visual field, has the same kind of crossed laterality (see Trevarthen,
1968a and 1974, for review of the effects of commissurotomy on the
cerebral motor system).

Recent anatomical studies show that the commissures interconnect
association cortex on both sides, contributing to a bilateral representation
in each hemisphere. This has important significance in relation to the
effects of commissurotomy (Trevarthen, 1972). An alternative input
to the association cortex derives from the sub-hemispheric neural fields
in which functions of the body as a whole in the space surrounding it are

unified (Trevarthen, 1970; Trevarthen and Sperry, 1972). Proximal or axial parts of the body are known to have both motor and sensory representation within the parts of the cortex bordering the primary fields, and in the association cortex. These represent the body bilaterally in each cortex; through ascending projections which pass from receptors on both sides through more medial parts of the thalamus, and via efferent projections to the medial, core motor system.

Commissurotomy, therefore, separates functions of the primary sensory projection systems and of refined distal praxis completely, but it does not divide the duplicate, bilateral input to association cortex for the sensory processes governing whole body orientation or posture. This last category of function includes ambient vision (Trevarthen, 1970; Trevarthen and Sperry, 1973). Likewise, whole-body motor patterning and integration is maintained through the core motor system after the hemispheres are deconnected. The little we know about visceral and autonomic functions and regulation of emotional state indicates that they remain undivided after commissurotomy.

The design for functions in the brain shown in Figure XI-1 B incorporates recent anatomical discoveries (see Trevarthen, 1970; 1975, for references). A great leap forward in neuroanatomical understanding has been achieved in the last ten years, largely as a result of the application of electrophysiological mapping of receptor fields of central sensory receiving neurones, and tracing of pathways by experimental procedures involving silver staining of degenerating terminals or pre-terminals. A remarkably beautiful pattern is emerging, which, though complex, has unity of design which, I should think, any biologist must take as a sign of a unitary adaptive functional principle. Perhaps more than most neurobiologists, I believe we can now see a functional morphology in the brain, and that a psychoneural isomorphism of the bisymmetric brain and "behavioural field," discussed elsewhere (Trevarthen, 1968b; 1974), is coming to light. Split-brain work offers one of the best methods of testing this hypothesis of an integrated cerebral functional system based on anatomical bisymmetry and somatotopic representation.

In my opinion, the most important finding is that the anatomical components concerned with coordinated action of separate parts of the body and separate receptor fields in relation to external events are formed as a vertically unified core system. At all levels commissures appear to give cross-communication for these interior systems which initiate voluntary behaviour and the psychological syntheses involved in perception, motivation and memory. It now seems impossible to regard psychological functions in terms of reflexes in associative combinations, for the sensory information is received and analysed by parts of the nervous system which

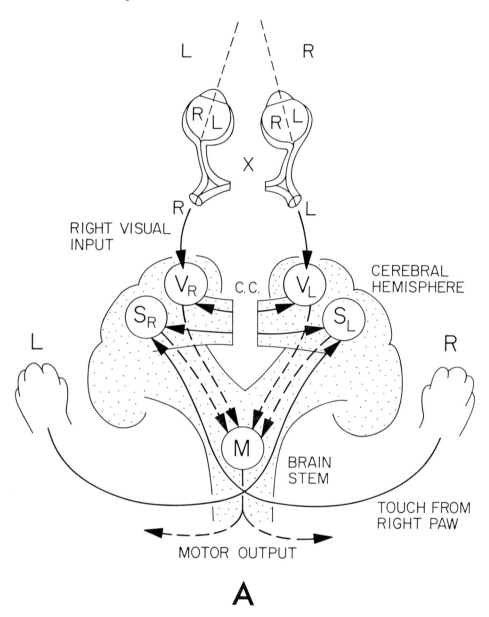

A

are appendages of the more central "nonspecific" mechanisms. On the motor side the data is equally clear.

Both striate visual cortex and precentral hand area in one hemisphere, having no direct access to their partners in the opposite hemisphere, work under direction of centers which move eyes or arm and hand. Their functions are regulated by hemisphere parts with rich reciprocal connections to lower levels of the brain as well as abundant com-

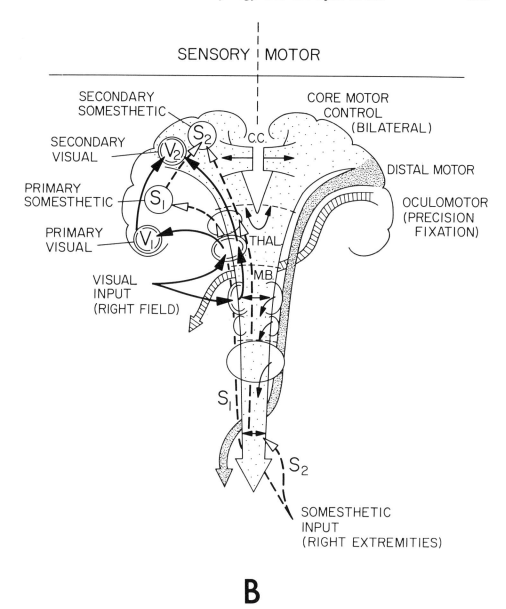

Figure XI-1a and b. Diagrams to explain concepts of function in split brains (See text, Trevarthen, 1969).

missural contacts with each other. Split-brain effects in man, and certain deconnection effects observed with unilateral cerebral injuries throw light on the elaborations in the cerebral hemispheres of the brain mechanisms in which psychological integrations are performed.

It is the purpose of this paper to review the relationship between the general scheme of the brain shown in Figure XI-1 b and brain growth. The embryology of the human brain is a unique process. Not only is it certainly the most complex of all biological growth phenomena, producing an intricacy of form far beyond our present understanding or imagination. It is also a very protracted process. Like the growth of a tree, brain growth and differentiation does not stop until the individual dies. This growth process is a way of incorporating structure through experience, like a tree forms a record of the direction of the sun, of every cold winter, every severe storm or axe blow; though of course, the neural process of assimilation is immensely more complex and discriminating and in command of its fate.

As we shall see, the embryology of the higher functional components of the brain which govern psychological activities, a process which I call "psychogenesis" (Trevarthen, 1972c), begins at birth. The human brain goes through growth and differentiation of components circuits mainly after birth, and not all parts of the brain develop at the same rate or appear at the same time (Trevarthen, 1972c; references for the following account may be found in this paper).

Body Form and Action Space

Bisymmetry and antero-posterior polarization are features of all free-moving forms of life. A body of that form is a sign of an automotive intelligence, and the psychological functions which regulate behaviour use the language of bisymmetry and forward progression to effect control over the body in relation to the external world. This is not so when polarization of space by gravity is insignificant, as floating plankton and space vehicles show.

In the first steps of the formation of a vertebrate embryo, the undifferentiated cells move in a delicate choreography shown in Figure XI-2 a. As a result, a bilaterally symmetrical dorsoventrally arranged, antero-posteriorly polarized individual is built by cells adhering selectively and moving past one another in a remarkably regulated process, the mechanical causes of which are now beginning to be understood. The important thing is that the *first* step is to establish such a body, and already at this stage one can take the organism and say, here is the head, here are the left and right halves of the body; here is where the nervous system will appear in the midline with an anterior brain thickening; the guts are going to be underneath and the outside world is going to impinge on top. You can talk about this early stage, less than 1 mm long, as a map of potential processes and anatomical elements which are going to eventuate later. The three germ layers, with their diverse function fates, are an expression of this same principle.

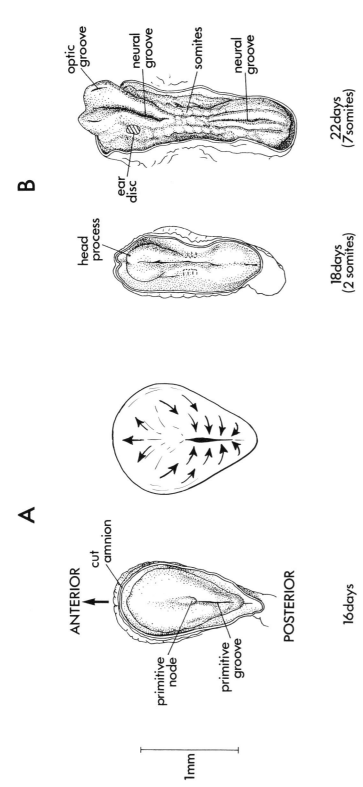

Figure XI-2. Human embryos from the embryonal disc stage to appearance of the nervous system. In A, cell motions observed in the chick embryo.

Thenceforth, there is a rapid accentuation of the polarity that has been so early stamped upon the body (Fig. XI-2b). The central nervous tissue is set out very early, and the spinal tube and brain tube appear within the pattern of body form. Like the body, the central nervous system shows a bilateral symmetry from the start. There is an axial notochord through the body which is the primordial skeletal axis and the contractile tissue antecedent is aggregated on either side of this to form a double chain of muscle blocks, one pair per body segment. At this stage the myotomes are, of course, not functional as muscles; they are preformed to be the elementary motor system and may already be identified as such.

Integrating the Nervous System with the Body

Analytical experiments testing the causal relationships at early stages show that while the different parts of the embryo may develop an intrinsic automatic ability to go part way on their own to a particular form, communication between the local regions affects the process and causes them to be related or integrated within an overall scheme.

In particular, the regions of the nervous system are instructed from the adjacent body parts as to their destiny in later development. What neurectoderm in a particular part of the early embryo nerve cord will be later depends, in part, upon the arrangement of body cells, ectoderm, notochord, mesoderm and endoderm, near it. If the neural tube is moved about surgically at an early enough stage, its further development may be redirected according to its new cell surroundings. If embryonic cells already differentiated as nerve ectoderm, skin ectoderm and muscle mesoderm are mechanically separated and mixed up, they may sort themselves out in tissue culture and regroup to form a neural mass with skin ectoderm and mesoderm surrounding it. What the nerve tissue in the resultant mass will differentiate into depends upon the ratio of ectoderm/mesoderm nearby. A high ratio switches the neuroblasts to form brain tissue, a low ratio, i.e. a high proportion of muscle mesoderm, induces spinal cord. One can rearrange the longitudinal differences, the dorso-ventral polarity and left-right symmetry of the nervous system by altering the body configurations round it. Clearly the body system and the impressionable neural tube within it have a common design obtained through their initial inductive relationships in the embryo.

So, what we have in the body and nervous system of an embryo is a preformed mechanism for activity in the world. You know which direction it will swim or walk, pushed by the posterior skeleto-motor mechanism. You know about its left-right turning tendencies, and about intake of metabolic requirements anteriorly under control of forwardly situated sense organs, etc.; all this can already be made out. The machinery or engine which will be able to act like this (one might think of it as a car with no one sitting in it) is formulated and built before the driver or nervous system appears, and there is, early on, an inductive relation from body to the nervous system. The embryo nervous system becomes imprinted with something which is very like an inner representation (a programme) of the uses to which the body may be put in later life.

Growth of a Controlling Nerve Net

Nerve fibers do not begin to express the latent structural organization of the nervous system in a pattern of connections until the late embryo, after morphogenesis has made a passable outline of all body parts, including special receptor organs, mouth, limbs, as well as internal heart, main blood vessels, gut etc. At this point, however, an embryo man looks much like an embryo chicken or donkey (Fig. XI-3a).

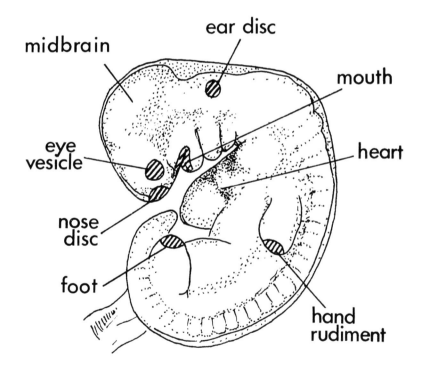

32 days (5mm)

Figure XI-3a. Human embryo showing sensory and motor structures.

When nerve fibers do grow out they clearly express different intrinsic powers of selection with respect to the tissues among which they must find their way. The apex of each outgrowing nerve cell extension is an intensely active mechanism. In tissue culture, free of tissue surroundings, it is a fan-like structure with minute radiating tentacles or filipodia. These are evidently capable of exploration and choice among a spread of alternative routes in a maze of tissue membranes and cavities. Consistent choices build up a directed growth path of the main thread of nerve plasm, the different cell-types producing axons which criss-cross each other, each indifferent to the others, but each guided by a particular bio-chemical or molecular-biological trace within the complexly patterned extraneural medium. No other explanation can be given for the patterns observed.

Until axons and dendrites have extended in this way and made their selective connections, the nervous system as such does not exist. Immature neuroblasts, like other embryonic cells, are in communication through contact points, and they can conduct electrical potentials. Their positions and migrations are determined in early stages by their amoeba-like motility and selective adhesion, but integration of a nervous system requires interconnection between remote points in a systematic net through outgrowth of dendrites and axons.

At the time the first nerve fibers appear, the body already has limbs, jaws and special sense organs locally developed on it, and these continue to differentiate in a somewhat self-sufficient manner, later to become pulled together or reintegrated within the overall body scheme by outgrowth of a nervous system (Fig. XI-3a). Here, again, we see the dialectic between individuality and collective action which is characteristic of all biological development. Inductive processes impose a representation of the common plan of the space of behavioural action on each primordium; inner ear, eye, limb, etc. This subsequently serves as a basis for their reintegration by growth of a nerve network linking them together (Fig. XI-3b).

If the nerve fibers are to make their connections correctly by choice as they grow out, the neuroblasts must already be stamped with the field of this action space as a population. We still do not remotely understand how the requisite instructions are given, but instructions there must be so that once nerve fibers do start to grow they will perform the extremely regular and complex pathfinding we see.

The Universal Brain Map of Visual Space

Most of what is known of this extraordinary process comes from studies not of embryogenesis, but of regrowth of nerve cables in lower vertebrates; especially those between retina and brain, after they have been broken up surgically. Rearrangement experiments have proved that a useful visual field in which a fish or a frog can aim its locomotion or food catching is the outcome of inherent patterning of connections between eye and brain (Sperry, 1951; 1965).

Now, thirty years after Sperry began to put the problem of specification of nerve nets on a solid experimental foundation, we know from histological and electrophysiological mapping work that all vertebrates map the external visual world onto the brain according to the same plan. Fish, amphibia, reptiles, birds and many mammals have been mapped. It has been found that the map on the midbrain roof is the same no matter which way the eyes point in the head (Fig. XI-5). For a rabbit the optical axis of each eye points to where he moves to turn far left or right. For a cat the optic axis is near straight ahead, where the animal looks to center his attention or aim his body. Nevertheless, straight ahead and 45° left to 45° right are mapped in the same relation to the bisymmetric midbrain roof in cat and rabbit, with only minor deformations which may be explained in terms of the relative sizes of other

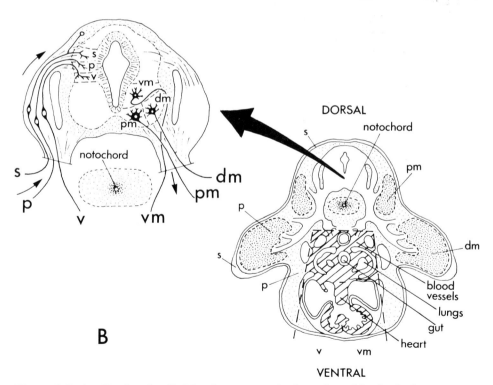

Figure XI-3b. Regional affinities between spinal cord and body in human embryo of 35 days.

neighboring brain structures such as the thalamus. The same is true for goldfish and frog which have an equally big difference between the direction of their optic axes. The midbrain map is, in vertebrates, a universal map of the visual projection of the space in which each animal acts (Trevarthen, 1968a, b).

Sensory-Motor Coupling for Segmental Reflexes

The fundamental relationship between the body form and nerve-cell fields in the brain may also be seen in the layout of sensory and motor zones within one segment of the nerve cord of the trunk (Fig. XI-3b). The orderly arrangement of distal, proximal and internal sensory and motor fields would seem to assure mapping of body surface, body inside structures and viscera onto the C.N.S. and thence via the effector circuit onto the motor machinery of body and limbs.

To Map the Visual Orientation Field on the Motor System, the Eye Map Must be Inverted

In the case of vision it is outer space which has to be mapped via the eye onto the motor map of the body by which locomotor coordination is effected. The motor integrator which directs the coupled actions of the spinal motor segments in locomotion to orient and aim the body within visual space is located in the midbrain. This is what Coghill called "the head ganglion of the motor system." There must be a map of the whole body in there which is connected appropriately to the downstream final common path motor mechanism that pulls the strings to move the trunk and limbs. And onto the midbrain motor map is projected an orderly representation of directions in visual space.

No matter which way the eyes are fixed in the head this map is always laid out on the optic tectum with anterior facing forwards in the midline, outside left on the right half of the brain, outside right on the left half of the brain; somewhat like a general will lay out his campaign map in front of him on the table with north ahead, east to the right and west to the left. The shape of the body first formed in embryogenesis determines where in front, left, right, up, down and behind will be, for goldfish and general alike.

Experiments indicate that these directions are also given by the body to the brain tissues and eye primordia which will connect up accordingly. The orientation of the tectal map agrees with the general principle that notochord and mesoderm concentration relative to ectoderm are reference structures for the labelling of the assembly of neuroblasts with the coordinates of the body.

But, here the argument encounters a serious difficulty. The eyes of true vertebrates have lenses which rotate the image of the external world 180° relative to the body. How does the brain growth take care of this? Is the matter taken care of only after birth, through experience? If so, what of the demonstrations that retino-tectal specification of circuits is established in the early embryo?

In the early somite embryo in man about three weeks after conception, each eye primordium is merely a small dimple along the anterior dorsal edge of the as yet unclosed brain platform (Fig. XI-4). This depression develops into a spherical outpushing or optic vesicle. Surgical experiments with amphibia show that early on the cells of this vesicle are still open to retyping; they are pluripotent in the sense that if the vesicle is transplanted elsewhere, the principle anteroposterior and dorsoventral axes will be impressed from the body field onto them no matter which way the vesicle is oriented in the body. At a critical point the cells are irreversibly typed, first with the A-P axis then with the D-V axis, and thereafter if the vesicle is taken out and put back upside down it will permanently have an upside down map relative to the body.

Preceding this point in time there is a remarkable growth change at the anterior ends of all vertebrate brains; shark, human or Coelacanth.* While the orienting field is maturing in the retinal neuroblasts, the optic territory moves forward, away from a position adjacent to the midbrain visual field, and rotates 180° as if it were rolling round the end of the notochord (Fig. XI-4). At the close of this rotation the notochord end is *above* the eye and later the oculomuscle rudiments come to lie *above* and *anterior* to the vesicle.† Early blood vessels likewise are related to the eye stalk in a configuration which is inverted when compared with the situation for other regions of the C.N.S. All the relations between the eye and the field established with respect to the notochord and myotomes are now rotated as compared to every other part of the C.N.S. and the body. In particular, they are inverted relative to the midbrain slice of the neural tube and the position in which it lay in relation to the body when its cells were, we presume, typed.

This morphogenetic trick would certainly appear to provide for the inversion of the visual image which is consequent on having a lens, for it means that the visual field will be mapped on the brain so that it works with respect to the motor system of the body. The casual mechanism proposed for induction of the retinal field has not been tested experi-

---

* For illustrations of the shark brain showing the early rotation of the anterior end, See Johnston (1911) and Kingsbury (1922).

† The detailed anatomy of the anterior end of the closing and down-curling neural plate in human embryos, with location of the optic area before its inversion, is given by Bartelmez, 1922; Bartelmez and Blount, 1954; and Bartelmez and Dekaban, 1962.

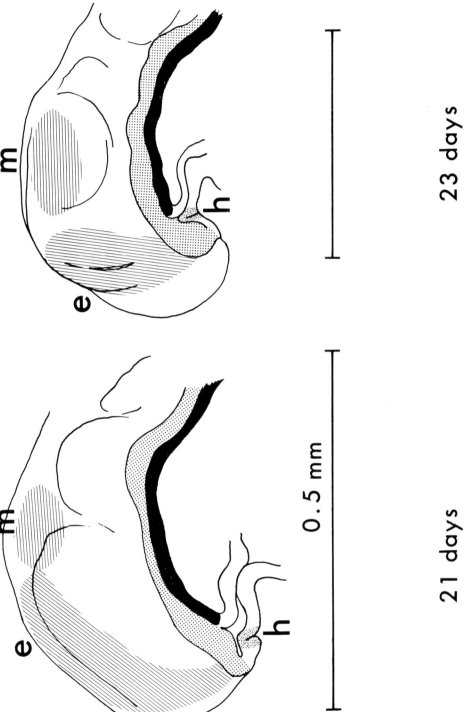

21 days

23 days

0.5 mm

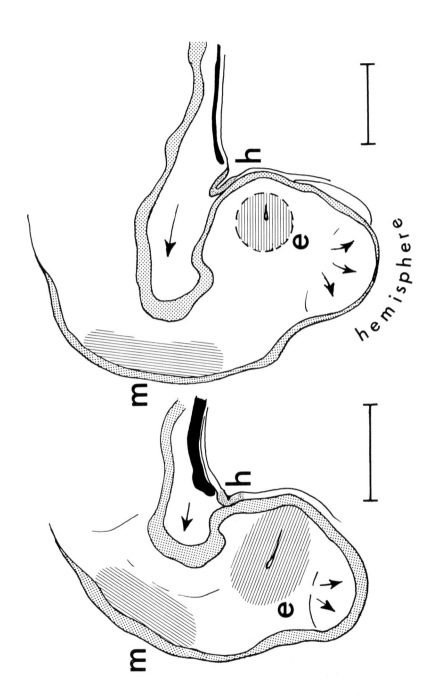

31 days   34 days

Figure XI-4. Human embryos. Changes in the position and orientation of the eye territory, e, relative to the optic projection field in the midbrain roof, m. Notochord, black; Rathke's pouch (pars anterior of hypophysis), h. Based on Bartelmez and Dekaban (1962) and others.

mentally, but I believe it is true, especially in view of the fact that *Amphioxus* and lamprey larvae which do not have lateral eyes with lenses also do not exhibit the 180° twist at the front ends of their brains.

Visuomotor Coordination is Primarily Innate Due to Embryogenesis

In psychology there is a centuries old argument about how on earth do we see the world upright when the image on the retina is rotated upside down. The explanation appears to be that in embryogenesis the behavioural field comes to be stamped on the retina when it is upside down relative to its final alignment to the rest of the system of the body. Consequently, when ganglion cells send out their axons to find their tectal destinations in the precise way they do, they automatically reerect the visual field image so that it is correct with respect to the body. All those wonderful arguments about the power of psychological symbolism and coding and what not now have lost their point in this particular case. More importantly, the evidence shows that acts are coordinated in visual space primarily because in the embryo, months before there is a visual space, the nervous system is connected up appropriately. This is a blow for psychobiology, the science of biological causes in psychology, and a more mystifying yet more satisfying explanation of a basic psychological function than an empiricist, who seeks to explain psychological functions by the effects of experience, may provide.

Recent studies of infants in the first weeks after birth make it clear that, contrary to long persisting belief, man is born with an immature but properly integrated visuo-motor space which has grown in his brain. The embryological phenomena we have just reviewed show how the determination of innate equipment for space perception starts off in development of the human brain.

Having found strong anatomical evidence for believing in an embryological process which builds an integrated neural system for regulating acts in a visual space, we shall consider the embryology of the cerebral hemispheres. But first I must define "behavioural space," as I use this term, and discuss the different functions which are incorporated in it.

Behavioural Space

Once the body begins to swim and behave, one can see how the territory in which the body acts is related to the brain through the embryological processes indicated. If one could envisage the whole population of forward motions, changes of course, jumps and turns to obtain or avoid, which a vertebrate makes in its lifetime, and plot them as a dis-

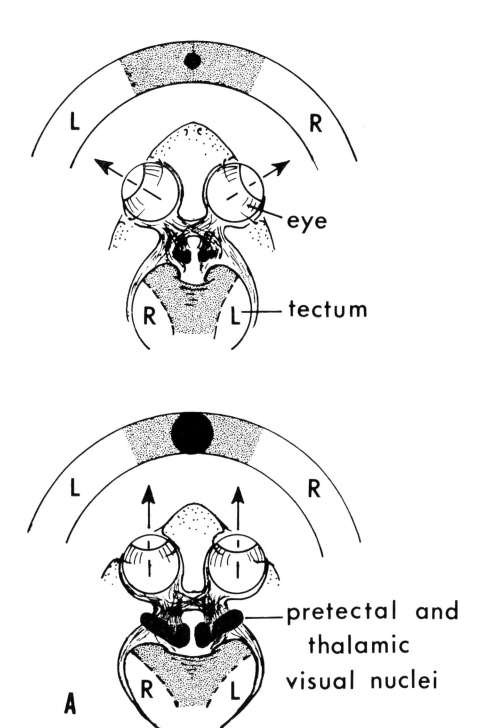

Figure XI-5a. Projection of regions of external space on midbrain tectum in animals with eyes facing different directions. Frontally oriented eyes are characteristically associated with greater development of diencephalic visual nuclei and elaboration of the geniculo-striate projection. Cerebral hemispheres not shown (c.f. Trevarthen, 1968a).

tribution of movement vectors centered on the body, a space would be generated which would be, like the body is, of a forward polarized, bisymmetric, horizontally poised form. This is behavioural space. Each locomobile animal has the potentiality to behave in such a bisymmetric polar space centered on the body; even the flatfish, which shows a rare abuse of its first swimming body, in the course of its metamorphosis into a new coordinate system turned 90° to the larval one so that it can swim on its side.

We can chart behavioural space, both with respect to its intake of information and its output of motor acts, by reference to body form. The reason we can do so is, of course, that it all originates in the symmetry of that body in early embryology.

The map of visual space on the surface of the midbrain, much studied in fish and amphibia, serves as an example of how behavioural space is represented in a dominant brain segment embryologically (Fig. XI-5). In it forward central space, the part in front of the head, where consummatory acts are performed under optimal attention control, where objects must be identified, is represented antero-medically on the two halves of the tectum and in duplicate.‡ Each central territory is mapped onto the other by orderly commissural connections which involve synaptic transmission of information through neurones somewhere in the midbrain core. This map on the midbrain roof bears obvious resemblance to the diagram of the functional system revealed by studies of the effects of cerebral deconnection (Fig. XI-1b).

The behavioural field has two components. Coordinated action of body parts produces acts of orientation which are aimed in the bisymmetric orientation space mapped out early in brain development. Inside this, at the center, is a group of functions concerned with psychological representation of special forms, objects, systems, etc., as such, after they have been oriented to. Orienting and identifying are represented in different parts of the brain networks.

Growth of the Cerebral Hemispheres in the Fetus
Development of Higher Capacities for Object Recognition
and Discriminatory Action

We have traced the embryology of primary visuomotor connections in the *embryo*. Now, in order to observe the formation of the cerebral hemispheres, which are the most anterior of brain parts, we must look

---

‡ There is also a mapping from surface to depth, with more medial parts concerned with multimodal control of central integrations, the surface being devoted to analysis of incoming sensory information and resolution of locations in orientation space.

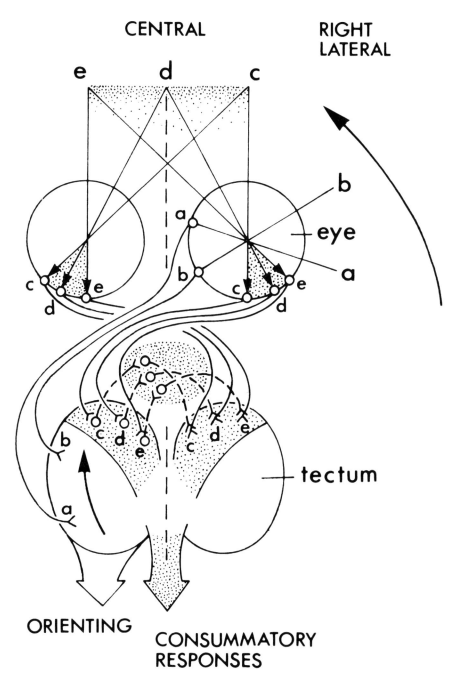

Figure XI-5b. Generalized map of visual field on midbrain of vertebrates (Trevarthen, 1972c).

at what occurs in the *fetus,* the phase which in man begins two months after fertilization.

An early fetus has a form showing the main characteristics of the species to which it belongs. Its body is essentially complete in form. It has, however, performed no motor contractions on neural command. The neurones are growing out, but the first functional contacts have not been formed between them. Nevertheless, the fetus looks as if it is oriented, hands, mouth, eyes, nose attentive to one point a short distance ahead (Fig. XI-6). This posture of coordinated orientation of parts remains the rest position or null position of the hands and head a month

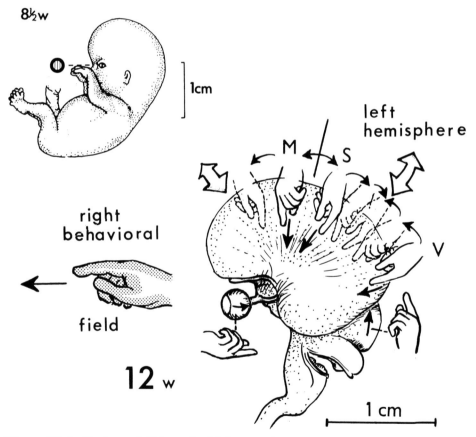

Figure XI-6. Posture of 8½ week old human fetus before any neurogenic movements occur. Speculative map of projections from the right half of the behavioral field onto the left cerebral hemisphere. Based on maps obtained for adult primates. M = motor; S = somesthetic; V = visual. White arrows indicate frontal and parietal regions richly interconnected by commissures with the other hemisphere.

or two later, after reflex responses appear to touch round the mouth or hands, and spontaneous turning patterns occur.

The body of a human fetus grows some two hundred times in weight and ten times in length, but this growth is accompanied by but slight elaboration of a structure already human at the start. The fetus is a time for growth of the brain, not the body; for differentiation of cerebral and cerebellar tissues. Even at birth major components of these organs are in rudimentary condition.

The brain of a fetus appears to grow by elaboration from a unified central mechanism, and the cerebral circuits which will control the perceptual exploration and voluntary motor employment of the world develop out of the anterior central components of the embryo brain, parts closely integrated anatomically with the midbrain map center. Thus, the human cerebral hemispheres grow after the brain of basic sensory-motor intelligence, equivalent to a fish brain, has been laid down in the late embryo. They swell rapidly in the early fetus as if they were balloons inflated from an attachment near the hypothalamus and as they expand they curl to form the characteristic ram's horn with temporal lobe curled forwards underneath. At the same time the diencephalon, especially the thalamus, expands greatly (Fig. XI-6).

Histogenesis of the cerebral cortex is very complex, but in outline it confirms the external appearance that the forebrain enlarges by an unrolling of nerve tissue from within. Indeed the tissues grow inside out over the cortical mantle. The reticular core of the brain stem and cord has close affinity with the cortex and all appearances lead to the conclusion that hemisphere growth is by an evagination. In the space exposed by separation of the rotated eye field and midbrain in the late embryo the forebrain billows out, incorporating cells which have built-in affinities to sensory and motor fields downstream in the brain. When nerve fiber tracts grow in the last week of the embryo and on into the fetus, they connect the hemispheres and basal ganglia with sensory or motor derivatives of the reticulum of brain stem and cord. This inaugurates the integrative core mechanism of Figure XI-1B.

In the first sixteen weeks of fetal growth the hemispheres attain their characteristic form, with forward pointing temporal lobe, and the primary olfactory, motor somesthetic and visual cortices are laid down. At this same time the cerebral commissures, which are of such particular interest to us, make their appearance; first the anterior commissure then the hippocampal cammissure and the corpus callosum growing by addition of fibers dorsally and caudally. But even at term (40 weeks) they are still disproportionately small (Fig. XI-7). Clearly they belong to a hemispheric component system which matures very late indeed.

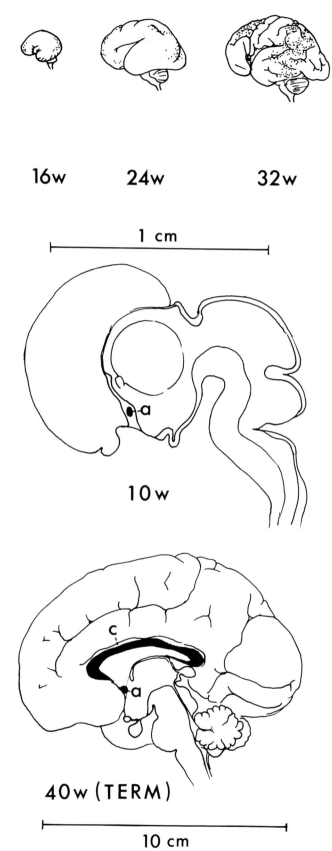

16w   24w   32w

1 cm

10 w

40w (TERM)

10 cm

Figure XI-7. Above: Human cerebral hemispheres to same scale showing the late maturation of association cortex (stipple).

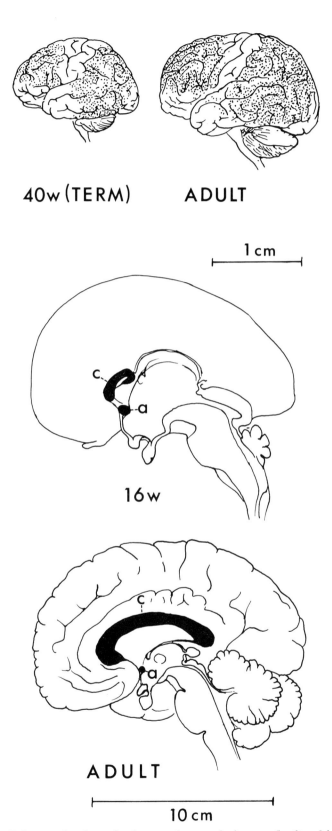

40w (TERM)   ADULT

1 cm

16w

ADULT

10 cm

Below: Parallel growth of cerebral commissures before and after birth.

Regional studies of the fetal and neonate cortex reveal that, in the last 16 weeks of intrauterine development, anterior (frontal) and posterior (parietal, occipito-parietal and posterior temporal) association cortex grow in size more than the regions near the central sulcus, inferior frontal surface, occipital pole or temporal pole. The association cortex in each hemisphere grows along with the commissures through which it is in direct communication to the corresponding cortex in the opposite hemisphere (Fig. XI-7).

Somatotopic (body-shaped) maps in the cerebral cortex, and indeed in thalamic nuclei, basal ganglia, cortico-bulbar and cortico-spinal fiber projections, all show that the imprint of body form is common currency throughout the brain. Recent maps of the primate cortex disclose a consistent layout related to simpler plans of lower mammals. The multiple maps are oriented in parallel and interconnected in orderly way by arcuate association fibers. Their arrangement appears to bear a definite relation to the relative growth movements of populations of cortical neuroblasts and this, together with the evidence for orderly connection of corresponding somatotopic points, for example, as between the visual midbrain map and the cortical maps, would appear to support the view that these connections all derive from morphogenetic fields impressed on the nervous system from the body in the embryo long before the hemispheres appear.

Postnatal Growth of the Brain

The human brain increases about two and one-half times in length from birth to adulthood. This size change, which is small compared with body growth, hides a complexity of internal regional differentiation, especially in infancy and early childhood.

As in fetal stages, the main increase in brain bulk after birth, is caused by the extension of dendrites and the proliferation of connecting axons, especially in the first two years. Cortical cells develop elaborate branching dendrites, covered with astronomical numbers of small dendritic spines to which a high proportion of synaptic connections are made. Postnatal production of new nerve cells is restricted to the cerebral hemispheres and cerebellum, and this results in the appearance of interstitial microneurones which may have a role in modification of circuits in later stages of development.

The larger nerve fibers gain a myelin sheath as the attached nerve cell body and dendritic tree attain maturity. Myelination therefore indicates growth of whole neurones, and studies of its patterning confirm that many human brain structures change greatly after birth.

Indeed, the hemispheres and brain stem exhibit three zones which mature at contrasting rates (Yakovlev and Lecours, 1967). The central core or *median zone* (hypothalamus and midline reticular nuclei of the thalamus) is concerned with visceral activity and behaviour patterns regulating metabolic and reproductive functions and it shows maturation over two to three decades, through the years of reproductive life. Outside this, the *paramedian zone* (cingulum, limbic cortex, basal ganglia) has a short cycle of development completed at puberty. This is the mechanism governing more complex innate motor patterns for signalling of internal states; gestures and mimicry, postural mannerisms and expressive vocalization. Finally, the commissural and association systems of the *outermost or supralimbic cerebral cortex zone* has the longest cycle of maturation extending through maturity to old age. Its growth and development corresponds with the continuation of cognitive learning from individual experience and with the acquisition of skills important in human society, including symbolized thought, language and manufacture.

Studies of commissurotomy patients support the view that cerebral maturation continuing beyond the first two decades is responsible for a progressive lateralization of functions of visual perception, thought and language (Levy, 1969; Sperry, 1968a, b; Levy, Trevarthen and Sperry, 1972). Evidently the slow-maturing association cortex-commissure system is responsible for a selective consolidation of experience differently in the two sides of the brain, a process which requires the connections of the corpus callosum (Sperry, 1968b; 1969).

Environmental Determination of Cerebral Circuits

All growing biological systems are in changing dynamic equilibrium, and the growth elements interact competitively, permitting various degrees of influence from external factors when these may change the balance of components as the system is formed. Nevertheless, the effects of external factors on the growth of form, especially in the more complex biological systems including the nervous system, are conditional on an initial closed phase of differentiation in which rules and programmes of potential action are laid down.

Up till this point we have been more concerned with bringing to light the primary embryology of the integrative nervous system, the process which sets the context for the selective assimilation later of specific and detailed structure from contacts with the environment. There are, of course, many grades of plasticity between the self-controlled dynamics of primary and closed morphogenesis, and the secondary, more open systems in later stages of growth and differentiation. The effectiveness of higher intelligence must certainly be due to the ability of highly elaborated brains to develop patterns of neurone interconnection that store regular occurrences in experience and make future acts more likely to be adaptive.

Recent experimental studies have brought to light a capacity for regulatory adjustment in the growth of certain late-maturing nerve networks. There is evidence from microelectrode studies of receptor units that the growth process connecting nerve cells in parts of the visual system may be modified greatly by influences from the environment through use (Gaze, 1970). In any attempt to assess the significance of the experimental results it should be remembered that rather extreme partial deprivation or distortion of input is required to bring them about. However, recent work with the frog *Xenopus* indicates that plasticity of nerve connections plays a highly significant role in changing relations between the growing retina of the embryo and the growing area to which it projects in the brain.

The environmentally determined balance of nerve connections recorded in the central binocular part of the midbrain visual map in *Xenopus,* and the selective redistribution of visual cortex connections in the neonatal kitten both appear to be correlated with adjustment of secondary components after the main form of the mid-brain visuomotor mechanism has been completed by closed morphogenesis in early brain embryology. It is also interesting that neural plasticity in both these cases is concerned with binocular convergence of inputs in a visual field which, through metamorphosis, has a much larger area of binocular overlap than would have occurred if the eyes had retained the lateral position in which they were first formed. In *Xenopus,* commissural neurones are involved in the convergence.

The late maturation of the cerebral commissures, and the association cortices they interconnect, suggests in mammals that this component of the cerebral circuits is more likely to be open to environmental or experimental specification than those laid down earlier.

In man, cerebral lateralization of function, and functional specialization of each hemisphere, result from slow post-natal development of asymmetric control within association cortex regions, and it would appear that the process requires intact commissures which communicate, not primary sensory information, but integrated perceptual and volitional programmes. There is, apparently, no cerebral lateralization when the corpus callosum fails to grow, as in acallosal subjects (Sperry, 1969).

CONCLUSIONS

The above account describes a basic principle of brain design derived from the embryological growth process. Body and brain grow as a unit and the psychological functions of the brain develop by elaboration of a principle of control which may be exemplified by the midbrain center for integration of visual orienting behaviour (Fig. XI-5b).

Consummatory or assimilatory acts, performed in central behavioural space under bilateral cerebral control follow exploratory and orienting behaviour which requires the body to be adjusted by locomotion and posture to the locations and times of events in the outside world. Consummatory acts also must be coloured by affect, which is a function of the self-regulatory (autonomic) neural systems by which the internal milieu is regulated and for which the hypothalamus is the chief ganglion. To do this predictively they draw on detailed sensory data which is assimilated by a process of controlled reorientation in a bisymmetric field approximately isomorphic to the brain.

The cerebral hemispheres have evolved and still grow by elaboration of the intrinsic integrative functions which we associate with the reticular formation of brain stem and cord. They provide for psychological functions of consciousness and volition which override the more immediate "reflex" adjustments that the early laid down circuits of brain stem and spinal cord can control.

Exploratory orienting functions of the hemispheres are under the direct influence of circuits in primary cortex (somesthetic, motor, visual etc.) but they are also coupled with brain-stem circuits and with association cortex in which bilateral representations come to predominate. The association cortex areas are interconnected by commissures; the primary, assimilatory cortex areas are not.

As the association cortex and commissures become more elaborate in the postnatal development of man, cerebral asymmetry expresses itself, the bilateral "whole organism" functions of each hemisphere taking a somewhat different path from the other. What developmental stratagem underlies cerebral asymmetry of function remains a mystery. But, as we shall see from later contributions to this volume, some consistency of rules emerges from which we may hope eventually to decipher a morphogenetic function underlying the formation of the more complex psychological mechanism of human intelligence.

One fascinating aspect is the suggestion, from Jerre Levy's studies of differences between left and right handers, that in normal psychogenesis different individual men and women may end up expressing different kinds of intelligence which have evolved as genetically regulated compliments in a cooperative society of minds. If this is so, psychologists' crude genetic ideas supporting the notion of a single scale of more or less "intelligence," however this is measured, will need revision to permit recognition of essentially different intelligences.

Finally, in reference to our special interest in the cerebral commissures in man, the developmental story leads to three conclusions, one concerning the effects of commissurotomy, the others related to the development of commissural function.

1. We should not be surprised if cutting the connections between the hemispheres in the adult does not either destroy or duplicate cerebral "processing" of motor patterning or attention, even if detailed information for consciousness and certain higher schemata for action are separately handled in deconnected hemispheres. The central somatotopic principle of brain organization, being of early embryogenic origin, is too widespread throughout lower levels, and vertical communication between them and the hemispheres is too rich to permit complete dissociation at the level of the hemispheres.

2. Infants are not likely to behave as if they have split-brains as has been lightly suggested. They do have very poorly developed hemispheric commissures, but the cortical tissues these interconnect are also poorly differentiated. Rather is it likely that what a neonate can do with his brain is what cannot be split in two by commissurotomy in the adult, i.e. peripheral awareness of self in relation to surroundings, and a relatively little differentiated, but unified, sensory-motor basis for action and intelligence.

   Recent studies of eye-hand coordination and perception of objects in infancy by Bower (1972) fit well with this idea. Coordinated looking movements of the two eyes are integrated in one field with earliest prereaching orientations of the hands, and feet, in the first weeks after birth. Bower and his students have even shown that babies a few weeks old expect an object to have touch properties when the hand is carried to the place where the object is seen to be (Bower, Broughton and Moore, 1970). This means that the neurally integrated orientation space is a space in which different modalities converge for the detection of objects, from the start. Nevertheless, discrimination of details in objects is clearly rudimentary for some time after birth.

3. It would appear that post-infancy maturation with intact commissures is essential to development of complimentary functions of higher order asymmetrically in the human brain. There is evidence that the basis of a particular direction of cerebral asymmetry of function may be already determined and produce effects in any given individual at birth, but most of cortical asymmetry grows much later on in life.

REFERENCES

Bartelmez, G. W.: The origin of the otic and optic primordia in man. *J Comp, Neurol, 34:* 201–232, 1922.

Bartelmez, G. W., and Blount, M. P.: The formation of neural crest from the primary optic vesicle in man. *Carnegie Inst Wash Publ 603, Contribs Embryol, 35:* 55–71, 1954.

Bartelmez, G. W., and Dekaban, A. S.: The early development of the human brain. *Carnegie Inst Wash Publ 621, Contribs Embryol, 37:* 15–32, not including plates, 1962.

Bower, T. G. R.: Object perception in infants. *Perception, 1:* 15–30, 1972.

Bower, T. G. R., Broughton, J. M., and Moore, M. K.: Demonstration of intention in the reaching behaviour of neonate humans. *Nature, 228:* 679–681, 1970.

Gaze, R. W.: *The Formation of Nerve Connections.* London and New York, Acad Pr, 1970.

Johnston, J. B.: The telencephalon of selachians. *J Comp Neurol, 21:* 1–114, 1911.

Kingsbury, B. F.: The fundamental plan of the vertebrate brain. *J Comp Neurol, 34:* 461–491, 1922.

Levy, J.: Possible basis for the evolution of lateral specialization of the human brain. *Nature, 224:* 614–615, 1969.

Levy, J., Trevarthen, C., and Sperry, R. W.: Perception of bilateral chimeric figures following hemispheric deconnexion. *Brain, 95:* 61–78, 1972.

Sperry, R. W.: Mechanisms of neural maturation. In: S. S. Stevens (Ed.): *Handbook of Experimental Psychology.* New York, Wiley, 1951.

Sperry, R. W.: Cerebral organization and behavior. *Science, 133:* 1749–1757, 1961.

Sperry, R. W.: Embryogenesis of behavioral nerve nets. In De Haan, R.L., and Ursprung, H., (Eds.): *Organogenesis.* New York, HRW, 1965.

Sperry, R. W.: Hemisphere deconnection and unity in conscious awareness. *Am Psychol, 23:* 723–733, 1968a.

Sperry, R. W.: Plasticity of neural maturation. In Locke, M., (Ed.): *The Emergence of Order in Developing Systems. Dev Biol, Suppl 2.* New York and London, Acad Pr, 1968b.

Sperry, R. W.: Perception in the absence of the neocortical commissures. *Res Publ Nerv Ment Dis, 48:* 123–138, 1969.

Trevarthen, C. B.: Two mechanisms of vision in primates. *Psych Forsch, 31:* 299–337, 1968a.

Trevarthen, C. B.: Vision in fish: The origins of the visual frame for action in vertebrates. In Ingle, D. (Ed.): *The central nervous system and fish behavior.* Chicago, U Chicago Pr, 1968b, pp. 61–94.

Trevarthen, C. B.: Cerebral-midbrain relations reflected in split-brain studies of higher integrative functions. Paper presented at the XIXth International Congress of Psychology, London. July 1969.

Trevarthen, C. B.: Experimental evidence for a brain-stem contribution to visual perception in man. *Brain, Behav Evol, 3:* 338–352, 1970.

Trevarthen, C. B.: Manipulative strategies of baboons and the origins of cerebral asymmetry. In Kinsbourne, M. (Ed.): *Hemispheric asymmetry of function.* Cambridge University Press (in press), 1975.

Trevarthen, C. B.: 1972b. Brain bisymmetry and the role of the corpus callosum in behavior and conscious experience. In Cernacek, J., and Podivinsky, F. (Eds.): *Proceedings of the Colloquium on Interhemispheric Relations.* Bratislava, Slovak Academy of Sciences, 1972, pp. 321–333.

Trevarthen, C. B.: Behavioral embryology. In Carterette, E. C., and Friedman, M. P., (Eds.): *Handbook of Perception.* New York, Acad Pr, 1973, pp 89–117.

Trevarthen, C. B., and Sperry, R. W.: Perceptual unity of the ambient visual field in commissurotomy patients. *Brain, 96:* 547–570, 1973.

Yakovlev, P. I., and Lecours, A. R.: The myelogenetic cycles of regional maturation of the brain. In Minkowski, A., (Ed.): *Regional Development of the Brain in Early Life.* Oxford, Blackwell, 1967.

[PART IV]

INTEGRATION

CHAPTER XII

LATERAL INTERACTIONS
IN THE BRAIN

Marcel Kinsbourne

MANY INVERTEBRATES AND ALL vertebrates are constructed bisymmetrically in both their locomotor and their neural control systems. This arrangement may have evolved as part of the development of effective unidirectional progression. Once a particular end of the animal is designated as its leading point, distance receptors may with advantage be organized around it. These will subserve two functions: (1) to detect ambient changes in the environment which it might be expedient to explore, and (2) when the organism has swung around to confront the location of change, to examine it further before making the fundamental decision to approach, to retreat, or to continue with previous activity. An initial orienting response is followed by analysis of the stimulus. Because relevant external events will with equal overall probability occur to the right and to the left, the input-processing facilities needed for orienting are bilaterally and symmetrically represented on the animal. The facilities for further stimulus analysis are not necessarily so reduplicated, though in subhuman species they still seem to involve both hemispheres equally. If the bilateral facilities that mediate lateral orientation were autonomous, then coincident events on the two sides of the animal could lead to simultaneous incompatible decisions. Furthermore, to secure the animal's coordinated whole-body movement, the unilateral decision mechanism must have access to effectors on both sides; otherwise, the animal would turn with the limbs on one side, but those opposite would fail to budge. Neural integration is required and must be of a type that would ensure that, when incompatible decisions are simultaneously formulated, one overrides the other and commands the bilateral musculature. The mechanism for this is reciprocal innervation, which involves mutual inhibition between symmetrically-located neural decision points, at least at a spinal level (Sherrington, 1906). The reciprocal inhibition that Sherrington inferred from the characteristics of the interaction of spinal reflexes also occurs in the interaction of individual neurons on the input side (Hartline, 1938). It will here be

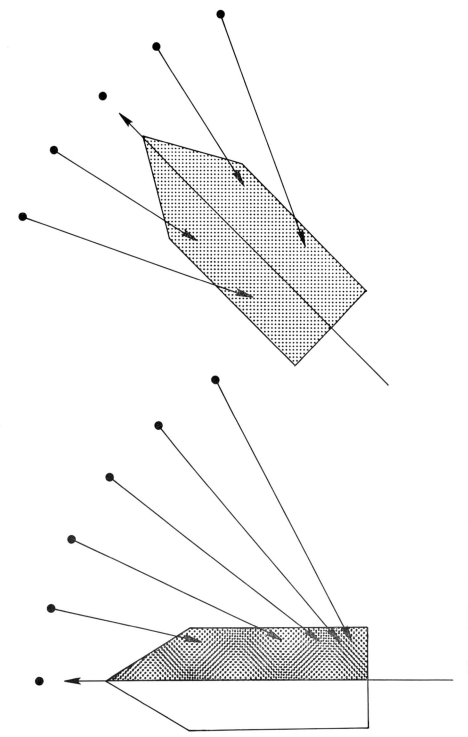

Figure XII-1. Asymmetric stimulation leads to turning, until stimulation becomes equalized.

proposed that the same principle applies to the selection between individual neurons and between processing facilities located at the complex level of the human cerebral cortex.

A simple bisymmetric animal will deviate sideward from its forward path of movement if it encounters oblique stimulation. It will turn toward that straight path along which stimulation of the two sides of its body is once again equalized (Loeb, 1918; see Fig. XII-1). This "tropotaxic" behavior is modified if the animal suffers some unilateral damage which makes one of its sides less sensitive to stimulation than the other (Fig. XII-2). This introduces a bias into the tropism, so that when the animal orients sideward, it points and moves to one side of the band of stimulation, rather than to its center. Indeed, if stimuli surround the organism on all sides, stimulation remains unequal wherever the animal is pointing, and so the animal continues to turn (Fig. 2). Since Goltz (1876), who induced it by unilaterally injuring the dog's cerebrum, this "circling" (or "circus movement") has been elicited by appropriately-placed unilateral lesions in a great number of bisymmetric species from the snail (Jordan, 1901) up to higher vertebrates. We have argued that certain consequences of stroke in humans essentially represent such circling (Kinsbourne, 1970). The phenomenon is most simply explained as due to a pathological bias introduced into a system that is in a state of mutually-inhibitory balance. Its ubiquitous occurrence is evidence that reciprocal relations between mirror-image loci in a bisymmetrical nervous system are a basic neural arrangement which is as crucial to primates and man as to the bee and the worm. This balance between opponent systems at a given segmental level is mediated by transverse commissures, of which the great forebrain commissure is both the evolutionarily most recent and the most impressively developed example.

We shall now marshall some evidence to support these generalizations, first in relation to the opponent systems as they recur at various neural levels and then with specific reference to the role of the corpus callosum in mediating interhemispheric opposition.

LATERAL INTERACTIONS THROUGHOUT THE CNS

Reciprocal relationships between bisymmetric structures have been defined in the invertebrate octopus (Messenger, 1967). The paired optic lobes analyze input and formulate response. The paired peduncle lobes, informed of the decisions, interact to reconcile them with each other and generate a superordinate, fully-coordinated orienting response rather than a stalemate or oscillation between incompatibles. When one peduncle lobe is excised, then receipt of visual input causes turning to one side only, and "circling" results. If the peduncle lobes are disconnected

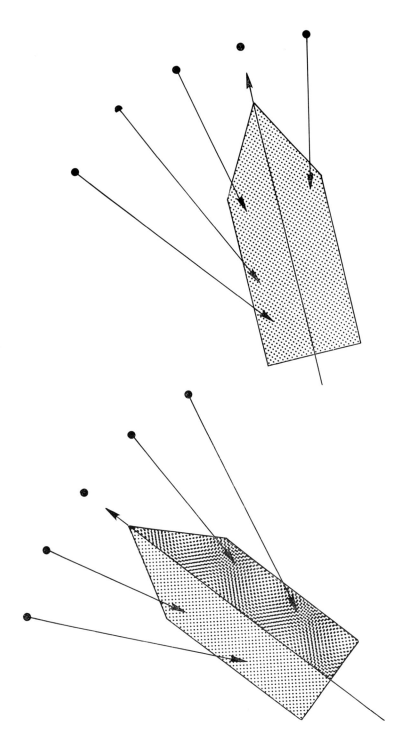

Figure XII-2. Where one side is insensitive, turning continues further before equalizing.

from each other, each still subserves orientation to one side but now only by the limbs on one side; the others remain behind ("half-attack"). This invertebrate model will be seen in essence to represent the situation right up the vertebrate scale to man.

Collicular stimulation in cats leads to contraversive turning of eyes, head, and forequarters in a coordinated "visual grasp" response by means of which laterally-moving targets are held in the center of view (Apter, 1945; Hess, Bürgi, and Bucher, 1946; Hyde and Eliasson, 1957). Stimulation of the optic tectum in monkeys leads to contraversive turning, dilatation of pupils, and widening of palpebral fissures (Ferrier, 1876); stimulation of the inferior colliculus results in pricking of the ears and vocalization (Denny-Brown, 1962). Midline stimulation of the anterior tectum in the frog causes symmetrical head-raising or -lowering, pouncing, and snapping (at imaginary food?) (Schneider, 1954).

Conversely, unilateral superior collicular destruction in dogs results in contralateral visual neglect (Sprague and Meikle, 1965), and destruction of inferior colliculus in monkeys results in contralateral auditory neglect (Denny-Brown, 1962). Movement contralateral to the lesion is only elicited as avoidance of ipsilateral threat (Horenstein, 1969). After bilateral collicular excision the monkey is practically unreactive to stimulation, staring aimlessly into space, there being "gross reduction in all types of externally-directed behavior" (Denny-Brown, 1962). Optokinetic responses are diminished for movement toward the destroyed colliculus but enhanced for movement away from it (Smith and Bridgeman, 1943). The evidence supports the view that the colliculi are in mutual inhibitory balance in the control of lateral orientation.

Bianchi (1895) ablated the middle and inferior frontal gyrus in dogs and monkeys and found them apparently blind contralateral to the lesion, with a tendency toward ipsilateral circling. Morin *et al.* (1951) in dogs and Kennard and Ectors (1938) and Welch and Stuteville (1958) in monkeys made similar observations, and Welch and Stuteville (1958) also noted disregard of the nonvisual modalities and poverty of spontaneous movement in the contralateral direction. There is "an enduring predilection for events that occur at the periphery of the field ipsilateral to the cerebral lesion" (Horenstein, 1969). Electrical stimulation of frontal areas involved in these ablation studies triggers contralateral gaze (Mott and Shafer, 1890; Leyton and Sherrington, 1917; Smith, 1936; Berkowitz and Silvertone, 1956; Jeannerod *et al.*, 1960; Schlag and Schlag-Rey, 1970). When anticholinergic agents are injected into the carotid artery of rabbits, cats, dogs, and monkeys, this results in chemical stimulation of the cerebral hemisphere on that side. The animals circle to the ipsilateral side (Essig *et al.* 1950). The movement

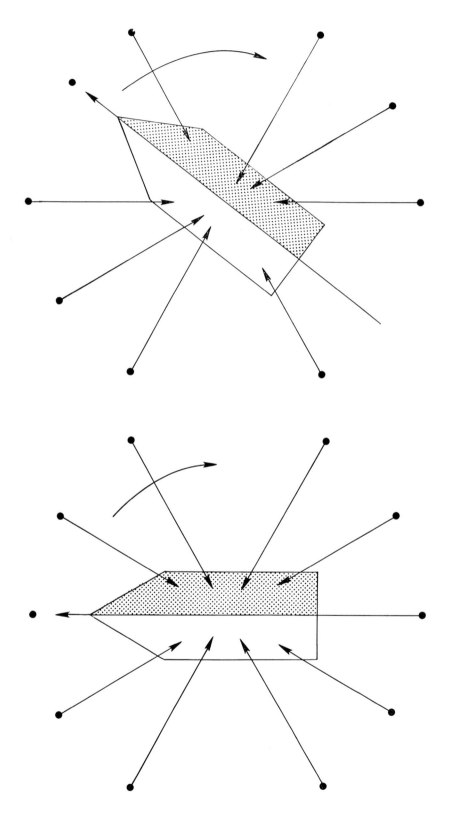

Figure XII-3. When display surrounds organism, circling results.

elicited by frontal stimulation is a coordinated deviation of the optic axes and head turning. If the head is held still, the eye movement increases in amplitude (Brown, 1922), so that the goal of lateral orientation is still achieved. Eye fields can also be discovered by electrical stimulation of portions of the other lobes of the cerebral cortex (Tower, 1936).

"Neglect" of stimulation contralateral to acute unilateral hemispheric damage is common. In man it has been reported for somatic sensation (Babinski, 1914; Denny-Brown, 1950; Gowers, 1893; Jackson, 1876; Zillig, 1941), vision (Zutt, 1932; Scheller and Seidemann, 1932; Paterson and Zangwill, 1944; Lawson, 1962), and audition (Scheller and Seidemann, 1932; Wortis and Pfeiffer, 1940). There is a striking tendency to turn head and eyes ipsilaterally (Prevost, 1868; Bard, 1922) and to overreact to stimuli introduced into the field of vision from the side ipsilateral to the lesion (Barany, 1913; Silberpfennig, 1941). Patients with lateralized cerebral lesions who show no gross neglect have been observed to initiate visual search ipsilateral to the lesion and only later to attend to the other side (deRenzi, Faglioni, and Scotti, 1970; Chedru and Leblanc, 1972). In its minor form, neglect is manifested by "inattention" to one side when both sides are stimulated simultaneously. This is often observed in the course of spontaneous unilateral cerebral disease in man (Denny-Brown and Banker, 1954) and has been induced by frontal and parietal excisions in monkeys (Schwartz and Eidelberg, 1968).

The tendency toward asymmetrical orientation that follows unilateral cerebral disease also appears as symmetrical autokinetic movement. When a patient views a point of light in the dark, he experiences illusory movement of the light toward the side of his lesion (Battersby *et al.*, 1956). Patients mislocate objects in space toward the side (Corvin and Bender, 1970), and when asked to bisect a horizontal line they mark it in such a way that the segment on the intact side is shorter (Fuchs, 1920). When a line of randomly-selected letters is briefly exposed, patients better report those letters that are located opposite the intact hemisphere, even if there is no visual field defect in the field of view. It appears that they sequentially read out the information starting with the letters on the unaffected side, ipsilateral to the lesion (Kinsbourne, 1966).

Thus, patients underestimate space and imperfectly attend to information on the side opposite the lesion. Conversely, they make inferences about that side of space on the basis of what would normally be regarded as inadequate information. The phenomenon of completion of incomplete forms across hemispheric field defects was discovered by Poppelreuter (1917). Patients with unilateral posterior cerebral disease are presented briefly-exposed forms that are incomplete on the side facing the lesion. They are apt to report having seen a complete figure. They fail to attend to the absence of the expected one, and they base their judgment exclusively on information from one side of the figure (Warrington, 1962). When incomplete words are briefly exposed in a similar manner, they also are imaginatively completed. This occurs not only when the word fragment is exposed hard upon the midline but also when it is presented well within the intact field (Kinsbourne and Warrington, 1962). It is the location of the missing part *relative* to the exposed letters which is crucial for completion, not its absolute location in the visual field. If the lesion is in the right hemisphere, even when the part-word appears well within the right visual field, the patient reports seeing a whole word, if the word fragment comes from the end (right) rather than the beginning (left) of the word.

In summary, there is ample evidence from studies of humans that unilateral cerebral lesions may produce a neglect syndrome analogous to that found in animals after experimental unilateral ablations. This neglect does not represent an ascendancy of one side of space over the other in the control of behavior but rather an ascendancy of the turning (orienting) tendency to one side over the turning tendency to the other. Thus, wherever in the environment a stimulus display appears, there is conflict between a tendency to orient to the left side of that display (right-hemispheric) and to its right side (left-hemispheric). In intact organisms these tendencies balance precisely, so that resultant orientation is to the center. In the unilaterally-lesioned individual with neglect, turning under control of the intact hemisphere gains ascendancy over turning programmed by the lesioned hemisphere, so the resulting orientation is biased contralateral to the intact side. A dramatic illustration of the fact that direction of gaze is a resultant of opposing hemispherically-programmed influences is afforded by temporary anesthetizing of one hemisphere through intracarotid injection of sodium amobarbital (Wada and Rasmussen, 1960). One consequence of the acute inactivation of one hemisphere is a sudden extreme deviation of gaze toward the side of cerebral anesthesia. Each hemisphere must exert a tonic influence on the direction of gaze: When one component of the opponent system is made inactive, the release of tonic influence from the other component is revealed by the resulting deviation of gaze.

When both right and left control centers are inactivated, then in the resting state, the direction of orientation remains straight ahead. But loss of this frontal control system introduces instability into the conflict between opposing turning tendencies. If both frontal lobes are ablated, the animal remains inert and centered in space (Horenstein, 1969). But he responds with vigorous ipsilateral circling to unilateral stimulation of the skin on either side of his body (Rademaker, 1931). A cortical control function has been lost through the ablation, and a more primitive and overreactive brainstem mechanism has assumed control over behavior. Bilateral lesions in man, admittedly more posteriorly located, lead to a state of inert underresponsivity to all stimulation, failure of scanning eye movements, and spatial disorientation (Balint, 1909; Tyler, 1968).

Sprague (1966) clarified the interaction between cerebrum and brainstem in the control of attention. By unilateral cerebral excision, he induced contralateral neglect; then, he excised the superior colliculus on the opposite side. This excision abolished the neglect. Even dividing the inter-collicular commissure, without encroaching on either superior colliculus, sufficed to reduce the neglect. The simplest explanation of these findings is that each hemisphere controls contralateral orientation through its excitatory effect on the ipsilateral superior colliculus. Each colliculus is in reciprocal inhibitory relationship wth the other. Damage to one hemisphere reduces its exciting effects on its colliculus, which then can no longer maintain balance with the colliculus on the opposite side. The imbalance in favor of the opposite colliculus is normally abolished by excising it. But even severing the commissure between the colliculi relieves neglect by protecting the colliculus that has lost hemispheric support from contralateral inhibition. We conclude that with respect to their control of laterality of orientation, the two colliculi are in mutually inhibitory balance.

There is further evidence of inhibitory interaction between cortical areas in opposite hemispheres, and some of these interactions appear to be callosally mediated. Welch and Stuteville (1958) made unilateral frontal excisions. They found that the failure of contralateral visual exploration that resulted could be relieved by excising contralateral occipital cortex. This result can be understood if frontal cortex is assumed to facilitate occipital cortex (Crosby, 1953). Deprived of that facilitation, the occipital cortex is inhibited by its contralateral fellow. Contralateral occipital excision then releases the residual occipital cortex from this inhibition.

Woolsey and Bard (1936) reported that proprioceptive placing, lost after ablating one parietal lobe, returned after the other parietal lobe was also removed. Bogen and Campbell (1962) hemicerebrectomized cats. Forelimb placing on the opposite side, which was abolished by the operation, recovered after frontal lobectomy on the spared side. Bard (1937) mentioned a monkey who, after unilateral ablation of cortical territory, lost the ability to hop; ablation of cortical territory contralateral to that already removed restored this motor skill. Denny-Brown and Botterell (1948) found that limbs made hemiplegic by ablating pre-central cortex could be better used when pre-central cortex on the other side was also ablated. Observations such as these make it hard to escape the conclusion that some bisymmetric cortical areas are in mutually inhibitory relationship. They do not resolve the question of whether the corpus callosum mediates this interaction, because callosal section was not compared in its effect with contralateral excision.

Callosal Mediation of Hemispheric Interaction

Neurophysiological findings are consistent with the view that the corpus callosum transmits inhibitory messages. There is a continual transcallosal traffic of nerve impulses in the unanesthetized cat in proportion to its degree of alertness (Berlucchi, 1965, 1966). Excitation of a given cortical region markedly enhanced excitability of the homologous region on the other side (Bremer, 1953; 1967). However, though their electrical rhythms desynchronize, the hemispheres do not lose in activation level after callosectomy (Koella and Ferry, 1963). This leads to the inference that inhibitory and excitatory transcallosal traffic occurs to an overall roughly equivalent extent. Branch and Martin (1958) found it possible to inhibit Betz cell activity by contralateral motor area stimulation, and the effect can be replicated by stimulating the free end of the sectioned corpus callosum (Asanuma and Okamoto, 1959; Asanuma and Okuda, 1962). Evidence from electrical recording for transcallosal inhibition was also observed by Li and Chou (1960), Jung (1961), Eidelberg (1969), and Hossman (1969) and for inhibition between olfactory bulbs mediated by the anterior commissure by Callens, Boisacq-Schepens, and Colle (1964).

What, then, are the effects of callosal section on lateral orientation and on bilaterally-represented cerebral processes?

In split-brain (chiasma- and callosum-divided) animals, each hemisphere can be privately stimulated through one eye. The situation resembles that which naturally prevails in birds. Mowrer (1937) found that in pigeons optokinetic stimulation elicited from each eye separately a preponderance of optokinetic nystagmus on movement of the rotating stripes toward the stimulated hemisphere. Pasik and Pasik (1964) report similar findings in split-brain monkeys. Even in normal humans, when optokinetic stimulation is arranged so as to occur both to the left and the right simultaneously, there is alternating preponderance in one and the other direction. This suggests that control of the ocular output mechanisms oscillates between the hemispheres (Enoksson, 1961, 1963). An attentional bias of each hemisphere in the predicted direction was observed by Trevarthen (1974) during manipulative behavior of split-brain baboons. In 1965 he observed that split-brain baboons at times reach for an object almost simultaneously with both forelimbs. Unlesioned animals do not do this. Perhaps because of mutual inhibition between cerebral hemispheres, only one hemisphere normally gains the control needed to program the reaching movement. If this inhibitory interaction is transcallosal, this would explain why callosal section makes it possible for each hemisphere to arrive at its own decision, to the detriment of the organism's mental unity.

There is some circumstantial evidence of inhibitory interaction at higher processing levels. Kaas *et al.* (1967) simultaneously presented different temporal click patterns to the two ears of cats and taught them to respond to a target pattern when it was presented to one ear but not when it was presented to the other. The habit was lost after auditory cortex ablation contralateral to the ear to which it had learned to respond; the habit was not lost after ipsilateral ablation. But if the corpus callosum was split before the contralateral ablation, the habit was not lost. This could be due to prevention of transcallosal inhibition of damaged by undamaged cortex. Larsen *et al.* (1969) taught chiasma-sectioned cats a light-dark discrimination. Unilateral occipital lobectomy abolished the discrimination as tested through the eye corresponding in side to the ablation. The discrimination could be relearned through that eye, but this occurred much faster if the corpus callosum was first sectioned, presumably protecting the damaged cortex from contralateral inhibition.

When Doty (1967) stimulated monkeys' occipital area 18, this resulted in coordinated grasping (of a hallucinated object?) only if the callosum had been previously cut. Doty (1969) suggests that normally the unstimulated homologous contralateral area would "disconfirm" the electrically elicited visual experience. It would presumably do so by means of transcallosal inhibition, because the response which should have been disconfirmed is released by callosal section.

We can now review the role of reciprocal inhibition between mirror-symmetrical neural loci in its biological context, guided by Sherrington's (1906) classification of movements into three types: synergic, reciprocal, and independent.

Synergisms that facilitate directional progression must have arisen early in the evolution of the bisymmetrical organism. The earliest such organisms exhibit such tropotaxis. They move along the plane of maximal stimulation. If that stimulation emanates from a single source, they will progress directly toward, or recede from, that source. But if there are two or more separate sources of comparable stimulation, then the organism's trajectory may follow a plane that passes between competing sources of stimulation. For tropotaxic arthropods like Ephestia larva and the pill lug, reciprocal inhibition need not be postulated. A simple additive model of the effect of stimulation would suffice. But when reciprocal movements such as walking or the undulations of swimming evolve, mutual inhibition at each segmental level becomes the logical mechanism. This was demonstrated by Sherrington (1906) for the mammalian spinal cord, by Horridge (1906) for invertebrates, and argued more generally by Reiss (1962) and Riss (1969). When a choice must be made between two possible directions of movement, and when the futile tropotaxic compromise of passing between two targets and thereby missing both (Loeb, 1890; Patten, 1914) is to be avoided, then mutual inhibition sharpens minor inequalities between the two approach tendencies; this permits the organism to make an unequivocal decision in favor of one or the other direction (Loeb's "teletaxis"). The same reasoning applies to the resolution of an approach-avoidance conflict. Whatever the conflicting pay-offs of the two behaviors, it is adaptive to adopt one or the other rather than to freeze into an immobility of indecision. The difference-amplifying effect of positive feedback by mutual inhibition would facilitate such an outcome. This logic remains valid through the vertebrate line to man.

In a simply organized animal the consummatory act that follows approach is not necessarily complex or highly skilled. But at the higher reaches of evolution the consummatory act may be exquisitely differentiated as regards input analysis and highly skilled as regards output programming. At this stage and for this purpose, the highly integrated type of brain organization that we have been discussing is no longer adaptive. These precise acts are not furthered but rather impeded by linkage with postural responses. This needed independence is reflected in the relative freedom of the first cortical relay for input and the final common pathway for output from direct homotopic callosal linkage (Trevarthen, 1969).

In the course of evolution of neocortex, archaic sensory projection systems are bypassed by newer ones, and the cortex differentiates to accomodate each separately (Diamond and Hall, 1969). The older systems with their diffuse cerebral projections are bypassed by newer high-velocity systems which have more specific and circumscribed cerebral destination. Each system has a sensory and a motor component. This evolutionary trend is best understood in terms of the anatomical basis of the "two visual systems" (Ingle, 1967; Schneider, 1967; Trevarthen, 1967; Held, 1967). An archaic projection from the retina with cell stations in the tectum and thalamus reaches a general sensory cortex (as in the hedgehog). In more recently-evolved vertebrates this is bypassed by a high-velocity genicular-striate projection, while the older system retreats to putamen and a prestriate ("visual belt") projection. The older system is integrative in function. It relates the source of stimulation to the orientation of the body. The newer system acts within an orienting context established by the old to perform a specific analysis (distinctive feature extraction) on the stimulus, to gain information for specific decision-making. The prestriate area, conventionally regarded as associative, and therefore by definition "higher" in function, actually has the more primitive roots. The callosal linkage of the prestriate area and the freedom from linkage of the striate area reflect this dichotomy.

Flechsig (1901) first proposed the general "law" that callosal projections link association cortex but not primary sensory cortex. This statement must be qualified with respect to the midline of space. While the cortical somatosensory representations of hands and feet and of the lateral extremes of visual space are indeed not directly interconnected, the cerebral representations of axial parts of the body (Eidelberg and Jenkins, 1966; Jones, 1967) and the median vertical meridian (Curtis, 1960; McCulloch and Garol, 1941; Whitteridge, 1965; Berlucchi, Gazzaniga, and Rizzolati, 1967; Hubel and Wiesel, 1967) are directly linked. A similar differentiation between median and lateral representations perhaps also occurs in the auditory system (Pandya, Mallett, and Mukherjee, 1969). This design of the forebrain commissure could be related to its well-established informational function. Although peripheral stimuli are likely to be completely within the territory of one cerebral hemisphere, ones near the midline are liable to extend across it, so that it is useful for information about the stimulus to be shared by the hemispheres (Karol and Pandya, 1971). But it can be related to a more fundamental dichotomy, both in the sensory and the motor sphere: that between bodily orientation in space (highly linked) and discrete differentiated sensorimotor programs, free of direct callosal linkage. Flechsig's proposition has been found to apply to the motor area also and to the secondary sensorimotor areas. Maximally peripheral structures like the fingers are to the greatest extent free of callosal interconnection as regards both their sensory and their motor representation. In terms of Diamond and Hall's (1969) analysis, the phylogenetically recent projections are discrete and autonomous, the ones of longer evolutionary standing more highly linked. Another aspect of cerebral motor control achieves a similar goal. While the somatic musculature is primarily under contralateral cerebral control, each hemisphere does also project to ipsilateral motor output systems (Bucy and Fulton, 1933). This projection is most effective for crude and proximal movements, whereas a hemisphere has least control over a highly differentiated movement of the ipsilateral fingers, both in primates (Brinkman and Kuypers, 1972) and in man (Gazzaniga, 1970). So there is both a structural and a functional distinction between the mechanism that reorients the body with respect to external change, and the analytic mechanism which is brought into play by this reorientation to determine and exploit the sensory change on the basis of its relevant detail (Trevarthen, 1967).

In summary, just as an ancient integrative sensory system is by-passed by a more recent differentiating projection, so on the motor side the pyramidal system, in control of finely differentiated detailed move-ments, bypasses the evolutionarily older projections which chiefly control the axial musculature by their relation to the motor integrating mech-anisms of the brainstem (Kuypers, 1964). These considerations high-light two functions of the corpus callosum. One is the phylogenetically ancient function of integrating the bisymmetric control systems to yield an adaptive reorientation of the whole organism. The split-brain cray-fish, stimulated in one visual field, responds with "half-attack." The limbs under control of the informed hemisphere advance, the ones on the other side remain stationary (Doty, 1968). The superordinate func-tion is behavioral unity. Its mechanism includes two elements—synchro-nization in timing of opposing motor programs (Preilowski, 1972) and graduated balance between opposing tendencies. The organizing prin-ciple for this synchronization and balance is the goal to be achieved. Callosal section releases alternative responses to a particular situation from the superordinate decision process that makes for behavioral unity, so that limbs on either side may move in ways that are in themselves clearly goal-directed but redundant from the perspective of the organism as a whole, or even mutually obstructive. This again has been ob-served on an anecdotal basis both in animals and man. Only highly automatized activities, such as walking, seem exempt from the hazard, perhaps because their motor programs are laid down at brainstem level and freed from observing response control by either hemisphere. A very simple and practiced response, reaching for an object, can cross the mid-line even in a monkey split down to the cerebellum (Mark and Sperry, 1968). But at some level, however low, commissural integration is needed.

The role of the callosum is different with respect to the more recently-evolved modality-specific information processing systems. The infor-mational output of such a system gains access to the contralateral hemi-sphere indirectly, by polysynaptic pathways. Rather than unite with information derived from the opposite mirror-image locus in the spatial field, the information first advances to a new stage of processing. Sim-ilarly as regards distal motor control the thrust of motor development is here toward greater autonomy, as the organism divests itself from the constraints of synergic and other associated movements. After section of the corpus callosum the information extracted from unilateral input cannot be communicated to the opposite hemisphere. Although this fact has been invaluable for studies of hemispheric specialization, it is biologically trivial, as minor adjustments in personal orientation readily distribute the same information to both sides, even if cross-cueing in animals (Gazzaniga, 1969a) or man (Gazzaniga, 1969b) fails. Unless the patient is taken to the limits of his performance, as in the laboratory, he remains socially competent, and these people are socially indistinguishable from others. If they have proved not very ambitious, fatigable, and not apt to maintain regular employment, this could be a consequence of the antecedent brain damage that caused the intractable epilepsy which served as justification for the operation in the first instance.

Even when visual stimulation is strictly unilateral and too brief to permit central (hemispheric) fixation of the stimulus, or when auditory stimulation is by two different but exquisitely synchronized messages, the informational insulation of the hemispheres is less than complete. Trevarthen (1965) has reported exceptions in relation to some simple perceptual judgments and has addressed himself to the effect of asymmetrical stimulation of the cerebrum on the perceptual readiness of the unstimulated hemisphere. At least some of the inability of the disconnected hemisphere to respond to contralateral stimulation is due to the demands of the active hemisphere on the overall attentional resources of the individual. When one hand-eye combination is consistently used, the other eye-hand combination tends to lapse into unresponsivity (Trevarthen, 1962). Preperceptual processes, that make no demands on attention (Neisser, 1967), presumably take their customary course, but only if the stimulation is of great biological significance to the patient will the inert hemisphere resume control of responding and thus participate in the flow of conscious experience.

The equalizing of hemispheric activity is the other biologically significant function of the corpus callosum. The corpus callosum minimizes disparities in the distribution of mental capacity ("attention") between the two hemispheres, so that both can be rapidly involved in any activity for which such involvement might be beneficial. Insofar as this is a stabilizing or difference-minimizing feedback function (Maryjama, 1963), it has the attributes of a negative feedback loop. Of all species, those that have greatest asymmetry of neurological representation have greatest need for such a stabilizing control system. One corollary of this fact is that in the course of their mental life, humans more than any other bisymmetrical animals are likely to manifest grossly asymmetrically distributed activity at the highest neural level, and in them the stabilizing effect of the corpus callosum is particularly vital.

In the human, the cerebral areas that subserve postural sensorimotor integration and are highly-linked callosally are also the areas richest in unilateral cortico-cortical connections. These support information flow within each hemisphere in the service of the higher mental functions for which the two human cerebral hemispheres are contrastingly specialized. In the next chapter we will explore the consequences of this great asymmetry of cerebral representation and therefore of moment-to-moment cerebral activity on the functioning of the positional system whose cerebral territory it shares.

REFERENCES

Apter, J. T.: Eye movements following strychninization of the superior colliculus of cats. *J Neurophysiol, 9:* 73–86, 1946.

Asanuma, M., and Okamoto, K.: Unitary study on evoked activity of callosal neurons and its effect on pyramidal tract cell activity in cats. *Jap J Physiol, 9:* 437–483, 1959.

Asanuma, M., and Okuda, O.: Effects of transcallosal volleys on pyramidal tract activity of cats. *J Neurophysiol, 25:* 198–208, 1962.

Babinski, J.: Contribution à l'etude des troubles mentaux dans l'hemiplegie organique cérébrale. *Rev Neurol, 27:* 845–848, 1914.

Bálint, R.: Seelenlähmung des Schauens, optische Ataxie, raumliche Störung der Aufmerksamkeit. *Mschr Psychiat Neurol, 25:* 51–81, 1909.

Barany, R.: Latente Deviation der Augen und Vorbeizeigen des Kopfes bei Hemiplegie und Epilepsie. *Wein Klin Wochenschr, 26:* 597–599, 1913.

Bard, L.: De l'origines sensorielle de la déviation conjugée des yeux avec rotation de la tête chez les hémiplégiques. *Sem Medicale, 24:* 9–13, 1904.

Battersby, W. S., Kahn, R. L., Pollock, M., and Bender, M. B.: Effects of visual, vestibular, and somatosensori-motor deficit on autokinetic perception. *J Exp Psychol, 52:* 398–410, 1956.

Berkowitz, E., and Silvertone, T.: Studies of the cortical eye motor fields of the cat. *Fed Proc, 15:* 16, 1956.

Berlucchi, G.: Callosal activity in unrestrained unanesthetized cats. *Arch Ital Biol, 102:* 623–634, 1965.

Berlucchi, G.: Electroencephalographic studies in "split brain" cats. *EEG Clin Neurophysiol, 20:* 348–356, 1966.

Berlucchi, G., Gazzaniga, M. S., and Rizzolati, G.: Microelectrode analysis of transfer of visual information by the corpus callosum. *Arch Ital Biol, 105:* 583–596, 1967.

Bianchi, L.: The functions of the frontal lobes. *Brain, 18:* 497–522, 1895.

Bogen, J. E., and Campbell, B.: Recovery of foreleg placing after ipsilateral frontal lobectomy in the hemicerebrectomized cat. *Science, 135:* 309, 1962.

Branch, C. L., and Martin, A. R.: Inhibition of Betz cell activity by thalamic and cortical stimulation. *J Neurophysiol, 21:* 380–390, 1958.

Bremer, F.: Un aspect de la physiologie du corps calleux. *Arch Int Physiol, 61:* 110–113, 1953.

Bremer, F.: An aspect of the physiology of corpus callosum. *EEG Clin Neurophysiol., 22:* 391, 1967.

Brinkman, J., and Kuypers, H. G. J. M.: Split-brain monkeys: cerebral control of ipsilateral and contralateral arm, hand and finger movements. *Science, 176:* 536–538, 1972.

Brown, T. G.: Reflex orientation of the optic axes and the influence upon it of the cerebral cortex. *Arch neerl de physiol, 7:* 571, 1922.

Bucy, P. C., and Fulton, J. F.: Ipsilateral representation in the motor and premotor cortex in monkeys. *Brain, 56:* 318–342, 1933.

Callens, M., Boisacq-Schepens, N., and Colle, J.: Le rôle des grains internes dans les phenoménes de dépression du bulbe olfactif. *J Physiol* (Paris), *56:* 310–311, 1964.

Chedru, F., and Leblanc, M.: Application of a visual searching test to the study of unilateral inattention. *Int J Ment Health, 1:* 55–64, 1972.

Corvin, M. S., and Bender, M. B.: Mislocalization in visual space with particular reference to the midline at the boundary of a homonymous hemianopia. *Proc Am Acad Neurol,* Miami, 1970.

Crosby, E. C.: Relations of brain centers to normal and abnormal eye movements in the horizontal plane. *J Comp Neurol, 99:* 437–479, 1953.

Curtis, H. J.: Intercortical connections of corpus callosum as indicated by evoked potentials. *J Neurophysiol, 3:* 407–413, 1940.

Denny-Brown, D.: Disintegration of motor function resulting from cerebral lesions. *J Nerv Ment Dis, 112:* 1–45, 1950.

Denny-Brown, D.: The mid-brain and motor integration. *Proc R Soc Med, 55:* 527–538, 1962.

Denny-Brown, D., and Banker, B. O.: Amorphosynthesis from left parietal lesion. *Arch Neurol Psychiatry, 71:* 302–313, 1954.

Denny-Brown, D., and Botterell, E.: The motor functions of the agranular frontal cortex. *Res Publ Assoc Res Nerv Ment Dis, 27:* 235–345, 1948.

de Renzi, E., Faglioni, P., and Scotti, G.: Hemispheric contribution to exploration of space through the visual and tactile modality. *Cortex, 6:* 191–203, 1970.

Diamond, I. T., and Hall, W. C.: Evolution of neocortex. *Science, 164:* 251–262, 1969.

Doty, R. W.: On butterflies in the brain. In Rusinov, V. S. (Ed.): *Current Problems in Electrophysiology of the Nervous System.* Moscow, Science Press, 1970, pp. 96–103.

Doty, R. W.: Electrical stimulation of the brain in behavioral cortex. *Ann Rev Psychol, 20:* 289–320, 1969.

Eidelberg, E.: Callosal and non-callosal connexions between the sensori-motor cortices in cat and monkey. *EEG Clin Neurophysiol, 26:* 557–564, 1969.

Eidelberg, E., and Jenkins, J.: Organization of somatic sensory mechanisms in the macaque cerebral cortex. *EEG Clin Neurophysiol, 21:* 451–460, 1966.

Enoksson, P.: A method for investigation of ocular dominance based on optokinetic nystagmus. *Acta Ophthalmol, 39:* 115–140, 1961.

Enoksson, P.: Binocular rivalry and monocular dominance studied with optokinetic nystagmus. *Acta Ophthalmol, 41:* 544–563, 1963.

Essig, C. F., Hampson, J. L., McCauley, A., and Himwhich, H. E.: An experimental analysis of biochemically induced circling behavior. *J. Neurophysiol, 13:* 269–275, 1950.

Ferrier, D.: *The Functions of the Brain*. London, Smith-Elder, 1876.

Flechsig, P.: Developmental (myelogenetic) localization of the cerebral cortex in the human subject. *Lancet, 2:* 1027–1029, 1901.

Fuchs, W.: Untersuchungen über das Sehen der Hemianopiker und Hemiamblyopiker, 1. Verlagerungserscheinungen. *Z Psychol, 84:* 67–169, 1920.

Gazzaniga, M. S.: Cross-cueing mechanisms and ipsilateral eye-hand control in split-brain monkeys. *Exp Neurol, 23:* 11–17, 1969a.

Gazzaniga, M. S.: Eye position and visual motor coordination. *Neuropsychologia, 7:* 379–382, 1969b.

Gazzaniga, M. S.: *The Bisected Brain*. New York, Appleton, 1970.

Goltz, F.: Uber die Vernichtungen des Grosshirnes. *Arch ges Physiol, 13:* 1–44, 1876.

Gowers, W. R.: *Diseases of the Nervous System,* 2nd ed. London, Churchill, 1897.

Hartline, H. K.: The response of single optic nerve fibers of the vertebrate eye to illumination of the retina. *Am J Physiol, 121:* 400–415, 1938.

Held, R.: Dissociation of visual functions by deprivation and rearrangement. *Psychol Forsch, 31:* 338–348, 1968.

Hess, R. W., Bürgi, S., and Bucher, V.: Motorische Funktion des Tektal-und Tegmentalgebietes. *Mschr Psychiat Neurol, 112:* 1–52, 1946.

Horenstein, S.: Sensorimotor concomitants of visual defects in monkeys. In Locke, S. (Ed.): *Modern Neurology*. Boston, Little Brown, 1969.

Horridge, G. A.: *Interneurons*. London, Freeman, 1965.

Hossman, K. A.: Untersuchungen über transcallosale Potentiale an der akuten Corpus Callosum Katze. *Dtsch Z Nervenhlk, 195:* 79–102, 1969.

Hubel, D. H., and Wiesel, T. N.: Cortical and callosal connections concerned with the vertical meridian of visual fields in the cat. *J Neurophysiol, 30:* 1561–1573, 1967.

Hyde, J. E., and Eliasson, S. G.: Brain stem induced eye movements in cats. *J Comp Neurol, 108:* 139–172, 1957.

Ingle, D.: Two visual mechanisms underlying the behavior of fish. *Psychol Forsch, 31:* 44–51, 1967.

Jackson, J. M.: Case of large cerebral tumour without optic neuritis and with left hemiplegia and imperception. *Royal London Ophth Hosp Rep, 8:* 434, 1876.

Jeannerod, M., Kiyono, S., and Mouret, J.: Effects des lesions frontales bilaterales sur le comportement oculomoteur chez le chat. *Vision Res, 8:* 575, 1968.

Jones, E. G.: Pattern of cortical and thalamic connections of the somatic sensory cortex. *Nature, 216:* 704–705, 1967.

Jordan, H. J.: Die Physiologie der Locomotion bei Aplysia limacina. *Z Biol, 41:* 196–238, 1901.

Jung, R.: Summary of the conference. In Mountcastle, V. V. (Ed.): *Interhemispheric Relations and Cerebral Dominance*. Baltimore: Johns Hopkins press, 1961.

Kaas, J., Axelrod, S., and Diamond, I. T.: An ablation study of the auditory cortex in the cat using binaural tonal patterns. *J Neurophysiol, 30:* 710–724, 1967.

Karol, E. A., and Pandya, D. N.: The distribution of the corpus callosum in the Rhesus monkey. *Brain, 94:* 471–486, 1971.

Kennard, M., and Ectors, L.: Forced circling in monkeys following lesions of the frontal lobe. *J Neurophysiol, 1:* 45–54, 1938.

Kinsbourne, M.: Limitations in visual capacity due to cerebral lesions. Paper to the International Congress of Psychology, Moscow, 1966.

Kinsbourne, M.: A model for the mechanism of unilateral neglect of space. *Trans Am Neurol Assoc, 95:* 143–145, 1970.

Kinsbourne, M., and Warrington, E. K.: A variety of reading disability associated with right hemisphere lesions. *J Neurol Neurosurg Psychiatry, 25:* 339–344, 1962.

Koella, W. P., and Ferry, A.: Cortico-subcortical homeostasis in the cat's brain. *Science, 142:* 586–589, 1963.

Kuypers, H. G. J. M.: The ascending pathways to the spinal cord, their anatomy and function. In Eccles, J. C., and Schade, J. P. (Eds.): *Progress in Brain Research, 2.* Amsterdam, Elsevier, 1964.

Larsen, J. W., Winans, S. S., and Meilke, T. H.: The effects of forebrain commissurotomies on the rate of learning a dark-light discrimination by cats. *Brain Res, 14:* 717–731, 1969.

Lawson, L. R.: Visual spatial neglect in terms of the right cerebral hemisphere. *Neurology, 12:* 23–33, 1962.

Leyton, A. S. F., and Sherrington, C. S.: Observations on the excitable cortex of the chimpanzee, orang-utan and gorilla. *Q J Ex Physiol, 11:* 135, 1917.

Li, C. L., and Chou, S. N.: Inhibitory interneurons in the neocortex. In Inhibition in the Nervous System and Gamma-amino Butyric acid. Proceedings of International Symposium, Duarte, California.

Loeb, J.: *Das Heliotropismus der Tiere und seine Ubereinstimmung mit dem Heliotropismus der Pflanzen.* Würtzburg, Hertz, 1890.

Loeb, J.: *Forced movements, tropisms and animal conduct.* Philadelphia, Lippincott, 1918.

Mark, R. F., and Sperry, R. W.: Bimanual coordination in monkeys. *Exp Neurol, 21:* 92–104, 1968.

Maryjama, M.: The second cybernetics: deviation-amplifying mutual causal processes. *Am Sci, 51:* 164–179, 1963.

McCulloch, W. C., and Garol, H. W.: Cortical origin and distribution of corpus callosum and anterior commissure in monkey. *J Neurophysiol, 4:* 555–563, 1941.

Messenger, T. B.: The effects of locomotion of lesions to the visuomotor system in Octopus. *Proc R Soc Lond (Biol), 167:* 252–281, 1967.

Morin, G., Donnet, V., Maffre, S., and Naquet, R.: Sur les troubles de la vision consecutifs aux decortications frontales chez le chien. *J Physiol* (Paris), *43:* 825–826, 1951.

Mott, F. W., and Shafer, E. A.: On associated eye movements produced by cortical faradization of the monkey's brain. *Brain, 13:* 165–173, 1890.

Mowrer, C. H.: A comparison of the reaction mechanisms mediating optokinetic nystagmus in human beings and in pigeons. *Psychol Monogr, 47:* 294–305, 1937.

Neisser, U.: *Cognitive Psychology.* New York, Appleton, 1967.

Pandya, D. N., Mallett, M., and Mukherjee, S. S.: Intra- and interhemispheric connections of the neocortical auditory system in the rhesus monkey. *Brain Res, 14:* 49–65, 1969.

Pasik, P., and Pasik, T.: Optokinetic nystagmus: an unlearned response altered by section of chiasm and corpus callosum in monkeys. *Nature, 203:* 609–611, 1964.

Paterson, A., and Zangwill, O. L.: Disorders of visual space perception associated with lesions of the right cerebral hemisphere. *Brain, 67:* 331–358, 1944.

Patten, B. M.: A quantitative determination of the orienting reaction of the Blowfly larva (Calliphora erythrocephala Meigen). *J Exp Zool, 17:* 213–280, 1914.

Poppelreuter, W.: *Die psychischen Schädigungen durch Kopfschuss im Kriege 1914–1916: die Störungen der niederen und höheren Sehleistungen durch Verletzungen des Okzipitalhirns.* Leipzig, Voss, 1917.

Preilowski, B. F. B.: Possible contribution of the anterior forebrain commissures to bilateral motor coordination. *Neurpsychologia, 10:* 267–277, 1972.

Prevost, J. L.: De la déviation conjugee des yeux et de la rotation de la tétè dans certains cas d'hemiplegie. Paris, Masson, 1868.

Rademaker, G. G. J.: *Das Stehen.* Berlin, Springer, 1931.

Reiss, R. F.: A theory and simulation of rhythmic behavior due to reciprocal inhibition in small nerve nets. *Proc AFIPS Spring Joint Computer Conference, 21:* 171–194, 1962.

Riss, W.: Introduction to a general theory of spinal organization. *Brain Behav Evol, 2:* 51–82, 1969.

Scheller, H., and Seidemann, H.: Zur Frage der optisch-räumlichen Agnosie Zugleich ein Beitrag zur Dyslexie. *Monatschr Psychiat Neurol, 81:* 97–188, 1931.

Schlag, J., and Schlag-Rey, M.: Induction of oculomotor responses by electrical stimulation of the prefrontal cortex in the cat. *Brain Res, 22:* 1–13, 1970.

Schneider, D.: Das Gesichtsfeld und der Fixiervorgang bei einheimischen Anuren. *Zeit-vergl Physiol, 36:* 147–164, 1954.

Schneider, G. E.: Contrasting visuomotor functions of tectum and cortex in the golden hamster. *Psychol Forsch, 31:* 52–62, 1967.

Schwartz, A. S., and Eidelberg, E.: "Extinction" to bilateral simultaneous stimulation in the monkey. *Neurology, 18:* 61–68, 1968.

Sherrington, C. S.: *Integrative action of the nervous system.* New Haven, Yale U Pr, 1906.

Silberpfennig, J.: Contributions to the problem of eye movements. III. Disturbances of ocular movements with pseudohemianopsia in frontal lobe tumors. *Confin Neurol, 4:* 1–13, 1941.

Smith, K. U., and Bridgeman, M.: The neural mechanism of movement vision and optic nystagmus. *J Exp Psychol, 33:* 165–187, 1943.

Smith, W. K.: Ocular responses elicited by electrical stimulation of the cerebral cortex. *Anat Rec, 64,* supp. 45, 1936.

Sprague, J. M.: Interaction of cortex and superior colliculus in mediation of visually guided behavior in the cat. *Science, 153:* 1544–1547, 1966.

Sprague, J. M., and Meikle, T. H.: The role of the superior colliculus in visually guided behavior. *Exp Neurol, 11:* 115–146, 1965.

Tower, S. S.: Extra pyramidal action from the cat's cerebral cortex: motor and inhibitory. *Brain, 59:* 408–444, 1936.

Trevarthen, C. B.: Double visual learning in split-brain monkeys. *Science, 136:* 258–259, 1962.

Trevarthen, C. B.: Functional interaction between the cerebral hemispheres of the split brain monkey. In Ettlinger, M. E. G. (Ed.): *Functions of the Corpus Callosum.* Ciba Foundation Study Group No. 20, London, Churchill, 1965.

Trevarthen, C. B.: Two mechanisms of vision in primates. *Psychol Forsch, 31:* 299–337, 1967.

Trevarthen, C. B.: Brain bisymmetry and the role of the corpus callosum in behavior and conscious experience. Paper to the Int. Colloquium on Interhemispheric Relations, Smolenice, Czechoslovakia, 1969.

Trevarthen, C. B.: Manipulative strategies of baboons, and the origins of cerebral asymmetry. In: Kinsbourne, M. (Ed.): *Hemispheric Asymmetry of Function,* London, Tavistock (in press) 1974.

Tyler, H. R.: Abnormalities of perception with defective eye movements. (Bálint's syndrome). *Cortex, 4:* 154–171, 1968.

Wada, J., and Rasmussen, T.: Intracarotid injection of sodium amytal for the lateralization of cerebral speech dominance. *J Neurosurg, 17:* 266–282, 1960.

Warrington, E. K.: The completion of visual forms across hemianopic field defects. *J Neurol Neurosurg Psychiatry, 25:* 208–217, 1962.

Welch, K., and Stuteville, P.: Experimental production of unilateral neglect in monkeys. *Brain, 81:* 341, 1958.

Whitteridge, D.: Area 18 and the vertical meridian of the visual field. In Ettlinger, M. E. G. (Ed.): *Functions of the Corpus Callosum.* Ciba Foundation Study Group No. 20. London, Churchill, 1965.

Woolsey, C. N., and Bard, P.: Cortical control of placing and hopping reactions in macaca mulatta. *Am J Physiol, 116:* 165–166, 1936.

Wortis, S. B., and Pfeiffer, A. Z.: Unilateral auditory spatial agnosia. *J Nerv Ment Dis, 108:* 181–186, 1940.

Zillig, G.: Beobachtungen bei einem Kranken mit rechtsseitiger Hemiplegie. *Arch Psychiat Nervenkr, 112:* 110–135, 1941.

Zutt, J.: Rechts-Linksstörung, Konstruktive Apraxie und reine Agraphie. *Mschr Psychiat Neurol, 82:* 253–305 and 355–396, 1932.

[CHAPTER XIII]

MECHANISMS OF HEMISPHERIC
INTERACTION IN MAN

Marcel Kinsbourne

THIS VOLUME HAS SUMMARIZED much of what is known about the different and distinctive contribution of the isolated left cerebral hemisphere and that of the isolated right cerebral hemisphere to human cognitive processes. This knowledge was derived from observing the limitations on human behavior imposed either by lack of one cerebral hemisphere or by the isolation of one hemisphere from the other by callosal section. In either case it becomes possible to interrogate one hemisphere in virtual isolation and to observe what it can do alone. The extent to which use of one hemisphere alone limits the subject's performance is taken to indicate what the other hemisphere would have contributed to behavior if it had taken part.

This simple subtractive logic, which virtually dominates neuropsychology, can be misleading, because it ignores certain factors and takes others for granted. The central problem is illustrated by a major paradox in neuropsychology which has virtually eluded discussion. This is that *the function of the whole appears to be less than the sum of its parts.* Focal lesions within a lobe result in deficits that are not observed after loss of the whole lobe. Focal lesions within a hemisphere result in deficits not found after hemispherectomy. Left occipital disease results in color agnosia (Kinsbourne and Warrington, 1964), but left hemispherectomy does not (Smith, 1966). Right occipital disease results in prosopagnosia (defective recognition of faces: Hécaen and Angelergues, 1962), but right hemispherectomy does not (Smith, 1969). Unilateral parietal disease may cause gross neglect of contralateral space (Gainotti, 1972), but bilateral parietal disease does not (at least, in that gross form).

To accommodate these facts we need to add two further explanatory principles to the simple information-flow models that are customarily invoked. These are: (1) *Compensatory activity by surviving cortex*— This activity is determined by the time course of disease, the time elapsed since the lesion occurred, the maturational state of the brain, and the integrity or interruption of commissural connections between damaged and preserved brain tissues. (2) *The organization of cerebral processes as opponent systems*—Damage to one polar element of the system will cause imbalances that generate symptomatology which does not occur when *both* elements are approximately equally impaired. Symptoms may even become less obtrusive as impairment spreads (either naturally or through operative intervention) from one element to the other.

COMPETITION AND COMPENSATION

The purpose of the first part of this paper is to show that we can explain features of behavior following hemispherectomy or callosal section that defy explanation in terms only of disconnection between cortical loci and loss of cortical processing capability. To do this we must assume:

    A. Areas of cortex that subserve specific functions inhibit other areas which are potentially capable of that same function.

    B. Destruction of such primarily responsible areas releases homologous areas from inhibition.

    C. This disinhibition permits compensatory functioning by the disinhibited area.

    D. The compensatory functioning is effective in proportion to the severity and extent of the primary lesion.

Before discussing the experimental findings, we shall draw attention to sampling difficulties in studying these patients. These difficulties add a dimension of uncertainty to the findings.

Hemispherectomy is performed only as a last resort in the face of gross cerebral disease, which is usually long-standing. This situation gives rise to two complications. First, although disease is no doubt centered upon the hemisphere that is excised, the causal pathological process is often one whose bounds are hard to define, and it is usually impossible to be sure that the residual hemisphere is totally intact. The occasional occurrence of cases with contralateral extension of damage would lead one to underestimate the functional potential of the residual hemisphere when cases are considered as a group.

The opposite error can also be made. The residual intact hemisphere may compensate for its absent partner; this would lead to a falsely elevated impression of the functional capability that the intact hemisphere would normally possess. When the hemispherectomy is performed after long-standing disease has proved intractable to more conservative measures, it is usually unclear whether the contralateral compensatory rearrangements began post-operatively or whether the damaged hemisphere was already so damaged before operation that the compensation began at some (usually indefinite) date prior to the hemispherectomy. This complicates the use of evidence from hemispherectomy to determine the course of developmental change in cerebral plasticity.

Damage extraneous to the excised hemisphere or to the sectioned forebrain commissure may be incurred during the operation. Thus, mutism quite often occurs during the early weeks following callosal section (Smith and Akelaitis, 1962) and may even be permanent (Bogen, personal communication). Although the interesting possibility exists that this reveals a role for the anterior corpus callosum in the coordination of vocal output, it could more simply be explained by incidental damage to the medial frontally-located and therefore vulnerable left supplementary motor area.

A few hemispherectomies have been performed on adults suffering from relatively recently acquired disease (Hillier, 1954; Smith, 1972; Ueki, 1966; Gordon, 1972; Zaidel, 1973). Such cases are sources of comparatively uncomplicated information about the function of the excised hemisphere in its mature state. Callosal sections are practically never performed for acute disease of adult onset. The patients have epileptogenic lesions of long standing, and one or both hemispheres are liable to be impaired and also to have developed compensatory functions of an indeterminate kind. Split-brain patients are notoriously different from one another, to an extent which makes it rarely justifiable to report them as a group. Their data must be analyzed and reported individually. We shall later argue that these individual differences result at least partly from a pathologically-exaggerated tendency for transitory mental sets to influence these patients' performance. But probably this source of individual differences is supplemented by a miscellany of coincident forms of brain damage (and anticonvulsant treatment).

Probably most static cerebral deficits of limited extent are in time mitigated by some measure of compensatory rearrangement in intact cortex. We shall limit ourselves to evidence for that compensation which occurs through activity of the contralateral hemisphere. Such compensation takes time and becomes increasingly effective during at least the first several months following the occurrence of the lesion. It is more far-reaching, the earlier in life the lesion occurs. Most is known of compensation for language deficit or for damage to areas preprogrammed to subserve language function.

CONTRALATERAL COMPENSATION FOR LANGUAGE DEFICIT

Typically, following the abrupt onset of aphasia in an adult, a period of overwhelming language deficit is followed by gradual recovery. This recovery may lead to apparently complete restoration of function or to a limited degree of recovery with residual, static, milder language disability. One might be tempted to suppose that, in the latter case, some cortical areas were irrevocably destroyed and others temporarily precluded from function. Recovery might be contributed by restoration of function to temporarily inactive cortical areas and also by compensatory assumption of the impaired function by neighboring cerebral areas. According to this view, the aphasic speech of a partially-recovered patient represents a left-hemispheric language system's best efforts to communicate after disease renders it imperfect. A further assumption that would follow is that the left hemisphere remains in control of whatever verbal behavior is available to the patient. One would then predict that further left-hemispheric inactivation should produce deepening language disability, whereas damage to the right hemisphere should not impair the speech of aphasics more frequently than it would do so in the general adult population.

The accuracy of these predictions could be determined by recording the effects of subsequent cerebral lesions on patients who were previously rendered aphasic by left-hemispheric damage. Nielsen (1946) reports a few patients who, after recovering partially or completely from aphasia precipitated by left-hemispheric damage, were apparently again rendered aphasic by lesions now affecting the right hemisphere. This report calls into question the accuracy of the assumption that aphasic speech comes from the damaged left hemisphere. It has recently become possible to obtain more systematic evidence by use of intracarotid amobarbital testing. This involves temporary anesthesia of one human cerebral hemisphere by mingling the carotid contribution to hemispheric blood flow with a very short-acting soluble barbiturate, a procedure introduced by Wada and Rasmussen (1960). Except in rare cases of anomaly of the Circle of Willis—the ring of blood vessels that mediates cerebral blood supply—such injection results in clinically obvious depression of ipsilateral cerebral functioning, as witnessed by contralateral hemiplegia, hemianesthesia, hemianopia, and extreme gaze deviation toward the side of the injection. Despite all of these evidences of hemispheric inactivation, one cannot logically assume that the hemisphere has been totally inactivated for the three minutes or so of full effectiveness of the injection. Also, the injection does not involve the posterior circulation, and so presumably at least the posterior pole of the hemisphere remains functional. Thus, if a function is impaired by unilateral amobarbital, this is evidence of participation of this hemisphere in the function in question. The converse does not hold. If a function remains effective in the face of such injection, that function might theoretically still be carried out by some part of that hemisphere that had not been fully suppressed by the barbiturate. To show that the other hemisphere had assumed that function, it is necessary to carry out a further procedure. This is on another occasion to anesthetize the opposite hemisphere and show that

the function is now abolished. An illustration may be found in the preserved ability of patients under Wada anesthesia to comprehend simple
instructions, as witnessed by their ability to respond with appropriate
movement of the unimpaired upper extremity of the face. This suggests
that either cerebral hemisphere has sufficient speech decoding capability
to deal with such instructions. But the possibility is not ruled out that
even during left-sided anesthesia, the relatively posteriorly-located speech
decoding areas on that side were still functioning.

When normal persons are subjected to a left-sided Wada procedure,
their ability to express themselves by spoken speech is almost invariably
abolished (Rosadini and Rossi, 1967), and a similar result was obtained
in 90 percent of cases when left-sided injection was made for purposes of
lateralizing speech in patients who were candidates for temporal lobectomy (Milner, Branch, and Rasmussen, 1964). We have carried out this
procedure on six aphasic patients (three of whom are reported in Kinsbourne, 1971). In four cases, left-sided injection failed to affect the patient's speech as tested during the injection. In three of these cases it
was clinically necessary to perform bilateral carotid arteriography, and
this afforded the opportunity to perform right-sided Wada testing also.
In each case, the right-sided injection did make it impossible for the patient to speak (or even to vocalize). Thus these right-handed people,
who had become aphasic in the usual way on account of left-hemisphere
damage, now were using their right (previously minor) hemisphere to
program speech output.

The limited number of cases precludes any attempt to estimate the
frequency with which aphasic speech represents the compensatory attempts of the previously "minor" hemisphere. Not all aphasic speech is
programmed by the minor hemisphere. In three other cases we found
that aphasic speech precipitated by left-hemisphere damage was abolished by anesthetizing that left side. But, if scattered case reports can
be believed, it even appears that the right hemisphere can at times compensate so completely that the patient is judged to have recovered full
language skill after his left-sided infarct, before a subsequent right-sided
stroke reveals the lateralization of the "recovered" language function
(Nielsen, 1946). However, there is no doubt that such successful compensation is far more likely to occur when disease strikes early in life.

ONTOGENY OF CEREBRAL DOMINANCE

There is precedent in the animal literature for far-reaching compensation even for massive cerebral excision, including hemispherectomy,
early in life. In man, it is now generally accepted that total destruction
of the left hemisphere perinatally or in infancy still leaves it possible

for the patient to gain language skills in normal developmental sequence and to achieve at least the lower echelons within the normal range of adult verbal functioning (Basser, 1962; Kinsbourne, 1974a). Particularly impressive is the absence of any difference in verbal intelligence quotient between left- and right-hemispherectomized groups (Kohn and Dennis, 1974). Paradoxically, when early unilateral disease is far less extreme in impact, giving rise to perhaps little more than a unilateral epileptogenic focus, then left-lesioned patients do have significantly lower verbal intelligence quotients than right-lesioned patients (Annett, Lee, and Ounsted, 1961). This could be a significant clue to the mechanism of compensation. The two hemispheres seem to be in mutually inhibitory competition. Damage to one will only release the other for purposes of compensation if the lesion is severe enough to disinhibit the other side of the brain. In left-hemispherectomized patients, the right hemisphere can compensate because it is totally free of competitive inhibition from the other side. But if the early left-sided damage is mild, it will suffice to impair the left hemisphere's language potential, but it will not release the right hemisphere for compensatory purposes. Evidence for the hypothesized interhemispheric suppression will be discussed below.

Putting together the information conveyed by reports of hemispherectomy or other early unilateral insult affecting language, Lenneberg (1967) concludes that left lateralization of language is not present at the very origins of language development but cumulatively increases until it reaches its definitive, mature status in early adolescence. Extensive lateral damage in the preverbal infant has an effect on early language development that does not depend on side of damage. During the first few years of language development, lesions on either side of the cerebrum are apt to disrupt speech with almost equal probability. Such regressions in language seem mostly to be on the output side, and they are temporary (Guttmann, 1942; McCarthy, 1963; Alajouanine and Lhermitte, 1965). When the child is more than five years old, right-hemisphere damage no longer seems to affect speaking, except in a very small percentage of cases that probably represents the incidence of right-brained language in the general population (Krashen, 1972). It is not clear whether the manner in which language behavior is disturbed by lateral cerebral damage before the fifth year of age depends on the side of the damage, but it does appear that at that stage both hemispheres supply necessary ingredients to the language processes. This could not merely involve identical instructions to the speech musculature from both hemispheres, as this would amount to redundancy rather than an essential role for both sides. More probably, each hemisphere contributes a different kind of programming. Or maybe there is at this early stage need for the maintenance of a certain interhemispheric balance of excitation as a basis for speech production. A role for the corpus callosum in such balance cannot be dismissed. In any case, after the fifth year, while right-hemisphere damage is no longer likely to disturb speech, the literature suggests that aphasias due to left-sided lesions prior to adolescence are milder and more transitory than would be expected were damage of comparable location and extent inflicted on the fully mature adult brain. Either residual intact left cerebral areas or the homologous areas on the right appear better and more completely able to compensate for language deficit in the immature individual than in the adult. In any case, left lateralization of language begins well after the origins of language and progresses throughout childhood. It entails both a more sophisticated control of language by the left hemisphere and a gradual corresponding impairment of the right hemisphere's ability to compensate when the need arises.

As either hemisphere, alone, is well able to support language development, the left-lateralized neuronal connections cannot be more preprogrammed than the right for future verbal functioning. What is the evolutionary advantage of lateral segregation of verbal control not prior to but during language development? Presumably, while the demands of early language can be met without lateral specialization, there is some change in language use at about the fifth year of life which demands lateral asymmetry as its neural substrate. The development of a processing strategy for speech input has been related to lateralization by Bever (1971). Or lateral asymmetry could be the basis of some propositional or categorical use of language not practiced by the younger child (Vigotsky, 1962; Mosher and Hornsby, 1966), but no evidence on this exists. A quite different possibility is that motor control of speech beyond a five-year level of fluency is facilitated by lateralization. The remarkably uniform onset of stuttering before that age could be related to the need for such lateralization, and in some of those persons whose stutter becomes permanent, failure of lateralization has been reported (Jones, 1966).

The origins of speech are inextricably embedded in motor behavior. The infant gurgles, babbles, and names, while he turns head, eyes, points his finger, and sets off toward the external referent. He cries in alarm, or for help, while his whole body exhibits a startle response. The syntax of early language and of gesture and mime are similarly simple and declarative.

At about the fifth year of life, speech has substantially separated out from its motor synergisms and, as Vigotsky (1962) has pointed out, is on the way to being internalized into verbal thought. In fact, speech never totally loses its somatic motor accompaniment. During verbal thought (Kinsbourne, 1972) and during hesitation pauses in speech, people tend to turn head and eyes to the right (driven by the active left hemisphere). But these are vestigial accompaniments which only affect the efficiency of verbal processing at the very limits of performance (Kinsbourne, 1974b). When people are not pressed to peak performance, the movements can be inhibited without obvious detriment to the ongoing activity. As language becomes internalized, its links with the motor system become irrelevant. Verbal thinking becomes categorical and analytic and no longer necessarily has specific reference to locations in space.

In contrast to the speech output system, the cerebral basis for decoding speech input has quite a different natural history. Lateralized lesions in children have rarely been documented to cause substantial receptive, as distinct from expressive, aphasia. Even among adults, receptive aphasia appears to be commoner in the older age group. Brown and Jaffe (1974) have raised the possibility that lateralization of receptive speech cumulatively increases at a much slower pace than lateralization for speech expression; he suggests that lateralization of receptive speech is still increasing throughout adult life. It is certainly clear from intracarotid amytal testing that both hemispheres can decode speech, at least with respect to the rough and hasty testing possible during the mere three minutes afforded by the Wada procedure. Using fewer cases but more thorough methods of investigation, a number of reports of split-brain humans (Gazzaniga and Sperry, 1967; and notably Zaidel, 1973) have shown that the mature right hemisphere can decode speech in both the auditory and visual modalities. Contrary to an early report (Gazzaniga and Hillyard, 1971), its semantic and syntactic competence differs only quantitatively from that of the left hemisphere (Zaidel, 1973). The substantial right-hemisphere ability to decode speech contrasts strikingly with its rudimentary control over speech output (Butler and Norsell, 1968; Levy, Nebes, and Sperry, 1971). Anderson and Jaffe (1973) have even suggested that some people habitually decode speech with their right rather than left Wernicke's area. Certainly, if a right-ear advantage in verbal dichotic listening is accepted as indicating left-hemispheric lateralization of language (Kimura, 1961), then the fact that only about 75 percent of right-handers show a right-ear advantage would, taken literally, indicate right-hemisphere dominance for decoding speech input in far more people than have right-hemisphere dominance for encoding speech output. From the perspective of the organism's overall adaptive needs, lateralization for programming of output seems far more important than lateralization for decoding purposes. Bilateral representation is immune from the hazard of competing responses so long as the function concerned is released in response to an external change or specific location; then the right-sided facility will respond to left stimulation and vice versa. Once a process can be initiated by internalized cues, then its dual representation serves no specific purpose and even incurs risk of competing and therefore inefficient response. Lateralization overcomes this risk.

There is no biologically essential restriction on input processing. Only the properties of the combined receptor surfaces limit the total input that can undergo preattentive processing (Neisser, 1967). There may be some logistic advantage in lateralizing input on the same side as output. But, in the presence of rich callosal connections, either side will serve.

But if this line of reasoning is correct, it would seem surprising that in ontogeny, decoding dominance appears by far to precede dominance for speech output. Whether the dichotic right-ear advantage for speech increases during childhood (Bryden, 1970) or does not (Kimura, 1963; Berlin *et al.*, 1972), it certainly is present even in the youngest children tested to date (Nagafuchi, 1970; Geffner and Hochberg, 1971), namely at three years of age, long before left-lateralization of language is indicated by the neuropsychological evidence. Even in newborns, there is anatomical asymmetry, with a larger planum temporale on the left than right (Witelson and Pallie, 1973). Behaviorally, newborns not only show a much greater rightward than leftward turning tendency during conditioning (Siqueland and Lipsitt, 1966; Turkewitz *et al.*, 1968) but even at that early age they can discriminate speech sounds (Eimas, 1971; Trehub and Rabinovitch, 1972), and there is reason to suppose that this function is lateralized. Molfese (1972) has recorded more striking evoked electrical response to speech sounds from the left and to nonspeech sounds from the right side of the scalp. From these findings, he infers preprogramming for language on the left and for nonverbal sound on the right. But this does not necessarily follow.

Lateral specialization cannot be inferred purely on the basis of electrical epiphenomena, the behavioral significance of which is quite unknown. Only differential performance can document such specialization. Now, asymmetry could be involved either in processing or in attention or in both. The electrophysiological findings do suggest that some asymmetry exists. Selective activity of one hemisphere biases attention (contralaterally), and electrical asymmetries may represent an attentional bias which is material-specific. This does not imply a processing superiority and in children appears well in advance of any specialization in processing. So the dichotic superiority of the left hemisphere for speech sounds in children before age five may reflect linkage of a tendency to orient to the right with speech input; it need not imply greater left- than right-hemisphere facility in processing verbal material. In the absence of definitive evidence, the most economical account of early language development is that both hemispheres are preprogrammed for language processes but in most people the left hemisphere is differentially stimulated by speech sounds. The left hemisphere will therefore show more impressive evoked response to speech sounds (Molfese, 1972). If the attentional ascendancy of the left hemisphere is accomplished with reciprocal inhibition of the right (Kinsbourne, 1970), then the possibility arises that over time this inhibition will have a cumulative effect on the right hemisphere; almost as a side effect of the left hemisphere's ascendancy for attention to verbal material, the left hemisphere's verbal processing facilities also would more and more completely take charge of the work to be done. Over time this suppression could have a deleterious effect on the right hemisphere's ability to process speech sounds even in noncompetitive situations (Zaidel, 1973). But in the early years of life the asymmetry is probably attentional rather than one of differing competences of the hemispheres.

If this account of right-hemisphere inhibition by left during speech is correct, which structure mediates this inhibition? Some indirect evidence on this point is afforded by studies of callosal agenesis. There is reason to suppose that not only motor control (Kinsbourne and Fisher, 1971) but also language lateralization is bilateral in such cases, and recently Saul and Gott (1973) have directly demonstrated bilateral language representation in one such case by use of intracarotid amytal. If this will be found to be generally true of acallosal people, then one could infer that the corpus callosum would normally have transmitted the inhibition which makes lateralization possible. However, it is clear from callosal section in the mature brain that, once established, the left-hemisphere ascendancy for language—at least on the output side—is by no means contingent on any continuing transcallosal effect.

Competition for control of language is the most striking instance of hemispheric rivalry, particularly because the ontogeny of those spatial functions for which the right hemisphere usually assumes major responsibility is only now beginning to be clarified (Witelson, 1974). But while the midline vocal mechanism clearly lends itself to competition for control, even paired structures such as the two upper extremities are not private and immune executors for the contralateral hemisphere. Where both hands of a split-brain subject are readied for response, one hemisphere quite often assumes control of both, whether in monkey (Brinkman and Kuypers, 1972) or in man (Kinsbourne, Trevarthen, and Sperry, 1974). Again, it might be that the corpus callosum mediates a mechanism that assures each hemisphere of primary control of the contralateral limbs.

After lateral hemispheric damage, movement on the intact side tends to contaminate and compromise any movement that is at the same time undertaken by the affected limbs (Cernacek, 1961). Again, it appears that a hemispheric balance safeguards the control of each hemisphere over its executive organs, and a lateralized lesion can disrupt this balance so as to render the affected side vulnerable to contralateral competition.

COLLABORATION
Hemispheric Control of Auditory Attention

So far we have considered the cerebral hemispheres as independent systems, each able to function in its own right, in the absence of communication with its partner, or even able to assume some of its partner's roles in times of necessity. The interactions between the hemispheres so far discussed were competitive, and a mutually inhibitory positive feedback model served to characterize them. We now consider the hemispheres as a collaborative system. Through precisely-balanced, callosally-mediated interaction they control shift of attention in the lateral plane.

Although there is interaction between the two auditory projection systems at several levels (Wegener, 1964), auditory spatial localization depends for its precision on the participation of the highest level, the auditory cortex. In the cat, after bilateral auditory cortex ablation (Arnott, 1953; Masterton and Diamond, 1964), precise auditory localization becomes virtually impossible, and the animal can judge only a complete shift of the source of stimulation from one side to the other. In terms of receptor orientation, cats with bilateral auditory cortex excision fail to orient toward the source of a sound (Thompson and Welker, 1963). This reduction of a precisely-graduated system to a crude, binary indicator is a typical consequence of the loss of cortical control which made fine adjustments on the cruder, dichotomous opponent processes contributed by the brainstem. While some balance between auditory cortices is clearly responsible for the precision of normal auditory localization, there is no experimental information as to whether the corpus callosum mediates this balance.

Each ear projects to both auditory cortices. The functional importance of the contralateral projection has not been questioned. The role of the ipsilateral projection is the subject of controversy. The question revolves around the manner in which speech coming into the left ear is processed (when it is in dichotic synchrony with a different right-ear message).

If it is assumed that speech processing necessarily occurs on the left, then two options are available for left-ear input. It reaches the left hemisphere either by ipsilateral projection (Kimura, 1961) or by contralateral projection to the right hemisphere and subsequent transcallosal traffic to the left (Sparks and Geschwind, 1968). If the right hemisphere is not only potentially a competent speech decoder, which it is known to be, but also actually normally participates in this function in the intact individual, then this raises the further possibility that left-ear input is processed after contralateral projection to the right hemisphere. Of course, if the required response is overt speech, then the information would presumably at some stage cross to the left-sided executive language facility. But if the task is one of search for a specific target, with perhaps a finger-press response to indicate match or mismatch, then according to this model the left hemisphere need not be involved at all.

When speech is presented to one ear only, there is little or no asymmetry in normal people, laterally-lesioned patients, or hemispherectomized or split-brain subjects. This result in the last two groups shows that the ipsilateral projection must be able to function efficiently when no competing input is presented. In a dichotic paradigm, what is the path of the left-ear message? If it were direct to the left hemisphere by ipsilateral projection, right-hemisphere disease should not affect it. But in fact such disease exaggerates the right-ear advantage (Schulhoff and Goodglass, 1969). A path through the right hemisphere (Sparks and Geschwind, 1968) would account for this finding and would also explain why split-brain patients sometimes (Milner, Taylor, and Sperry, 1968; Sparks and Geschwind, 1968), though not always (Gordon, 1971), virtually completely suppress the left of dichotic messages. But none of the models explains why lesions in either hemisphere far away from auditory projections and cortex can still profoundly bias ear advantage in favor of the intact hemisphere. Another explanation is needed.

Unilateral cerebral lesions bias attention even when they are located well clear of primary sensory projections and cortical receiving areas. Each hemisphere drives attention toward contralateral space, and the balance between them at any moment determines the direction in which the organism is attending. That balance is upset by a unilateral lesion. Stronger stimulation or concurrently-enhanced activity of the lesioned hemisphere is needed to enable it to shift attention counter to the direction of influence of the intact hemisphere; in the case of equivalent bilateral simultaneous stimulation, the organism's attention shifts contralateral to the intact half-brain. Thus, hemispheric lesions can either enhance or reverse premorbid ear preferences. They do so not by changing either hemisphere's ability to process the input but rather through attentional shifts, by affecting the choice of material for processing. This phenomenon is convincingly illustrated by dichotic effects in cases where only one hemisphere, and therefore only one processing facility, is available for use: in hemispherectomized patients.

Hemispherectomized patients show no ear advantage for a single message (Kinsbourne, 1974b). Yet with dichotic presentation, there is a striking advantage for input into the ear contralateral to the residual hemisphere (Netley, 1972; Kinsbourne, 1974b). In the dichotic situation, the natural selection bias of the residual hemisphere for contralateral input comes to the fore.

Kimura (1961) has explained the right-ear advantage for speech messages on the assumptions that (i) the left hemisphere is the processor for verbal material and (ii) contralateral projection is more effective than ipsilateral when both are carrying different messages. Sparks and Geschwind (1968) assent to (i) but suppose that (ii) only contralateral projections are used in the dichotic situation and (iii) the left-ear message goes first to the right hemisphere and then has to pass transcallosally to the left hemisphere; this imposes a relative disadvantage as compared to the direct contralateral route from the right ear to the left hemisphere.

These are passive models of cerebral processing. They invoke one of two explanations for the right-ear advantage in identifying speech sounds: (a) Material coming from the right side arrives at the left hemisphere before material coming there from the left side, *or* (b) The right-ear message blocks the left-ear message through some mechanism which is not speed of arrival but which is not specified. Both explanations stress the importance of the physical path through which speech input goes to the left hemisphere.

An alternative, active model would propose that what produces the right-ear advantage is not the physical path of the input but rather the side of space from which the sound seems to come. We would suggest that even if a hemisphere were to receive two equally clear messages, it would actively select for prior processing the one that seemed to come from contralateral space. To test this proposition, we need an experimental situation in which two messages come through the same channel but are localized to opposite sides of space. The dichotic method of investigation confounds channel of entry with direction from which the stimulation comes. This confounding is avoided by substituting for the earphones used in dichotic listening two externally-located loudspeakers, one on the subject's right and one on his left. If a different message comes from each speaker and they come simultaneously, then both ears receive both messages. Using this paradigm, right-sided advantage is still found (Morais and Bertelson, 1973). The message from the left side of space and that from the right now both go through the right ear to the left hemisphere. But since messages coming from both sides of space take the same physical path (e.g. to the left hemisphere, through the right ear), the physical explanations of Kimura and of Sparks and Geschwind are ruled out. It now appears that right-*ear* advantage found in dichotic listening experiments is a product of the fact that the right ear receives a message from the right *side of space*. The loudspeaker experiment demonstrates that when *two* messages go simultaneously into the right ear, the message that seemed to come from the right side of space is the one to which the subject responds. Both messages obviously were sent along the same physical path, but the left hemisphere's activation by verbal activity (the verbal nature of the messages) biased the subject's attention toward sounds which came from the right.

Even if hemispherectomized subjects are specifically instructed to ignore the preferred ear input and asked to report only the nonpreferred message, the inherent orienting tendency of the intact hemisphere breaks through, and much of the reported material is intrusion from the irrelevant message. These effects do not depend on the requirement of overt imitative verbal response. When subjects are asked to scan dichotic input for a target word and to indicate its presence or absence by button press, they show a pattern of results identical to that in the conventional verbal report paradigm. Presence of target is more often reported from the preferred side, and with attention distracted to the nonpreferred side, false positive matches indicate the presence of targets on the side the subjects were asked to ignore. This perceptual analysis gives priority to the preferred ear input. But the effect of the asymmetry goes beyond a mere temporal priority for one response over another. After responding to the preferred side, these patients are usually not able to report the contralateral message. Not only is attention biased in one direction but it is also sluggish in returning to pick up any material which might be in preperceptual state because it originated from the opposite side. In the absence of the contralateral hemisphere, the system for shifting attention laterally has become biased and sluggish. The balance between the hemispheres, which can normally be rapidly and flexibly changed as attention shifts sideward in pursuit of adaptive ends, is inoperative. It gives way to a cruder balance at brainstem level under the biasing control of the single remaining hemisphere. Cortical control of selective attention is revealed as primarily a mechanism that chooses between alternative opportunities for focal attention rather than a mechanism that directs attention toward one particular point or direction in space. When one hemisphere is inactive, subjects have difficulty in detaching from the existing focus of attention for a new focus in any direction.

The dichotic listening results with callosectomized subjects (Milner, Taylor, and Sperry, 1968; Sparks and Geschwind, 1968; Gordon, 1972) can now be explained. The virtual suppression of left-ear input is due to the activation of the left hemisphere by the verbal nature of the task which results in selective attention to the right-sided of two competing messages. The absence of the corpus callosum is decisive in setting up this situation. But this is not by virtue of its information-transmitting function, as hitherto supposed. Instead it is because lack of the callosum's excitation-equalizing function releases a gross imbalance of attention where in a normal person that imbalance is present but is so slight as to be biologically trivial.

Hemispheric Control of Visual Attention

The inertia and liability to bias of the attentional control mechanism after callosal section can be readily demonstrated in the visual modality. It is dramatically true that under selected conditions the two hemispheres of split-brain monkeys can be taught to respond in different, even contradictory, fashions to the same visual event, or to different visual events perceived at the same location (Trevarthen, 1962). This illustrates the cognitive independence of the separated hemispheres. They are capable, should the world be thus arranged, of building up contradictory life experiences on the two sides, within the same individual, a point to which we shall return when considering the implications of split-brain behavior for the notion of unitary consciousness, in the following chapter. Further, contradictory responses may occur simultaneously, and it has been argued that splitting the callosum doubles the animal's capacity because he can now perform a second task simultaneously without effect on main performance (Gazzaniga and Sperry, 1966; Gazzaniga and Young, 1967). However, so can a skilled subject with intact commissures. The critical question for the hypothesis of independent parallel functioning is whether the two parts of a single process performed sequentially by normal subjects can be performed in parallel by callosectomized man.

Gazzaniga (1968) tried to answer this question. He presented two split-brain subjects briefly-exposed letter groups (drawn from a set of 20 consonants), either four at a time in one half-field or eight simultaneously with four in each half-field. Whereas controls did no better on the eight-letter than the four-letter condition, the split-brain subjects learned nearly twice as well as with the bilateral exposure, in picking out target letters from an ensemble. However, overall scores were exceedingly low, and a forced-choice procedure was not adopted, although there were twice as many opportunities for successful guessing in the eight-letter condition. A more promising design would hold the total number of stimuli constant, varying only their distribution between the half-fields. However, the further problem of variable periods of elapsed time and possible memory decay as the subject searches through the ensemble makes it desirable to choose a different paradigm, in which a single latency measure is the decisive dependent variable.

In order to design such an experiment, the following facts were considered. Visual search through letters is a disjunctive reaction-time measure. Subjects are acquainted with one or more target letters ("positive set") and then presented one or more letter probes ("array"). Time taken to reach a decision as to the presence or absence of a letter from positive set in the array is a linear function both of the number of targets in memory (Sternberg, 1966) and the number in the array. A sequential search model postulating serial sameness-difference judgments for all possible combinations of letters in positive set and in array fits the data (Nickerson, 1972). Increments in size of positive set and of array have comparable effects on latency, which is a function of the overall number of decisions to be made. The question arises, if the two hemispheres are simultaneously presented each with half the array, is the process still sequential, or do the two hemispheres operate in parallel, with resulting changes in latency?

We performed the experiment on two patients who had undergone callosal section (Kinsbourne, Trevarthen, and Sperry, 1974). The subject sat facing a tachistoscopic screen. His head and eye movements were continuously monitored. Each index finger rested on the table in front of him. A finger lift interrupted a beam of light and was transduced into a response recorded on a polygraph. The subject was asked to lift a finger if a target appeared. Otherwise, he was to make no response. He was not specifically told which finger to raise in response to a target in either half-field. The displays consisted of one or two upper-case letters, briefly exposed in one half-field, or one in each half-field. When the target letter appeared to the left of the bilateral probe, the patients often totally failed to respond. On other trials, they made the appropriate positive response by raising their left hand, but only after long latency; presumably this occurred after, rather than at the same time as, the left hemisphere had arrived at its own decision, which was not to move the right hand. But when the target letter was located on the right, latency of right-hand response was usually equal to latency when the probe consisted of a single letter only. On those occasions on which bilateral presentation met with appropriate response, latencies were on the average much longer than those for two letters when they were both presented in the same half-field. Thus, when split-brain subjects do process simultaneously with both hemispheres, they do so inefficiently, and in no way can this be regarded as representing an increase in mental capacity as compared to that afforded by the normally-linked cerebral hemispheres or even by one hemisphere processing in isolation. A third subject could not be included in the analysis because, although his right-hand responding was appropriate, he also responded with his left hand to every left half-field stimulus, target or nontarget. He seemed unable to stop this automatic responding. Like the other two subjects, he could not efficiently process in both hemispheres at once. In his case, however, the right hemisphere, rather than failing to respond, responded automatically on the basis of a low level of visual analysis. Again, the left hemisphere had pre-empted the patient's mental capacity in this task; but in this case the right hemisphere, lacking access to attention, responded at an automatic, preattentive level.

Neglect of the left-sided stimulus was most severe when subjects were asked to respond verbally, by saying "yes" or "no," at the same time as making a finger response. When a subject used a single hand, then if that was the right hand, his neglect of the left side of the tachistoscopic field was absolute. If it was the left, there was no converse neglect of the right, but the number of missed responses to targets appearing on the left were minimal, and something approaching a balance of attention between the two sides appeared to have been achieved. So there was from the start a tendency for one cerebral hemisphere, namely the one specialized to represent language, to predominate when simultaneous bilateral inputs claimed attention. This tendency was enhanced by further selectively enlisting left-hemisphere participation by use of the right hand and by including the use of speech in the response. Use of the left hand only had the converse effect of enhancing the right hemisphere's efficiency in detecting events in the left visual field.

It was abundantly clear that the subjects were by no means exhibiting double capacity. The normally serial visual search process did not proceed in parallel on the two sides of the surgically-separated midline. After callosal section, lateral attentional shift from the fixation point to the target, and from target to target, was extremely slow. This slowness of shift occurred not only across the midline (from one hemispheric territory to the other) but also within one visual half-field. This reminds us that both hemispheres participate in attentional shifts even when they occur within a territory that projects wholly to one of them (Kinsbourne, 1974b). Further, performance was clearly biased to the right. This is an anomalous finding for horizontal rows of letters, which almost always are scanned from left to right by those accustomed to left-to-right reading (Heron, 1957). It suggests that the left hemisphere pre-empted the patient's mental capacity by virtue of the verbal set involved in the task and thus generated the rightward orientational bias proper to that hemisphere. The extreme degree of this bias vividly illustrates the consequences of loss of the equilibrating function of the corpus callosum.

Situations do exist in which both visual half-fields can be used for stimuli to which the subject successfully responds. Trevarthen and Kinsbourne (1974) found it possible to elicit bilateral response to simple geometric shapes presented to both half-fields simultaneously, and Levy, Trevarthen, and Sperry (1972) confirmed and extended these findings. But the perceptual processing involved was trivial. The more exacting the task, the more probable is a greater role of one hemisphere than the other and, consequently, a left-sided neglect due to the instability induced by loss of callosal connection (Trevarthen, 1962).

Hemispheric Sharing of Attention for Concurrent Performances

It may occasionally be the case that the disconnected cerebral hemispheres both concurrently perform in ways that demand attention. When they do, a problem arises if one hemisphere suddenly has an increased need for attention or mental capacity. Thus, when normal subjects tap with both index fingers while speaking aloud, there is neither much disruption of the tapping nor any asymmetry in the extent to which the tapping rate is decreased (Briggs and Kinsbourne, 1971). But with a split-brain subject, a revealing phenomenon recurred (Kreuter, Kinsbourne, and Trevarthen, 1972). While speaking was effortless, no effect on tapping was seen. When the subject was deep in thought in search of the next response, the tapping ceased on the right but continued on the left. When she made a mistaken response, then realized it and hesitated to pull herself together, both hands momentarily stopped tapping.

Kinsbourne and Cook (1971) and Hicks (1973), using a dowel balancing task concurrently with speaking, showed that speaking interferes more with right- than with left-hand performance. They suggested that "hemispheric sharing," the need to program both performances from the same hemisphere (when dowel balancing with the right hand was combined with speaking), left the subject open to interfering or cross-talk between these two acts. In the case of the split-brain subject, we can take the argument further. As she comes to a verbally difficult moment, attentional requirements of the left hemisphere rise sharply. This happens at the expense of the concurrent tapping. But the mental capacity used by the right hemisphere for left index finger tapping is unavailable on account of the callosal section. Therefore, the verbal process draws exclusively on the resources previously allocated to the left hemisphere-right index finger combination. This suggests the generalization that the corpus callosum aids in the rapid redisposition of the human's limited attentional resources as demand characteristics change. The ultimately unitary nature of this store is shown by the complete arrest of tapping at points of error. The total attentional resources are momentarily depleted.

INTERACTION OF PREATTENTATIVE AND FOCALLY ATTENTIVE PROCESSES

The terms "spatial" and "nonverbal" emphasize certain distinctions between the type of processing that the right hemisphere characteristically contributes to overall performance and the more familiar contributions of the "dominant" left hemisphere. But an exact formulation of the role of the "minor" hemisphere in perception is not yet available. Indeed, there is no logical reason why a single formulation should be expected to do justice to the various functions of a whole hemisphere. However, a tentative attribution may be attempted, which, even if it will emerge as incorrect, has the heuristic advantage of relating this field of neuropsychological inquiry to current experimental studies of human information processing.

Neisser (1967) has suggested that sensory input is subjected to the influences of "preattentive" processes before certain features are singled out for focal (and conscious) attention. Input is grouped according to Gestalt laws, so that the perceptual field is segmented or structured. The resulting perceptual units have a high probability of corresponding to distinct objects when they represent grouping over space, distinct events when the grouping is over time (Kahneman, 1973).

Patients with right posterior cerebral lesions who suffer from visuospatial agnosia (Paterson and Zangwill, 1966; Hécaen, 1962) behave as though this preattentive structuring had not occurred. Their focal attention wanders aimlessly across a chaotic field or adheres to a salient stimulus for lack of further direction.

At least some of the perceptual tasks for which left half-field or left-ear advantage has been demonstrated in normal people appear to make major demands on preattentive processing of a relatively complex stimulus field. The right hemisphere seems particularly adept at this in neuropsychological investigation. An especially striking example is the function of "perceptual closure" as exemplified by solving of the perceptual challenge posed by fragmented and depleted pictorial material in tests such as the Street Gestalt Completion and the Gollin and Mooney Closure Figures. Right-hemispheric superiority for such materials has been found in comparisons of right- and left-hemispherically lesioned groups (deRenzi and Spinnler, 1966; Lansdell, 1968; Kinsbourne, 1966; Warrington and James, 1967) and hemispherectomy (Kohn and Dennis, 1974). Insofar as the organization of the fragmented array into a meaningful figure does not appear to be facilitated by verbal coding or hypothesis generation and does not seem to result from investing effort or focal attention, it might be an instance of a task which gives the right hemisphere scope for its hypothesized preattentive function. Pre-attentive processing is automatically followed by focussing down of attention on some specific aspect that seems to call for further analysis. In the callosectomized person, the right hemisphere cannot transmit the structured field in its entirety to the left. Nevertheless, the patient seems to have no difficulty in grossly structuring space in the natural environment. Perhaps the right hemisphere assumes control of the direction of attention at brainstem level and so adjusts the direction of attention that left-hemisphere focus may be appropriately brought to bear. Thus in a test like "Embedded Figures," which calls both for a preattentive structuring of a complex display (right-hemispheric) and a focal extraction of the target figure from its redundant surround (left-hemispheric), one would expect that free vision would yield better performance than either half-field alone, and this is what Zaidel (1973) found.

We propose that the two hemispheres collaborate in the control of attention in two ways: (1) They control its disposition in space by establishing an appropriate balance between opponent directionalities. (2) They guide its focus by establishing preattentive structuring of the field and attentive focussing within it in appropriate temporal sequence.

Segregation of verbal-analytic and spatial-synthetic functions between the hemispheres is the rule. Insofar as this arrangement is the outcome of natural selection, it presumably conveys some substantial advantage over other possible lateralizations of function. Other arrangements may occasionally occur, in relation to early brain damage (Kinsbourne, 1974a); anomalous handedness, in which bilateral representation of language is relatively frequent (Subirana, 1969; Goodglass and Quadfasel, 1954) and which itself is more common after birth stress (Bakan, Dibb, and Reed, 1973); anomalous earedness (Anderson and Jaffe, 1973); and possibly even when none of these stigmata are to be found. Yet in spite of pilot studies (Levy, 1970; Miller, 1971) that indicate a performance deficit for left-handers, who must include some anomalously-lateralized individuals (Hécaen and Sauget, 1971), it has not proved possible to verify this discrepancy with samples of adequate size (Briggs, Nebes, and Kinsbourne, 1974; Swanson, 1974). The most economical explanation for the lack of obvious drawback for survival incurred by anomalous lateralization of function would be that the now customary dichotomy was of substantial use at some earlier stage of human evolution but that under present social conditions those functions have receded in importance or perhaps are performed on behalf of the whole society by those individuals who are endowed with them. It remains possible that less grave difficulties, such as slowness in learning to read (Orton, 1937; Zangwill, 1962; Witelson and Rabinovitch, 1972) or stuttering (Travis and Lindsley, 1933), are based at times upon anomalous cerebral representation of function.

In evolution, verbal skills are a new departure (Lenneberg, 1967). The very anatomical arrangements that underlie verbal utterance are lacking even in nonhuman primates (Lieberman, 1968; Lieberman, Klatt, and Wilson, 1969). No such unique attributes characterize human spatial orientation. This is a function man shares with many animals and one which could be regarded as more archaic than language, bilateral before language evolved, and partially crowded out of the left hemisphere by verbal function when it lateralized both in phylogeny and ontogeny. Language development is faster in women (Darley and Winitz, 1961; Garai and Scheinfeld, 1968) and perhaps sooner and more lateralized in them than in men (Buffery, 1971). In contrast, sex-linked inheritance of spatial skill favors males over females (Stafford, 1961; Buffery and Gray, 1972). This could imply a certain incompatibility between attaining a high level of spatial skill and a high level of verbal skill. Buffery and Gray (1972) have related the female language advantage to her biologically historical preoccupation with domestic and interpersonal roles, whereas males require more spatial skill to support their providing and protecting roles, which needs must cover a more extensive territory. The mechanism of verbal-spatial antagonism, if it exists, could be a simple mutual incompatibility between these mechanisms (Levy, 1974). Or perhaps some spatial skills are facilitated by a more bilateral type of cerebral organization (Buffery and Gray, 1972). This could be due to the bihemispheric spreading of a spatial map, which could be obscured in part by undue verbal lateralization. The neuronal basis of that incompatibility might be along lines suggested by Semmes (1968), who proposed more focalization of function on the left and more overlap on the right.

REFERENCES

Alajouanine, T., and Lhermitte, F.: Acquired aphasia in children. *Brain, 88:* 653–662, 1965.

Anderson, S. W., and Jaffe, J.: Eye movement bias and ear preferences as indices of speech lateralization in brain. *Scientific Report, 15,* Dept. of Comm Sci, New York, Psychiatry Institute, 1973.

Annett, M., Lee, D., and Ounsted, C.: Intellectual disabilities in relation to lateralized features in the EEG. In *Hemiplegic Cerebral Palsy in Children and Adults.* London, Heinemann, 1961.

Arnott, G. P.: *Impairment following ablation of the primary and secondary areas of the auditory cortex.* Unpublished Ph.D. Dissertation, University of Chicago, 1953.

Bakan, P., Dibb, G., and Reed, P.: Handedness and birth stress. Paper to the International Society for the Study of Behavioral Development, Ann Arbor, Michigan, August, 1973.

Basser, L. S.: Hemiplegia of early onset and the faculty of speech with special reference to the effects of hemispherectomy. *Brain, 85:* 427–460, 1962.

Berlin, C. I., Lowe-Bell, S. S., Hughes, L. F., and Berlin, H. L.: Dichotic right ear advantage in males and females—ages 5–13. Paper to the 84th meeting of the Acoustical Society of America, Miami Beach, Florida, 1972.

Bever, T. G.: The nature of cerebral dominance in speech behaviour of the child and adult. In Huxley, R., and Ingram, E. (Eds.): *Mechanisms of Language Development.* New York, Acad Pr, 1971.

Briggs, G. G., and Kinsbourne, M.: Unpublished observations, 1971.

Briggs, G. G., Nebes, R. D., and Kinsbourne, M.: In preparation, 1974.

Brown, J. W., and Jaffe, J.: Hypothesis on cerebral dominance. (In preparation) 1974.

Bryden, M. P.: Laterality effect in dichotic listening: relations with handedness and reading ability in children. *Neuropsychologia, 8:* 443–450, 1970.

Buffery, A. W. H.: Sex differences in the development of hemispheric asymmetry of function in the human brain. *Brain Res, 31:* 364–365, 1971.

Buffery, A. W. H., and Gray, J. A.: Sex differences in the development of spatial and linguistic skills. In Ounsted, C., and Taylor, D. C. (Eds.): *Gender Differences.* Baltimore, Williams and Wilkins, 1972.

Butler, S. R., and Norsell, U.: Vocalization possibly initiated by the minor hemisphere. *Nature, 220:* 793–794, 1968.

Cernacek, J.: Contralateral motor irradiation-cerebral dominance. *Arch Neurol, 4:* 165–172, 1961.

Darley, F. L., and Winitz, H.: Age of first word: review of research. *J Speech Hear Disord, 26:* 272–290, 1961.

De Renzi, E., and Spinnler, M.: Visual recognition in patients with unilateral cerebral disease. *J Nerv Ment Dis, 142:* 515–525, 1966.

Eimas, P. D., Siqueland, P. R., Jusczyk, P., and Vigonto, J.: Speech perception in infants. *Science, 171:* 303–306, 1971.

Gainotti, G.: Studies in the functional organization of the minor hemisphere. *Int J Mental Health, 1:* 78–82, 1972.

Garai, J. E., and Scheinfeld, A.: Sex differences in mental and behavioral traits. *Genet Psychol Monogr, 77:* 169–299, 1968.

Gazzaniga, M. S.: Short-term memory and brain-bisected man. *Psychon Sci, 12:* 161–163, 1968.

Gazzaniga, M. S., and Hillyard, S. A.: Language and speech capacity of the right hemisphere. *Neuropsychologia, 9:* 273–280, 1971.

Gazzaniga, M. S., and Sperry, R. W.: Simultaneous double discrimination response following brain bisection. *Psychon Sci, 4:* 261–263, 1966.

Gazzaniga, M. S., and Sperry, R. W.: Language after section of the cerebral commissures. *Brain, 90:* 131–148, 1967.

Gazzaniga, M. S., and Young, E. D.: Effects of commissurotomy on the processing of increasing visual information. *Exp Brain Res, 3:* 368–371, 1967.

Geffner, O. S., and Hochberg, I.: Ear laterality performance of children from low and middle socioeconomic levels on a verbal dichotic listening task. *Cortex, 7:* 193–203, 1971.

Goodglass, H., and Quadfasel, F. A.: Language laterality in left-handed aphasics. *Brain, 77:* 521–548, 1954.

Gordon, H.: *Verbal and nonverbal cerebral processing in man for audition.* Unpublished Ph.D. Dissertation, California Institute of Technology, 1972.

Guttmann, E.: Aphasia in children. *Brain, 65:* 205–219, 1942.

Hécaen, H.: Clinical symptomatology in right and left hemisphere lesions. In Mountcastle, V. B. (Ed.): *Interhemispheric Relations and Cerebral Dominance.* Baltimore, Johns Hopkins, 1972.

Hécaen, H., and Angelergues, R.: Agnosia for faces (prosopagnosia). *Arch Neurol, 7:* 92–100, 1962.

Hécaen, H., and Sauget, J.: Cerebral dominance in left handed subjects. *Cortex, 7:* 19–48, 1971.

Heron, W.: Perception as a function of retinal locus and attention. *Am J Psychol, 70:* 38–48, 1957.

Hicks, R. E.: *Role of cerebral hemispheric lateralization of function in concurrent verbal and unimanual performance.* Unpublished Ph.D. Dissertation, University of Texas at Austin, 1973.

Hillier, W. F.: Total left cerebral hemispherectomy for malignant glioma. *Neurology, 4:* 718–721, 1954.

Jones, R. K.: Observations on stammering after localized cerebral injury. *J Neurol Neurosurg Psychiatry, 29:* 192–195, 1966.

Kahneman, D.: *Attention and Effort.* Englewood, Prentice-Hall, 1973.

Kimura, D.: Cerebral dominance and the perception of verbal stimuli. *Can J Psychol, 15:* 166–171, 1967.

Kimura, D.: Speech lateralization in young children as determined by an auditory test. *J Comp Physiol Psychol, 56:* 899–902, 1963.

Kinsbourne, M.: Limitations in visual capacity due to cerebral lesions. Presented to the 18th Int. Congress Psychology, Moscow, 1966.

Kinsbourne, M.: The cerebral basis of lateral asymmetries in attention. *Acta Psychol, 33:* 193–201, 1970.

Kinsbourne, M.: The minor cerebral hemisphere as a source of aphasic speech. *Arch Neurol, 25:* 302–306, 1971.

Kinsbourne, M.: Eye and head turning indicates cerebral lateralization. *Science, 176:* 539–591, 1972.

Kinsbourne, M.: Minor hemisphere language and cerebral maturation. In Lenneberg, E., and Lenneberg, E. (Eds.): *Foundations of Language Development: A multidisciplinary Approach.* UNESCO, 1974a.

Kinsbourne, M.: The interaction between cognitive process and the direction of attention. In Rabbitt, P. M. A., and Dornic, S. (Eds.): *Attention and Performance, V.* London, Acad Pr, in press, 1974g.

Kinsbourne, M., and Cook, J.: Generalized and lateralized effects of concurrent verbalization on a unimanual skill. *Q J Exp Psychol, 23:* 341–345, 1971.

Kinsbourne, M., and Fisher, M.: Latency of uncrossed and crossed reaction in callosal agenesis. *Neuropsychologia, 9:* 471–472, 1971.

Kinsbourne, M., Trevarthen, C., and Sperry, R. W.: Bilateral visual search with deconnected cerebral hemispheres. In preparation, 1974.

Kinsbourne, M., and Warrington, E. K.: Observations on colour agnosia. *J Neurol Neurosurg Psychiatry, 27:* 224–228, 1964.

Kohn, B., and Dennis, M.: Patterns of hemispheric specialization after hemi-decortication for infantile hemiplegia. This volume, 1974.

Krashen, J.: Language and the left hemisphere. Working papers in phonetics, 26. University of California at Los Angeles, 1972.

Kreuter, C., Kinsbourne, M., and Trevarthen, C.: Are deconnected cerebral hemispheres independent channels? A preliminary study of the effect of uni-lateral loading on bilateral finger tapping. *Neuropsychologia, 10:* 453–461, 1972.

Lansdell, H.: Effect of extent of temporal lobe oblations on two lateralized deficits. *Physiol Behav, 3:* 271–273, 1968.

Lenneberg, E. H.: *Biological Foundations of Language.* New York, Wiley, 1967.

Levy, J.: Possible basis for the evolution of lateral specialization of the human brain. *Nature, 224:* 614–615, 1970.

Levy, J.: Cerebral asymmetries as manifested in split-brain man. This volume, 1974.

Levy, J., Nebes, R. D., and Sperry, R. W.: Expressive language in the surgically separated minor hemisphere. *Cortex, 7:* 49–58, 1971.

Levy, J., Trevarthen, C., and Sperry, R. W.: Perception of bilateral chimeric figures following hemispheric deconnexion. *Brain, 95:* 61–78, 1972.

Lieberman, P.: Primate vocalizations and human linguistic ability. *J Acoust Soc Am, 44:* 1574–1584, 1968.

Lieberman, P., Klatt, D. L., and Wilson, W. A.: Vocal tract limitations in the vowel repertoire of rhesus monkey and other nonhuman primates. *Science, 164:* 1185–1187, 1969.

Masterton, R. B., and Diamond, I. T.: Effects of auditory cortex ablation on discrimination of small binaural time differences. *J Neurophysiol, 27:* 15–36, 1964.

Miller, E.: Handedness and the pattern of human ability. *British J Psychol, 62:* 111–112, 1971.

Milner, B., Branch, C., and Rasmussen, T.: Observation on cerebral dominance. In deReuck, A. V. S., and O'Connor, M. (Eds.): *Disorders of Language.* London, Churchill, 1964.

Milner, B., Taylor, L., and Sperry, R. W.: Lateralized suppression of dichotically presented digits after commissual section in man. *Science, 161:* 184–186, 1968.

Molfese, D. L.: *Cerebral asymmetry in infants, children and adults: auditory evoked responses to speech and noise stimuli.* Unpublished Ph.D. Dissertation, Pennsylvania State University, 1972.

Morais, J., and Bertelson, P.: Laterality effects in diotic listening. *Perception, 2:* 107–111, 1973.

Mosher, F. A., and Hornsby, J. R.: On asking questions. In Bruner, J. S., Olver, R. R., and Greenfield, P. N. (Eds.): *Studies in cognitive growth.* New York, Wiley, 1966.

Nagafuchi, M.: Development of dichotic and monaural hearing abilities in young children. *Acta Otolaryngol, 69:* 409–414, 1970.

Neisser, U.: *Cognitive Psychology.* New York, Appleton, 1967.

Netley, C.: Dichotic listening performance of hemispherectomized patients. *Neuropsychologia, 10:* 233–240, 1972.

Nickerson, R. S.: Binary-classification reaction time: a review of some studies of human information processing capabilities. *Psychonom Monogr Supp, 4,* No. 17, 1972.

Nielsen, J. M.: *Agnosia, Apraxia, Aphasia: Their value in cerebral localization,* 2nd ed. New York, Hoeber, 1946.

Orton, S.: *Reading, writing and speech problems in children.* London, Chapman and Hall, 1937.

Rosadini, G., and Rossi, G. F.: On the suggested cerebral dominance for consciousness. *Brain, 90:* 101–112, 1967.

Saul, R. E., and Gott, P. S.: Compensatory mechanisms in agenesis of the corpus callosum. Paper to the 25th annual meeting of the American Academy of Neurology, Boston, 1973.

Schulhoff, C., and Goodglass, H.: Dichotic listening, side of brain injury and cerebral dominance. *Neuropsychologia, 7:* 149–160, 1969.

Semmes, J.: Hemispheric specialization: a possible clue in mechanism. *Neuropsychologia, 6:* 11–26, 1968.

Siqueland, E. R., and Lipsitt, L. P.: Conditioned head turning in human newborns. *J Exp Child Psychol, 4:* 356–377, 1966.

Smith, A.: Speech and other functions after left (dominant) hemispherectomy. *J Neurol Neurosurg Psychiat, 29:* 467–471, 1966.

Smith, A.: Nondominant hemispherectomy. *Neurology, 19:* 442–445, 1969.

Smith, A.: Dominant and nondominant hemispherectomy. In Smith, W. L. (Ed.): *Drugs, Development and Cerebral Function.* Springfield, Thomas, 1972.

Smith, K. U., and Akelaitis, A. J.: Studies on the corpus callosum. 1. Laterality in behavior and bilateral motor organization in man before and after section of the corpus callosum. *Arch Neurol Psychiatry, 47:* 519–543, 1942.

Sparks, R., and Geschwind, N.: Dichotic listening in man after section of neocortical commissures. *Cortex, 4:* 3–16, 1960.

Stafford, R. E.: Sex differences in spatial visualization as evidence of sex linked inheritance. *Percept Mot Skills, 13:* 428, 1961.

Sternberg, S.: High-speed scanning in human memory. *Science, 153:* 652–654, 1966.

Subirana, A.: Handedness and cerebral dominance. In Vinken, P. J., and de Bruyn, G. W. (Eds.): *Handbook of Clinical Neurology.* New York, Wiley, 1969, Vol. 4, pp. 248–272.

Swanson, J.: In preparation, 1974.

Thompson, R. F., and Welker, W. I.: Role of auditory cortex in reflex head orientation by cats to auditory stimulation. *J Comp Physiol Psychol, 56:* 996–1002, 1963.

Travis, L. E., and Lindsley, D. B.: Action current. Study of handedness in relation to stuttering. *J Exp Psychol, 16:* 258–270, 1933.

Trehub, S. E., and Rabinovitch, M. S.: Auditory-linguistic sensitivity in early infancy. *Devel Psychol, 6:* 74–77, 1972.

Trevarthen, C., and Kinsbourne, M.: Perceptual completion of words and figures by commissurotomy patients. In preparation, 1974.

Turkewitz, G., Gordon, B. W., and Birch, M. G.: Head turning in the human neonate effect of prandial condition and lateral preference. *J Comp Physiol Psychol, 59:* 189–192, 1968.

Ueki, K.: Hemispherectomy in the human with special reference to the preservation of function. *Prog Brain Res, 21:* 285–338, 1966.

Vigotsky, L. S.: *Thought and Language.* Cambridge, Massachusetts Institute of Technology Press, 1962.

Wada, J., and Rasmussen, T.: Intracarotid injection of sodium amytal for the lateralization of cerebral speech dominance. *J Neurosurg, 17:* 266–282, 1960.

Wegener, J. G.: A note on auditory discrimination behavior and the corpus callosum. In Ettlinger, E. G. (Ed.): *Functions of the Corpus Callosum.* Boston, Little, Brown, 1965.

Witelson, S. F.: Hemispheric specialization for linguistic and non-linguistic tactual perception using a dichotomous stimulation technique. *Cortex, 10:* 3–17, 1974.

Witelson, S. F., and Pallie, W.: Left-hemisphere specialization for language in the human newborn: neuroanatomical evidence of asymmetry. *Brain, 96:* 641–646, 1973.

Witelson, S. F., and Rabinovitch, M. S.: Hemispheric speech lateralization in children with auditory-linguistic deficits. *Cortex, 8:* 412–426, 1972.

Zaidel, E.: *Linguistic competence and related functions in the right cerebral hemisphere of man following commissurotomy and hemispherectomy.* Unpublished Ph.D. Dissertation, California Institute of Technology, 1973.

Zangwill, O. L.: Dyslexia in relation to cerebral dominance. In Money, J. (Ed.): *Reading Disability.* Baltimore, Johns Hopkins, 1962.

[CHAPTER XIV]

CEREBRAL CONTROL AND MENTAL EVOLUTION

THE SPECIES THAT EVOLVED relatively recently in the vertebrate line are in general capable of the most varied and flexible behavior. This development coincides with great gains in cerebral mass and complexity as well as of richness of callosal interconnection. It would therefore, be reasonable to expect to find in cortical organization a substrate of the capabilities that characterize the higher mammals and particularly man. In man this substrate is not found in some novel brain facility that has no evolutionary precedent. Rather, it represents a substantial elaboration on the ancient bisymmetric blueprint that dates from the origins of the lower worms, well before the initiation of the vertebrate line. Similarly, if consciousness is defined in biologically intelligible terms, there is no justification for limiting that concept to the human or for looking for its neurological basis in some uniquely human variant of brain anatomy. The momentary content of consciousness may be defined as the sum total of ongoing covert and overt voluntary responses, that is, responses that are not automatized but use mental capacity or "attention." The possible number of concurrent automatized responses is limited only by the availability of peripheral sensorimotor vehicles for response. But the number of attention-demanding responses is subject to central brain limitation. By this definition, one would expect human consciousness to be richer but not qualitatively different from consciousness of animals. In the intact human being, the responses that draw upon the finite fund of mental capacity, and thus constitute conscious awareness, typically arise in both cerebral hemispheres as well as parts of the brain stem. In the hemispherectomized patients consciousness is deprived of the potential contribution of the missing hemisphere. This diminishes the richness of consciousness but does not make the person less conscious. When the hemispheres, themselves intact, are disconnected from each other, both hemispheres remain able to control behavior. But instead of integrating their separate activities into a unified cortical contribution to the control of behavior, each hemisphere is apt to compete in maladaptive fashion with the other for control. The hemispherectomized individual practices consistent control with a diminished cerebral facility. The commissurotomized person practices intermittent control with one or the other half of an undiminished cerebral facility. While the intact brain is so organized that of competing responses to a single stimulus all but one are inhibited, in split-brain subjects two competing responses originating from the two sides may on rare occasions occur. However, it is not clear that both invoke attention; at least one may be automatized. As the overwhelming rule, in any case, the continuity of behavior is maintained. This is because the cerebrum is unstable, so that one hemisphere is likely to be in control at any time. During this time the other hemisphere probably takes little part either in controlling events, or rejecting them in divided memory. So the person is at times informed by the logico-analytic control system of the left hemisphere and at times by the global-synthetic strategies characteristic of the right. But this does not imply concurrent streams of consciousness. It does imply it in the sense of parallel processing systems each with its own exclusive resource of attention; a rather rapid alternation between two organizing principles which in the normal case combine rather than compete to determine the individual's plans and decisions.

There appear to be three possible arguments for the quality of consciousness in callosectomized people. The first makes assumptions about the existence of two independent parallel processors lodged in the two hemispheres. These assumptions we have already discussed and rejected. The second emphasizes the potential that each hemisphere has for building up an independent store of experience derived from strictly lateralized input (such as effectively can only be secured in the laboratory). This is the view of dual system of information flow. The third point of view emphasized the differences in cognitive style between the hemispheres.

In terms of information flow, callosal section produces a special case of a wide range of so-called disconnection syndromes. In these syndromes there is interruption of communication between separately localized neural facilities that underlie higher mental functioning. The specific consequence of the interruption depends on its location within the scheme of cognitive information flow. Thus a color agnosic can discriminate colors, but cannot retrieve their associates. The conduction aphasic can comprehend but not repeat words. Viewed from the vantage point of the response, certain inputs are not followed by the customary response; that is, just as in cerebral disconnection, certain response systems fail to reflect certain forms of input. In a normal person, the same behavioral consequence would occur if the response system in question were already fully occupied with a concurrently imposed task. In the split-brain subject this is the case to an extreme degree in that virtually any response programmed by one hemisphere fails to reflect virtually any input limited to the other. But in principle the phenomenon is the same as in the other disconnection syndromes and even in the normal person in a state of concurrent activity. Any duality of consciousness attributed to split-brain person on these grounds would logically also apply in a much wider range of circumstances.

The word "consciousness" is currently often used in a loose sense to designate a particular cognitive style, a manner of attending and responding selectively. With regard to these strategies, the hemispheres differ, and so from time to time; right or left hemisphere consciousness holds sway. A host of mental and cultural dichotomies spring to mind and enthusiasm is readily generated for the supposed underdog, the minor-hemisphere processing mode.

Throughout the ages, people have not been spared the copious advice of teacher, philospher, and sage on how to live. Insofar as all behavior is based on brain, and each control system of the brain has its particular localization, this advice can be viewed as support for use of one part of the brain in preference to another. However, to state the choice simply as between two opposing modes of processing corresponding to mutually exclusive life-styles is grossly authoritarian and undervalues a crucial feature of brain organization. This is the ability to switch and recombine the available mental capacity so as to deploy whatever combination of control systems, right-sided or left-, most adaptively deals with the problems at hand. There is no need for exclusive commitment to one problem solving mode. The associationist view of differing hemisphere-consciousness implicitly imposes a choice. The biological facts presented in the previous chapter contradict the view that cortex primarily harbors associations, and they render the implied advice meaningless.

Normal people are aware of events irrespective of whether their initial impact is on one side or the other. The callosum shares the information between the hemispheres. Normal people need not choose between left and right hemispheric cognitive styles as two packages. They can draw on any combination of faculties that they choose, irrespective of lateralization. Thus the resources of strategy and awareness that are available to the disconnected right hemisphere of a split-brain person are also available to the normal person. He may enlist some of them at will. The split-brain person is more at the mercy of uncontrollable surges of hemispheric preponderance, and to that extent is handicapped in his ability to select strategies to fit a given situation. Thus a split-brain person will more often than a normal adopt an extreme and rigid right or left hemispheric approach. But a normal person may choose to do so also, and in a normal person, an agony of indecision might closely mimic the oscillation of control between hemispheres that characterizes the split-brain state.

All the facilities and capabilities of the disconnected right hemisphere are freely available to the intact person. His right hemisphere is no passive fellow-traveler. He may use any or all of its capabilities at any time of his choice. The split brain person effectively has to choose at any time between using them all, or none at all.

We have attempted in these concluding chapters to show that the corpus callosum mediates collaboration between compatible response patterns and competition between incompatible response patterns. In this way it plays an important part in the moment-to-moment allocation of "attention" to parts of the central nervous system and thus necessarily also in the withdrawal of attention from its other parts.

In the absence of this great forebrain commissure the amount of attention, an epiphenomenon of which is consciousness, is unchanged. Nor is attention then vested in structures that were previously suppressed or functioned only at the automatic level. The unity and continuity of awareness is unchanged. Its content varies from moment to moment, depending on which hemisphere is mainly responsible for the attentional sifting of input and formulation of plans at that time. Lack of the forebrain commissure impairs the organism's ability to integrate certain faculties in unified action, to ensure stability and precision of certain dynamically balanced opponent processes, and to guarantee the organism relative freedom from competing response tendencies. In these respects it acts in a manner which differs in particulars but conforms in general plan to that of commissures anywhere in the bisymmetrical nervous system. Even more than an information transmitter, the corpus callosum is a regulator. Sherrington described this type of functioning as a "releasing force":

> Releasing forces acting on the brain from moment to moment shut out from activity whole regions of the nervous system, as they conversely call vast other regions into play. The resultant singleness of action from moment to moment is a keystone in the construction of the individual whose unity it is the specific office of the nervous system to perfect. The interference of unlike reflexes and the alliance of like reflexes in their action upon their common paths seem to lie at the very root of the great psychical process of *attention*.

AUTHOR INDEX

A

Acheson, G. G., 80, 90
Ades, H. W., 72, 84
Adevai, G., 180, 183
Adey, W. R., 56, 84
Adrian, E. D., 73, 84
Ajuriaguerra, J., 126, 135
Akelaitis, A. J., xi, 121, 122, 123, 125, 138, 150, 262, 284
Alajouanine, T., 265, 280
Albee, G. W., 17, 24, 31
Alexejeff, W. A., 56, 91
Alpers, B. J., 121, 124, 137, 150
Amassian, V. E., 78, 84, 94
Amosov, N. M., 95, 112
Anderson, S. W., 267, 279, 280
André-Balisaux, G., 138, 150
Angelergues, R., 173, 179, 182, 260, 282
Annett, M., 265, 280
Apter, J. T., 243, 254
Arbib, M. A., 95, 112
Arnott, G. P., 270, 281
Arora, H. A., 140, 152
Arrigoni, G., 179, 182
Asanuma, M., 248, 254
Austin, G. M., 95, 96, 97, 98, 99, 102, 104, 111, 112, 113
Axelrod, S., 249, 256
Ayala, G., 121, 124

B

Babinski, J., 245, 254
Bakan, P., 279, 281
Bakay, L., 98, 112
Baldwin, M., 84
Bálint, R., 247, 254
Banker, B. O., 245, 255
Barany, R., 245, 254
Bard, L., 245, 247, 254
Bard, P., 59, 61, 65, 66, 72, 79, 84, 85, 94, 247, 259
Barnet A., 72, 85
Barrett, R., 101, 109, 112
Barro, G., 79, 92
Bartelmez, G. W., 219, 221, 235
Bashore, W. D., 55, 56, 89
Basser, L. S., 11, 21, 28, 31, 34, 45, 265, 281
Battersby, W. S., 245, 254
Bazelon, M., 72, 85

Bazett, H. C., 52, 72, 85
Beller, A., 98, 114
Bender, M. B., 91, 245, 254, 255
Bendixen, H., 98, 112
Bennett, A. H., 6, 31
Bennett, G. K., 168, 182
Benton, A. L., 39, 40, 43, 45, 46
Berkowitz, E., 243, 254
Berlin, C. I., 268, 281
Berlin, H. L., 268, 281
Berlucci, G., 85, 248, 251, 254
Berman, A. J., 56, 85
Bertelson, P., 283
Best, C. H., 65, 85
Bever, T. G., 266, 281
Bianchi, L., 243, 254
Bianki, V. L., 140, 150
Bickford, R. G., 56, 94
Birch, M. G., 268
Black, P., 83, 85, 139, 151, 191, 204
Blagoveshchenskaya, W., 55, 85
Blount, M. P., 219, 235
Bogen, G. M., 86
Bogen, J. E., 6, 13, 16, 31, 44, 45, 53, 59, 60, 69, 72, 79, 80, 82, 85, 86, 126, 128, 129, 135, 141, 149, 151, 152, 154, 155, 156, 163, 164, 165, 182, 194, 203, 205, 206, 247, 254
Boisacq-Schepens, N., 248, 255
Bonhoeffer, K., 120, 124
Bonin, G. V., 86
Bossom, J., 188, 205
Botterell, E., 248, 255
Bouillaud, J., 86
Bour, H., 97, 112
Bowden, J. W., 56, 90
Bower, T. G. R., 234, 235
Boyle, B., 89
Bradford, F. K., 86
Brain, R., 82, 86
Bramwell, B., 17, 31
Branch, C. L., 248, 254, 264, 283
Braun, J. J., 72, 86
Bremer, F., 123, 124, 138, 151, 248, 254, 255
Bridgeman, M., 243
Bridgman, C. S., 122, 124, 138, 151
Briggs, G. G., 277, 279, 281
Brinkman, J., 192, 205, 252, 255
Bristowe, J. S., 137, 151
Broadbent, D. B., 132, 135
Broca, P., 6, 7, 31

SUBJECT INDEX

A

Akinetic mutism, 107
Alexia, 120, 122
Amnesia, 97
Amphioxus, 222
Amusia, 16
Anosognosia, 16, 17
Anterior cerebral artery occlusion, 107
Anterior commissure, 121, 143, 149
Anticonvulsant drugs, 22, 26
Aphasia, 6, 8, 12, 15, 17, 18, 20, 28–30,
    43, 120, 262–3, 266–7
  conduction, 287
  crossed, 17
Auditory cortex ablation, 170
Autokinetic movement, 245

B

Baboon, 82, 84, 193, 201, 249
Basal ganglia, 49
Basilar artery occlusion, 107
Benton visual retention test, 27
Betz cell, 248

C

Caffeine, 72
Callosal agenesis, 200, 232, 269
Callosal section (see Commissurotomy)
Caudate nucleus, 73
Cat, 48
Catatonia, 101
Cerebellum, 73, 188
Cerebral dominance (see Hemisphere)
Chicken, 49
Chimeric stimuli, 172–176, 200–202
Chimpanzee, 82, 83
Chronogenic localisation, 12, 19
Circle of Willis, 98
Circus movement, 241, 243, 246
Closure, speed of, 163
Coelocanth, 222
Color agnosia, 260, 287
Coma, 96
Commissurotomy, 16, 44, 138–144, 150, 156,
    165, 172, 187–195, 190–201, 208, 231,
    234, 248, 253, 261, 262, 267, 271–277,
    287
Commissurotomy anterior, 149–200
Completion, 172, 196, 199, 200, 245, 246

Consciousness, 193, 196, 198, 201, 233,
    234, 274, 286–288
Constructional dyspraxia, 165, 167
Convolution, first frontal, 68
Confusion, 96
Corpus collusum, 117–123, 137–141, 198
Corpus striatum, 49
Cribriform plate, 143
Cross-cueing, 145

D

Deja vue, 99
Delirium, 96
Dichotic listening, 126, 132, 134, 267,
    268, 270–273
Differential aptitude test battery, 168
Disconnection syndrome, 43
Dog, 6, 48
Double simultaneous stimulation, 28
Double volitional activity, 192
Duck, 48
Dysarthria, 15
Dyscopia, 44
Dysgraphia, 44

E

Encephalization, 80, 82, 83
Embedded figures test, 178, 279
Ephestia, 250

F

Facial agnosia, 16, 179, 200, 260
Feedback, 250, 253, 270
Finger tapping, 198, 277
Flat fish, 224
Flechsig's law, 251
Forebrain commissure (see Corpus
    callosum)
Frontal lobe, 55
Frontal lobectomy, 66, 72, 97, 98, 247

G

Gibbon, 83
Golden hamster, 189, 200
Gollin figures, 278